C000233256

quick and easy
low cholesterol
recipes

Grange BOOKS

CONTENTS

Published by Grange Books
an imprint of Grange Books Plc
The Grange
Kingsnorth Industrial Estate
Hoo, nr Rochester
Kent ME3 9ND
www.Grangebooks.co.uk
Copyright © Trident Press International 2002

Quick & Easy Low Cholesterol Recipes

EDITORIAL
Managing Editor: Catherine Saxelby
Editor: Diane Hodges
Food Editor: Sheryle Eastwood
Assistant Food Editor: Rachel Blackmore
Food Consultant: Frances Naldrett
Editorial Coordinator: Margaret Kelly
Editors: Marian Broderick, Ingaret Ward
Home Economist: Anneka Mitchell
Australian Editorial Coordinators: Claire Pallant,
Nadia Sbisa

PHOTOGRAPHY AND STYLING
Ashley Mackevicius
Rosemary De Santis

ILLUSTRATIONS
Carol Dunn

DESIGN AND PRODUCTION
Tracey Burt
Chris Hatcher

All rights reserved. No part of this book may
be stored, reproduced or transmitted in any form
or by any means without written permission of the
publisher, except in the case of brief quotations
embodied in critical articles and reviews.

Includes Index
ISBN 1-84013-484-4
EAN 9781840134841

This Edition 2002

Printed in China

NUTRITION AND DIET GUIDE

EASY A TO Z LOW CHOLESTEROL RECIPES

METRIC MEASURES		QUICK METRIC IMPERIAL CONVERTER			
Cups					
1/4 cup	60 mL	**g**	**oz**	**mL**	**fl.oz**
1/3 cup	80 mL				
1/2 cup	125 mL				
1 cup	250 mL	30	1	30	1
Spoons		60	2	60	2
1/4 teaspoon	1.25 mL	125	4	125	4
1/2 teaspoon	2.5 mL	250	8	125	8
1 teaspoon	5 mL	370	12	370	12
1 tablespoon	20 mL	500	16	500	16

FOREWORD

Nowadays most Australians are aware that the food we eat is important for good health. Heart disease is still the major cause of death in this country, accounting for more deaths than cancer and road accidents combined. The good news is that the death rate from heart attacks has been falling since the late 1960's, reflecting our healthier lifestyles and better medical care. The foods we eat, our exercise and smoking habits can all influence our health.

Fortunately we have a wide variety of foods available in this country but this can make it difficult to choose the right foods for healthy eating. This book provides useful information and excellent recipes which can help you and your family towards a healthier way of eating. The recipes are based on the National Heart Foundation's dietary guidelines and contain minimal saturated fat, cholesterol and salt but are rich in dietary fibre.

Whether you need to lower your blood cholesterol or are simply aiming to help your family with the good eating habit you will find this publication a useful companion in your kitchen.

Dr Robert Hodge
Director, National Heart Foundation

CHECK-AND-GO

When planning a meal, use the easy Check-and-Go boxes which appear beside each ingredient. Simply check on your pantry shelf and if the ingredients are not there, tick the boxes as a reminder to add those items to your shopping list.

NUTRITIONAL ANALYSIS EXPLAINED

Each recipe has been computer-analysed for its kilojoule (calorie) content and food value. At a glance, you can see whether a dish is LOW, MEDIUM or HIGH in fat, cholesterol, sodium (a measure of salt) and fibre. The following recommended daily intakes have been used to set guidelines.

Kilojoules	8500
Calories	2000
Fat (based on 30% of kilojoules)	67 grams
Cholesterol	300 milligrams
Sodium	920 – 2300 milligrams
Fibre	25 – 30 grams

Note: A serve for dressings and sauces throughout this book is one tablespoon.

What is cholesterol?

Forget cholesterol, think fat!

Cholesterol is a white fat-like substance, which is produced by all animals, including humans. It is an essential component of the body, being vital for the manufacture of several hormones and vitamin D; the structure of cell membranes; and the formation of bile acids, which help digest fat.

✧ Cholesterol only becomes undesirable when large amounts accumulate in the bloodstream and cause fatty build-up in the blood vessels. Research shows that the higher your blood cholesterol reading, the higher the risk of heart problems – which can eventually lead to a heart attack or stroke.

✧ Heredity, being overweight, and doing too little exercise all influence blood cholesterol; but the major contributor is your diet, and in particular, the type and amount of fat you consume.

✧ Despite the recent emphasis on cholesterol in food, recent studies show that food fat, especially saturated fat, has a more direct influence on blood cholesterol than does food cholesterol.

✧ Eating large amounts of cholesterol (say from eggs or liver) does not automatically raise the blood cholesterol, as our liver

simply compensates by 'switching off' its own natural cholesterol manufacture.

✧ For saturated fats, there is no feedback mechanism and they actually encourage the liver to produce more cholesterol.

✧ For most people, cutting back on saturated fats is healthier than eliminating foods with high cholesterol, many of which are nutritious – such as eggs, organ meats and shellfish.

✧ A small number of people are sensitive to dietary cholesterol, and should avoid both fat and cholesterol.

SEPARATING FAT FROM FICTION

Reducing your overall fat intake has other benefits for health, and is an important nutrition goal in Western countries. Fat, whether saturated or unsaturated, is a concentrated source of kilojoules (calories) and provides twice as many kilojoules as either protein or carbohydrate, weight for weight.

✧ Apart from heart disease, high fat diets have also been linked to the development of other illnesses such as gallbladder disease and certain cancers.

FAT IN FOODS

Foods containing fat carry a mixture of saturated, polyunsaturated and monounsaturated fats.
The predominant fat gives the food its classification.

SATURATED	MONOUNSATURATED	POLYUNSATURATED
butter, cream, dripping, lard, copha	olive oil, olives	most vegetable oils, including safflower, sunflower, maize or corn, cotton seed, soya bean, grape seed, walnut, sesame
coconut oil, palm oil	peanut oil, peanuts, peanut butter	
many cheeses, ice cream, chocolate	most nuts	margarine, reduced-fat spreads and oils labelled polyunsaturated
meat fat, poultry skin	avocado	
full cream dairy products	egg yolk	seeds, including sunflower, pumpkin, sesame
many commercial foods including snack foods, pies, pastries, biscuits, fast foods, chips	margarine (unless labelled poly-unsaturated)	nuts: walnuts, brazil nuts, pine nuts
	lean meat, chicken, salmon, tuna	fish, shellfish

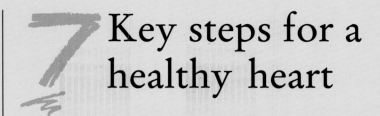

7 Key steps for a healthy heart

How to lower your blood cholesterol

The latest medical research around the world points to these 7 key steps in lowering cholesterol and blood pressure and preventing fatal heart disease.

Reduce fats

1 Reduce your intake of all fats. Only 30 per cent of your total kilojoule (calorie) intake should come from fats, with saturated fats contributing no more than 10 per cent and unsaturated fats (poly- and monounsaturated) contributing the remaining 20 per cent.

Reduce weight

2 Reduce your body weight, if you are overweight.

Reduce cholesterol

3 Reduce cholesterol intake from foods to under 300 milligrams a day. This means limiting cholesterol-rich foods such as brains, liver, kidney, egg yolks, prawns, fish roe and squid.

Increase fibre intake

4 Increase your fibre intake. Water-soluble fibre, such as pectins and gums can speed the removal of cholesterol from the body. Pay attention to oats, oat bran, barley, barley bran, rice, rice bran, dried beans, lentils, fruit and vegetables.

Reduce salt

5 Reduce your salt intake. Do not sprinkle salt on food or in cooking, and switch to salt reduced or no-added-salt products when next shopping.

Reduce alcohol

6 Drink less alcohol. No more than two standard drinks a day is advisable.

Exercise more

7 Try to maintain a moderate level of exercise on a regular basis.

WATCH WHAT YOU EAT

	EAT AND ENJOY	EAT OCCASIONALLY	THESE FOODS ARE NOT FOR YOU
Grains and bread	oats, rice, buckwheat, barley, brans, wholegrain cereals, rolled oats (porridge), bran cereal, wheatgerm flour, bread, crispbread, pasta, noodles, macaroni, water crackers, filo pastry (with minimal oil)	modified cakes, biscuits and loaves made with ingredients in 'eat and enjoy' column	most toasted muesli, croissants, cheese, bread, commercial pastry, cakes, most biscuits and crackers
Vegetables and fruit	all fresh and frozen vegetables (canned vegetables preferably no added salt) dried peas, beans, and lentils canned beans (preferably no added salt) fresh fruit canned fruit (preferably unsweetened or in juice) dried fruit	olives, avocado pears	potato chips and other vegetables cooked in fat
Fish	all fresh fish canned fish (preferably no added salt) oysters, scallops, mussels, crab, lobster	prawns, fish roe, squid (calamari), cuttlefish, octopus – limit once per week	fried fish or shellfish in batter
Meat and poultry	lean beef, pork, veal, rabbit, game (venison, buffalo), lamb, mutton, chicken, turkey (skin removed), lean mince	liver, kidney, heart, sweetbreads – limit once per week lean ham, low fat luncheon meats (pressed turkey, chicken)	visible fat on meat (including poultry skin and pork crackling), sausages, salami, pate, luncheon meats (unless lean), bacon, brains
Nuts	chestnuts	walnuts, Brazil nuts, pecans, almonds, hazelnuts, peanuts, pine nuts, macadamias, pistachio, cashews all nuts (except chestnuts) are high in fat	coconut

	EAT AND ENJOY	EAT OCCASIONALLY	THESE FOODS ARE NOT FOR YOU
Fats and oils	all fats should be limited to 1 tablespoon per day	polyunsaturated oils monounsaturated oils polyunsaturated margarine low fat spreads	butter, lard, suet, dripping, ghee, copha, cooking margarine, solid frying fats, palm oil, palm kernel oil, coconut oil, hydrogenated vegetable oil whole or full cream milk
Fast foods and snacks	barbecued chicken (remove skin) toasted sandwiches, steak sandwiches, rolls, pocket flat bread with lean filling popcorn, rice crackers	hamburgers, pizzas	fried foods (chips, crumbed chicken, spring rolls, dim sims, battered fish, potato scallops) meat pies, sausage rolls, pasties, hot dogs fried rice, quiche potato crisps, corn chips (and similar snack foods)
Eggs	egg white yolk-free egg substitute	egg yolks – limit 2 per week	
Sweets and spreads		boiled sweets, fruit pastilles, chewing gum, peppermints jam, honey, marmalade, sugar peanut butter – limit 1–2 teaspoons a day	chocolate, caramels, toffee, butterscotch, muesli bars, lemon butter chocolate nut spread carob confectionery
Dairy foods	skim milk, low fat milk low fat yoghurt, frozen yoghurt low fat cheeses (cottage or curd cheese, quark, ricotta)	reduced fat cheeses, e.g.reduced fat Cheddar, feta, mozzarella, Swiss, Edam, ice confection	cream, sour cream, cream cheese hard yellow cheeses (unless reduced fat), cheese spreads, ice cream

Avocado

Avocados are often wrongly avoided by people with high cholesterol. Like other fruit and vegetables, they contain no cholesterol, but, at 20–25 per cent fat, they are high in fat, although their fat is mainly mono-unsaturated, a type not considered to raise blood cholesterol levels.

The high fat content of avocados makes them somewhat fattening and so they should be eaten sparingly by anyone with a weight problem.

Half an avocado supplies 1070 kilojoules (255 calories), which is equivalent to three or four slices of bread. So enjoy them with lemon juice, freshly ground pepper and crusty bread, but don't overindulge!

You might like to try this creamy sauce. Place an avocado, a banana, a little honey and fruit juice, in a food processor or blender and process to make sauce of pouring consistency. Serve this delicious sauce with fresh fruit salad in place of cream or ice cream. Avocado is also perfect sliced and tossed through a green salad.

Brans

(Except oat bran – see Oats)

Bran, in the form of unprocessed wheat bran, came to public prominence in the early 1970s, when British doctors believed the UK diet was severely lacking in food fibre. Since then, there has been a great deal of research into the nutritional attributes of the bran (outer layers) of many grains. Oat bran, rice bran, barley bran and maize (corn) bran can all be used as sources of fibre.

Most brans can be sprinkled over cereal, fruit or yoghurt, for a quick high fibre breakfast. They are also processed into packet breakfast cereals or incorporated into breads, pasta, biscuits, cakes, and even sausages, meat dishes and drinks.

Try our healthy bran recipes and see how easy it is to put more fibre into your food.

BRAN FIBRE

Wheat bran	40%
Oat bran	18%
Rice bran	26%
Barley bran	16%

Values are dietary fibre expressed as average values per 100 grams consumed.

GOLDEN-COATED CHICKEN DRUMSTICKS

Serves 4

- ☐ 4 x 150 g chicken drumsticks, skin removed
- ☐ plain flour
- ☐ 1 egg, lightly beaten
- ☐ 1 tablespoon polyunsaturated oil

RICE BRAN COATING
- ☐ $1/2$ cup (45 g) rice bran
- ☐ $3/4$ cup (45 g) soft wholemeal bread crumbs
- ☐ $1/4$ teaspoon dried ground rosemary
- ☐ 3 tablespoons grated Parmesan cheese

1 To make coating, combine rice bran, breadcrumbs, rosemary and Parmesan cheese. Coat drumsticks with flour, dip in egg and coat well with crumb mixture.
2 Brush baking dish with oil. Add chicken and bake at 180°C for 1 hour, turning and basting frequently.

955 kilojoules (230 calories) per serve

Fat	12.2 g	med
Cholesterol	131 mg	med
Fibre	3.0 g	high
Sodium	229 mg	med

BRAN PASTRY

Makes 1 x 20 cm shell or 18 tartlets

- ☐ 1 cup (125 g) plain flour, sifted
- ☐ $1/2$ cup (45 g) rice bran
- ☐ 2 tablespoons polyunsaturated oil
- ☐ $1/2$ cup (125 mL) skim milk

1 Place flour and rice bran in a large mixing bowl.
2 Make a well in the centre and pour in oil and milk. Mix to a firm dough. Turn out onto a lightly floured board and knead lightly. Wrap in plastic food wrap. Refrigerate for 30 minutes. Roll out and line a pie plate. Bake at 200°C for 30–35 minutes.
To make a sweet pastry, add 2 tablespoons sugar and $1/2$ teaspoon ground nutmeg.

Favourite Family Meatloaf, Golden-Coated Chicken Drumsticks

FAVOURITE FAMILY MEATLOAF

Serves 6

- ☐ $1/2$ cup (60 g) bran cereal
- ☐ 1 onion, grated
- ☐ 1 carrot, grated
- ☐ 1 small zucchini, grated
- ☐ 3 tablespoons low fat unflavoured yoghurt
- ☐ 1 egg, lightly beaten
- ☐ 500 g lean minced beef
- ☐ 2 teaspoons grated lemon rind
- ☐ 1 tablespoon lemon juice
- ☐ $1/2$ teaspoon mixed dried herbs
- ☐ freshly ground black pepper

TOPPING
- ☐ 4 tablespoons tomato sauce (no added salt)
- ☐ 2 tablespoons Worcestershire sauce
- ☐ 1 tablespoon white wine vinegar
- ☐ 1 tablespoon red currant jelly
- ☐ 3 tablespoons Mexican pumpkin seeds
- ☐ 1 tablespoon toasted sesame seeds

1 Combine bran cereal, onion, carrot, zucchini, yoghurt and egg in a mixing bowl. Set aside for 10 minutes.
2 Mix in meat, lemon rind, lemon juice, herbs and pepper to taste. Press mixture into a lightly greased and lined 25 cm x 10 cm ovenproof loaf pan. Bake at 180°C for 30–35 minutes. Drain off any excess liquid. Turn out onto an ovenproof plate.
3 To make topping, combine tomato sauce, Worcestershire sauce, vinegar and red currant jelly. Combine pumpkin and sesame seeds and sprinkle over top of meatloaf. Spread topping over all surfaces of meatloaf. Bake at 180°C for a further 10 minutes. Serve sliced either hot or cold.

842 kilojoules (202 calories) per serve

Fat	9.1 g	med
Cholesterol	92 mg	med
Fibre	4.4 g	high
Sodium	169 mg	med

MICROWAVE IT

Prepare the loaf mixture as above. Press it into a microwave-safe loaf dish. Cook on HIGH (100%) for 10–15 minutes. Turn out onto a microwave-safe plate and top with seed mixture. Spread loaf with topping and cook on HIGH (100%) for 4–5 minutes.

CHEESY SPINACH PIZZA

If you didn't think you could have pizza on a low cholesterol diet, you're in for a surprise. Try ours. It's low in fat and cholesterol and high in fibre.

Serves 8

- ☐ **8 spinach leaves, stalks removed and shredded**
- ☐ **$^1/_2$ cup (20 g) unprocessed bran**
- ☐ **$^3/_4$ cup (190 mL) water**
- ☐ **2 tablespoons olive oil**
- ☐ **1 $^3/_4$ cups (215 g) self-raising flour**
- ☐ **pinch ground nutmeg**
- ☐ **freshly ground black pepper**

TOPPING
- ☐ **4 tablespoons tomato paste (no added salt)**
- ☐ **1 tablespoon finely chopped fresh basil**
- ☐ **100 g mozzarella cheese, grated**
- ☐ **4 shallots, finely chopped**
- ☐ **2 tomatoes, sliced**
- ☐ **3 tablespoons grated Parmesan cheese**

1 Steam or microwave spinach until tender. Drain and set aside to cool.
2 Place bran and water in a mixing bowl. Stand 10 minutes, then stir in oil, flour, nutmeg, pepper to taste and one third of the cooked spinach.
3 Turn mixture out onto a lightly floured board and knead lightly. Press to fit a lightly greased 30 cm metal pizza tray.
4 To make topping, combine tomato paste with basil and spread over pizza base. Top with mozzarella, remaining spinach and shallots. Arrange tomato slices on top and sprinkle with Parmesan cheese. Bake at 200°C for 30–35 minutes or until golden.

881 kilojoules (210 calories) per serve
Fat	8.6 g	med
Cholesterol	12 mg	low
Fibre	3.6 g	high
Sodium	345 mg	high

Quick Banana Pecan Loaf, Cheesy Spinach Pizza

QUICK BANANA PECAN LOAF

A must for banana lovers. Serve this delicious quick bread as an alternative to bread or as a morning tea treat.

Serves 12

- ☐ **1 cup (45 g) unprocessed wheat bran**
- ☐ **1 cup (170 g) brown sugar**
- ☐ **3 small bananas, mashed**
- ☐ **1 cup (250 mL) skim milk**
- ☐ **60 g finely chopped pecans**
- ☐ **1 $^1/_2$ cups (185 g) self-raising flour, sifted**
- ☐ **1 teaspoon mixed spice**

1 Combine bran, sugar, bananas and milk in a mixing bowl. Set aside for 5 minutes.

2 Stir in pecans, flour and mixed spice. Spoon mixture into a lightly greased and lined 23 cm x 12 cm loaf pan. Bake at 200°C for 1 hour or until cooked.

770 kilojoules (182 calories) per serve
Fat	3.1 g	low
Cholesterol	0 mg	low
Fibre	3.0 g	high
Sodium	180 mg	med

NUTRITION TIPS

Because different brans have different actions in the body it is good to eat a variety of fibre foods.
❖ Wheat bran with its high content of insoluble fibre, is effective in providing bulk and relieving constipation.
❖ Oat and barley bran have a smaller effect on the bowel, but are useful for lowering blood cholesterol.
❖ Rice bran appears to lie between these, being good for laxation and heart health.

Breads

One of the oldest foods, bread, today comes in an amazing array of shapes, sizes and types. Wholemeal or wheatmeal bread is the most nutritious, offering the goodness of the whole grain with its abundance of fibre, B vitamins, essential minerals and proteins.

Mixed grain bread contains pre-soaked grains which add crunch and fibre but, because the basic dough is white, has a medium fibre content.

Bran-enriched bread contains wheat, oat or rice bran, and is valuable when a high fibre intake is important.

All types of bread, whatever their colour, are good for your heart, as they are low in fat and high in energy-giving complex carbo-hydrate. They are also not as fattening as we once believed. Often what is spread on top contributes more kilojoules (calories) than the bread underneath! So take care to spread butter or margarine sparingly and even avoid it entirely with high fat toppings like peanut butter, cheese, pate, and sardines. Bread contains no cholesterol and usually less than 3 percent fat.

BAKER'S TIP

Stale bread need not be wasted, it can be made into breadcrumbs. Trim the crusts from the bread and place on a baking tray, dry out in the oven at 150°C until bread is crisp and golden in colour. Place in a food processor and crumb. When cool, store in an airtight container.

Pumpkin and Prune Damper

PUMPKIN AND PRUNE DAMPER

Serves 12

- ☐ **3 cups (375 g) self-raising flour, sifted**
- ☐ **1 cup (135 g) wholemeal self-raising flour, sifted**
- ☐ **2 teaspoons mixed spice**
- ☐ **¹/₂ cup (20 g) unprocessed bran**
- ☐ **3 tablespoons grape seed oil**
- ☐ **1 egg, lightly beaten**
- ☐ **300 g cooked mashed pumpkin**
- ☐ **1 tablespoon grated orange rind**
- ☐ **¹/₂ cup (90 g) chopped pitted prunes**
- ☐ **¹/₂ cup (125 mL) orange juice**
- ☐ **¹/₂ cup (125 mL) evaporated skim milk**

1   Place both self-raising flours, mixed spice and bran in a bowl. Combine oil, egg, pumpkin, orange rind, prunes, orange juice and milk. Make a well in the centre of the dry ingredients and pour in pumpkin mixture. Mix lightly with a knife until all ingredients are just combined.

2   Turn mixture out onto a lightly floured board and knead lightly.

3   Place dough on a greased oven tray. Shape into a circle 2 cm thick. Brush with a little extra milk and mark into eight wedges with a sharp knife. Bake at 200°C for 45 minutes or until golden brown.

1066 kilojoules (252 calories) per serve

Fat	5.7 g	med
Cholesterol	20 mg	low
Fibre	4.9 g	high
Sodium	473 mg	high

HERB AND CHEESE LOAF

This high fibre loaf is terrific served warm.

Serves 12

- ☐ 1 ¹/₄ cups (170 g) self-raising wholemeal flour
- ☐ 1 cup (90 g) rolled oats
- ☐ 1 cup (45 g) unprocessed bran
- ☐ ¹/₂ cup (60 g) grated low fat cheese
- ☐ 1 tablespoon grated Parmesan cheese
- ☐ 2 tablespoons chopped chives
- ☐ 2 tablespoons chopped fresh parsley
- ☐ 1 cup (250 mL) low fat milk
- ☐ 4 tablespoons safflower oil
- ☐ 3 egg whites

1   In a bowl combine flour, rolled oats, bran, low fat and Parmesan cheeses, chives and parsley. Make a well in the centre of the dry ingredients. Add milk and oil. Mix to combine.
2   Beat egg whites until stiff peaks form. Lightly fold through dough.
3   Spoon into a 23 cm x 12 cm non-stick loaf pan. Bake at 180°C for 40 minutes.

678 kilojoules (161 calories) per serve

Fat	8.2 g	med
Cholesterol	7 mg	low
Fibre	3.6 g	high
Sodium	202 mg	med

CARROT AND SESAME MUFFINS

Delicious light muffins are perfect weekend fare. Any leftovers can be frozen and used when time is short.

Makes 24

- ☐ 3 cups (375 g) self-raising flour
- ☐ ¹/₂ teaspoon bicarbonate of soda
- ☐ 1 teaspoon mixed spice
- ☐ ¹/₂ cup (85 g) brown sugar
- ☐ 1 large carrot, grated
- ☐ 4 tablespoons toasted sesame seeds
- ☐ 1 cup (170 g) sultanas
- ☐ 1 cup (250 g) low fat unflavoured yoghurt
- ☐ 1 cup (250 mL) skim milk
- ☐ 3 tablespoons melted poly- unsaturated margarine (salt reduced)
- ☐ 3 egg whites, lightly beaten

NUTRITION TIP

✧   For people who need to restrict salt as well as fat and cholesterol, try using a sodium-free baking powder in place of ordinary baking powder and self-raising flour, which supply a large amount of sodium. Based on potassium, it is available from pharmacies or specialty health food shops.
✧   Toasting bread does not reduce its carbohydrate or kilojoule (calorie) value. It merely drives off water and converts some of the starchy carbohydrate to dextrins and sugars.

1   Sift flour, bicarbonate of soda and mixed spice into a mixing bowl. Add brown sugar, carrot, sesame seeds and sultanas.
2   Combine yoghurt, milk, margarine and egg whites and stir into flour mixture. Mix until just combined. Spoon mixture into lightly greased muffin pans. Bake at 200°C for 20 minutes or until golden brown.

588 kilojoules (139 calories) per serve

Fat	3.6 g	low
Cholesterol	0 mg	low
Fibre	1.2 g	med
Sodium	214 mg	med

Above: Herb and Cheese Loaf, Carrot and Sesame Muffins
Left: Fruit Cheese Dip, Ricotta Hearts

Cheese

Hard yellow cheeses have to be restricted or avoided on cholesterol-lowering diets, due to their high content of saturated fat, cholesterol and salt. Cheddar, one of the most popular varieties, averages 33% fat and is classified as high fat, together with Swiss, Parmesan, blue-vein, feta, Brie and cream cheese.

It is best to select low fat soft cheeses such as cottage cheese, ricotta and quark, or use small quantities of reduced fat versions of your favourite varieties. Many manufacturers now provide reduced fat Cheddar, Edam, Parmesan, mozzarella and other kinds.

❖

RICOTTA HEARTS

Serves 6

- ☐ **2 teaspoons gelatine dissolved in 1 tablespoon hot water**
- ☐ **250 g ricotta cheese,**
- ☐ **¹/₂ cup (125 g) unflavoured low fat yoghurt**
- ☐ **2 tablespoons caster sugar**
- ☐ **1 egg white**
- ☐ **6 small strawberries, fanned**

STRAWBERRY COULIS
- ☐ **250 g strawberries, hulled**
- ☐ **1 tablespoon icing sugar**

KIWI COULIS
- ☐ **3 kiwi fruit, peeled and chopped**
- ☐ **1 tablespoon icing sugar**

1 Set gelatine mixture aside to cool. Rinse 6 heart shaped moulds in cold water and line with muslin.
2 Place ricotta, yoghurt, sugar and gelatine mixture in a bowl and mix well to combine.

3 Beat egg white until stiff peaks form and fold into cheese mixture. Fill moulds with cheese mixture. Place on a tray and leave to drain in the refrigerator overnight.
4 To make Strawberry Coulis, push strawberries through a sieve and mix in icing sugar. To make Kiwi Fruit Coulis, push kiwi fruit through a sieve and mix in icing sugar.
5 To serve, place a spoonful of each coulis on every plate and unmould the hearts in the centre. Garnish each heart with a fanned strawberry.

645 kilojoules (152 calories) per serve

Fat	4.0 g	low
Cholesterol	19 mg	low
Fibre	2.4 g	med
Sodium	111 mg	low

NUTRITION TIP

Low salt and reduced fat varieties of cheese are starting to appear in delicatessens and supermarkets. Salt is essential to cheese making, and cannot be completely eliminated, as it controls ripening and determines the final moisture content.

❖

FRUIT CHEESE DIP

Serves 6

- ☐ **¹/₂ cup (60 g) dried apricots, finely chopped**
- ☐ **¹/₂ cup (90 g) sultanas, finely chopped**
- ☐ **3 tablespoons glace ginger, finely chopped**
- ☐ **¹/₂ cup (125 mL) brandy**
- ☐ **250 g low fat ricotta cheese**
- ☐ **125 g reduced fat cream cheese**
- ☐ **¹/₂ teaspoon ground nutmeg**
- ☐ **2 teaspoons poppy seeds**

1 Place apricots, sultanas, ginger and brandy in a bowl, cover and soak overnight.
2 Place ricotta, cream cheese and nutmeg in a food processor or blender and process until combined. Drain fruit and mix into cheese mixture.
3 Chill until ready to serve. Sprinkle with poppy seeds and serve with melba toast or water crackers.

964 kilojoules (231 calories) per serve

Fat	10.7 g	med
Cholesterol	39 mg	low
Fibre	3.6 g	high
Sodium	180 mg	med

FILO CHICKEN PARCELS

For a wonderful luncheon, serve our tasty parcels with a green salad.

Serves 6

- ☐ **6 sheets filo pastry**
- ☐ **1 tablespoon olive oil**

FILLING
- ☐ **100 g broccoli, cut into small florets**
- ☐ **125 g cottage cheese**
- ☐ **1 tablespoon grated Parmesan cheese**
- ☐ **1 teaspoon Dijon mustard**
- ☐ **100 g cooked chicken, chopped**
- ☐ **freshly ground black pepper**

1　Brush each sheet of filo pastry with a little oil and fold in half.
2　Boil, steam or microwave broccoli until just tender. Drain and set aside.
3　Place cottage cheese, Parmesan cheese and mustard in a bowl and mix well to combine. Stir in broccoli and chicken. Season to taste with pepper. Place spoonfuls of mixture in the centre of each pastry sheet. Gather up the corners of the pastry over the filling to make a bag. Press together firmly and gently twist just above the filling to seal. Carefully fan out pastry tops and brush each parcel with remaining oil. Bake at 200°C for 20 minutes or until crisp and golden.

568 kilojoules (136 calories) per serve

Fat	5.4 g	med
Cholesterol	26 mg	low
Fibre	0.7 g	low
Sodium	163 mg	med

NUTRITION TIPS

✧　Cheese is a valuable source of calcium for strong bones and teeth, protein and riboflavin (vitamin B2). Because it is a concentrated form of milk, just 30 grams of cheese has the same food value as a 300 millilitre carton of milk. For people who do not consume milk or yoghurt, a small quantity of cheese each day is an important inclusion for calcium.

✧　Those who are unable to digest lactose (milk sugar) are usually able to eat firm varieties of cheese without ill effects. During cheesemaking, most of the lactose in milk is lost in the whey and any remaining is broken down as the cheese matures. Fresh unripened cheeses such as cottage cheese retain most of their lactose.

✧　Cheese makes a great snack. We have put together some cheesy snack ideas using low fat cheese which will allow you to indulge without worry.

✧　Season low fat cottage cheese with freshly ground black pepper and a few chopped fresh basil leaves. Place on a plain water cracker or crispbread and top with tomato and cucumber slices.

✧　Mix 2 tablespoons grated carrot, 1 tablespoon sultanas, 2 chopped dried apricots and a squeeze of lemon juice through 250 g ricotta cheese. Use as a topping on plain water crackers, crispbread or toast.

Filo Chicken Parcels, West Indian Chicken

KNOW YOUR CHEESES

LOW FAT	MEDIUM FAT	HIGH FAT
Cottage cheese	Edam	Cheddar
Creamed cottage cheese	Camembert	Gouda
Quark	Cheddar	Swiss
Ricotta (reduced fat)	Feta	Parmesan
	Mozzarella	Blue-vein
	Reduced-fat varieties of regular cheeses	Brie
		Stilton
		Gloucester
		Cream cheese
		Colby

Chicken

Chicken is a light and versatile white meat to include in a low fat, low cholesterol plan. Most of its fat lies just under the skin, which is easily removed for low fat cooking. The leanest cuts are breasts and breast fillets; the dark meat on thighs and drumsticks are higher in fat, although they can still be part of your diet. Sample our delicious recipes and discover how easy it is to prepare low fat fare.

❖

WEST INDIAN CHICKEN

Serves 4

- ☐ **750 g chicken pieces, skin removed**
- ☐ **1 teaspoon curry powder**
- ☐ **¹/4 teaspoon ground ginger**
- ☐ **¹/4 teaspoon ground cumin**
- ☐ **¹/4 teaspoon ground cardamom**
- ☐ **pinch chilli powder**
- ☐ **¹/4 teaspoon garam masala**
- ☐ **400 g canned pineapple pieces (no added sugar), drained and liquid reserved**
- ☐ **1 green capsicum, chopped**
- ☐ **freshly ground black pepper**

1   Score chicken pieces with a sharp knife. Combine curry powder, ginger, cumin, cardamom, chilli and garam masala and rub well into chicken pieces.
2   Place chicken in a shallow glass dish. Pour over reserved pineapple liquid and marinate for 2 hours. Remove chicken and grill slowly, turning and basting frequently with remaining pineapple liquid until tender.
3   Place pineapple pieces, any remaining liquid, capsicum and pepper to taste in a food processor or blender and process until smooth. Transfer to a saucepan and heat gently. To serve, place chicken on a serving platter and spoon over sauce.

856 kilojoules (206 calories) per serve

Fat	5.3 g	med
Cholesterol	86 mg	med
Fibre	1.9 g	med
Sodium	95 mg	low

Oriental Chicken Salad, Chicken and Spinach Parcels

❖

CHICKEN AND SPINACH PARCELS

If you are having a dinner party, these chicken parcels make a great main course. Prepare them earlier in the day and cook when required.

Serves 4

- ☐ **4 x 125 g boneless chicken fillets, skin removed**
- ☐ **4 tablespoons chicken stock**
- ☐ **4 tablespoons dry sherry**
- ☐ **freshly ground black pepper**

SPINACH FILLING
- ☐ **8 spinach leaves, stalks removed and leaves shredded**
- ☐ **1 large carrot, cut into thin strips**
- ☐ **1 stalk celery, cut into thin strips**
- ☐ **1 leek, cut into thin strips**
- ☐ **pinch ground nutmeg**
- ☐ **freshly ground black pepper**

1   Place chicken breasts between two sheets of plastic food wrap and pound lightly to flatten.
2   Steam or microwave spinach, carrot, celery and leek until tender. Refresh under cold running water. Pat dry on absorbent paper. Season to taste with nutmeg and pepper.
3   Cut four large squares of baking paper and top each with a chicken breast. Place spinach, carrot, celery and leek over half of each breast. Fold to enclose filling. Sprinkle with stock, sherry and pepper to taste. Seal the edges of the paper carefully and place on an oven tray. Bake at 200°C for 15–20 minutes or until tender. Season to taste with pepper. Chill for 1 hour before serving.

805 kilojoules (194 calories) per serve

Fat	*5.5 g*	*med*
Cholesterol	*86 mg*	*med*
Fibre	*2.7 g*	*med*
Sodium	*126 mg*	*low*

N U T R I T I O N T I P

Like all meats, chicken provides valuable protein, B vitamins, and minerals such as iron and zinc. Its iron content is only about one-third that of red meat, but is nevertheless well absorbed by the body.

❖

ORIENTAL CHICKEN SALAD

Our light chicken salad is easy to prepare and makes a tasty alternative to heavier, more traditional chicken salads.

Serves 3

- ☐ **2 x 125 g boneless chicken fillets, skin removed**
- ☐ **1 large carrot**
- ☐ **¹/₂ bunch watercress**
- ☐ **¹/₄ red cabbage, shredded**
- ☐ **100 g bean sprouts**
- ☐ **4 tablespoons lime juice**

MARINADE
- ☐ **2 tablespoons dry sherry**
- ☐ **1 tablespoon low salt soy sauce**
- ☐ **2 teaspoons hoisin sauce**
- ☐ **2 teaspoons peanut oil**
- ☐ **2 cloves garlic, crushed**

1   Place chicken fillets between two sheets of plastic food wrap and pound lightly to flatten.
2   To make marinade, combine sherry, soy sauce, hoisin sauce, peanut oil and garlic in a glass bowl. Add chicken fillets and marinate for 1–2 hours.
3   Remove chicken from marinade and barbecue or grill slowly, turning and basting frequently with remaining marinade. Cool and slice thinly.
4   Using a vegetable peeler, slice carrot thinly lengthways. Stand slices in iced water for 5–10 minutes. Drain and arrange attractively on individual serving plates with watercress, cabbage and bean sprouts. Sprinkle with lime juice and top with chicken slices. Serve chilled.

1310 kilojoules (313 calories) per serve

Fat	*6.9 g*	*med*
Cholesterol	*57 mg*	*med*
Fibre	*10.6 g*	*high*
Sodium	*320 mg*	*high*

Dressings and Sauces

Dressings and sauces are frequently a health hazard for the heart, with their rich content of butter, cream, oil, eggs or cheese. Ours have been designed with a minimum of these ingredients and yet are delicious and convenient – they will add a new interest to salads, vegetables, fish, lean meats and pasta. A serve for dressings and sauces in this book is one tablespoon.

HOT CURRY SAUCE

As a topping for baked potatoes or an accompaniment to steamed vegetables this easy-to-prepare sauce makes a tasty change.

Makes 2 cups (500 mL)

- ☐ **6 zucchini, peeled and chopped**
- ☐ **2 teaspoons polyunsaturated oil**
- ☐ **1 onion, chopped**
- ☐ **1 teaspoon curry powder**
- ☐ **¹/₂ teaspoon chilli sauce**
- ☐ **1 tablespoon chutney or relish**

1   Boil, steam or microwave zucchini. Drain and set aside to cool.
2   Heat oil in a non-stick frypan. Add onion and curry powder and cook for 4–5 minutes or until onion softens.
3   Place zucchini, onion mixture, chilli sauce and chutney in a food processor or blender and process until smooth. Pour into a saucepan and cook over low heat until sauce heats through.

44 kilojoules (11 calories) per serve

Fat	0.4 g	low
Cholesterol	0 mg	low
Fibre	0.5 g	low
Sodium	4 mg	low

CHEESE SAUCE

Use this cheese sauce when making cauliflower cheese or lasagne.

Makes 1 cup (250 mL)

- ☐ **1 cup (250 mL) skim milk**
- ☐ **pinch ground nutmeg**
- ☐ **1 tablespoon cornflour blended with 2 tablespoons skim milk**
- ☐ **1 tablespoon grated Parmesan cheese**
- ☐ **freshly ground black pepper**

1   Bring milk and nutmeg to boil. Whisk in cornflour mixture and simmer for 10 minutes, stirring constantly.
2   Stir in cheese and cook a further 2 minutes. Season to taste with pepper.

61 kilojoules (14 calories) per serve

Fat	0.3 g	low
Cholesterol	0 mg	low
Fibre	0 g	low
Sodium	23 mg	low

M I C R O W A V E I T

To make Cheese Sauce, place milk and nutmeg in a microwave-safe jug, whisk in cornflour mixture. Cook on HIGH (100%) for 2 minutes or until sauce thickens. Stir in cheese and season to taste with pepper.

FRESH TOMATO AND BASIL SAUCE

Fresh tomato sauces are great with vegetables, chicken, fish or lean meats.

Makes 2 cups (500 mL)

- ☐ **1 tablespoon olive oil**
- ☐ **1 large onion, sliced**
- ☐ **1 clove garlic, crushed**
- ☐ **6 large tomatoes, peeled and diced**
- ☐ **¹/₂ cup (125 mL) tomato juice (no added salt)**
- ☐ **2 tablespoons chopped fresh basil**
- ☐ **freshly ground black pepper**

1   Heat oil in a saucepan. Cook onion and garlic for 4–5 minutes or until onion softens. Stir in tomatoes and tomato juice and simmer for 5 minutes.
2   Add 1 tablespoon basil and simmer for a further 1 hour or until sauce thickens and reduces. Just before serving, stir in remaining basil and season with pepper.

84 kilojoules (20 calories) per serve

Fat	0.7 g	low
Cholesterol	0 mg	low
Fibre	1.3 g	low
Sodium	22 mg	low

From left: Fresh Tomato and Basil Sauce, Cheese Sauce, Hot Curry Sauce

APPLE AND HERB DRESSING

Use this dressing as an alternative to the traditional French dressing or try it as a tasty dressing for rice salad.

Makes 1 1/2 cups (375 mL)

- ☐ **1 cup (250 mL) unsweetened apple juice**
- ☐ **3 tablespoons apple cider vinegar**
- ☐ **1 clove garlic, crushed**
- ☐ **1 tablespoon finely chopped chives**
- ☐ **2 tablespoons finely chopped fresh parsley**
- ☐ **freshly ground black pepper**

Place apple juice, vinegar, garlic, chives and parsley in a screwtop jar. Season to taste with pepper. Shake well to combine.

20 kilojoules (5 calories) per serve

Fat	0 g	low
Cholesterol	0 mg	low
Fibre	0.1 g	low
Sodium	2 mg	low

NUTRITION TIP

✦ When using commercial sauces, look for the many new 'no-oil' and 'fat-reduced' products now available.

✦ Check ingredients on the label; many mayonnaises are labelled 'poly-unsaturated' or 'egg-free', but are nevertheless high in fat.

MINTY LEMON DRESSING

Makes 1 cup (250 mL)

- ☐ **3/4 cup (190 mL) unflavoured low fat yoghurt**
- ☐ **1 clove garlic, crushed**
- ☐ **2 tablespoons lemon juice**
- ☐ **2 tablespoons chopped fresh mint**
- ☐ **freshly ground black pepper**

Combine yoghurt, garlic, lemon juice, mint and pepper in a bowl. Whisk to combine.

37 kilojoules (9 calories) per serve

Fat	0.2 g	low
Cholesterol	0 mg	low
Fibre	0.1 g	low
Sodium	13 mg	low

MOCK SOUR CREAM

One of the first foods to go when you start thinking about lowering your cholesterol intake is sour cream. Use our Mock Sour Cream in its place as a topping on potatoes, in soups or blended into casseroles.

Makes 3/4 cup (190 mL)

- ☐ **3 tablespoons low fat milk**
- ☐ **1 teaspoon skim milk powder**
- ☐ **3/4 cup (190 g) low fat cottage cheese**
- ☐ **2 teaspoons white vinegar**

1   Whisk together low fat milk and skim milk powder

2   Combine half the milk mixture with half the cheese in a blender and blend until smooth. Add remaining milk mixture and cheese and continue to blend until a smooth mixture resembling sour cream is formed. Mix in vinegar.

94 kilojoules (23 calories) per serve

Fat	0.3 g	low
Cholesterol	3 mg	low
Fibre	0 g	low
Sodium	32 mg	low

COOK'S TIP

If kept in an airtight container in the refrigerator, Mock Sour Cream will keep for two to three days. You may add a little more vinegar if you prefer a more sour taste.

ITALIAN DRESSING

This tasty dressing can be prepared in advance and kept in the refrigerator to use as required.

Makes 1 cup (250 mL)

- ☐ ³/₄ cup (190 mL) red wine vinegar
- ☐ 2 tablespoons olive oil
- ☐ 1 clove garlic, crushed
- ☐ 2 teaspoons chopped fresh oregano
- ☐ 1 teaspoons chopped fresh basil
- ☐ freshly ground black pepper

In a screwtop jar combine vinegar, oil, garlic, oregano and basil. Shake to combine. Season to taste with pepper.

100 kilojoules (24 calories) per serve

Fat	2.7 g	low
Cholesterol	0 mg	low
Fibre	0.1 g	low
Sodium	0 mg	low

❖

TOFU MAYONNAISE

This delicious mayonnaise made with tofu is a cholesterol free alternative.

Makes 1¹/₂ cups (375 mL)

- ☐ 250 g tofu
- ☐ 1 teaspoon Dijon-style mustard
- ☐ 3 tablespoons cider vinegar
- ☐ ¹/₂ cup (125 mL) olive oil
- ☐ freshly ground black pepper

1 Place tofu, mustard and 1 tablespoon vinegar in a food processor or blender and process until smooth.
2 With the machine running, slowly add 2 tablespoons oil then 1 tablespoon vinegar. Continue in this way until all the oil and vinegar is used. Season to taste with pepper.

243 kilojoules (67 calories) per serve

Fat	7.1 g	med
Cholesterol	0 mg	low
Fibre	0 g	low
Sodium	0 mg	low

From left: Minty Lemon Dressing, Apple and Herb Dressing, Italian Dressing, Tofu Mayonnaise, Mock Sour Cream

FAT FIGHTER

Flavoured vinegars are a boon as they add taste and interest without kilojoules (calories) or fat. Try making your own flavoured vinegars by steeping herbs, fruit or garlic in white or cider vinegar. Use flavoured vinegars in dressings, sauces and pickles that normally call for vinegar.

Eggs

Eggs are limited to two per week, because of their high cholesterol content. At around 250 milligrams, just one egg brings you close to the recommended maximum of 300 milligrams a day. Virtually all the cholesterol and fat lies in the yolk; the white can be used freely, as can yolk-free substitute mixes.

Remember that the number of eggs eaten must be assessed in terms of your overall diet and blood cholesterol reading. If your intake of fats is low, and your blood cholesterol level within limits, then you could well enjoy more eggs more often. Check with your doctor or dietitian first.

Egg substitute is made from egg whites, skim milk powder, polyunsaturated vegetable oil, emulsifier and beta-carotene (the yellow-orange colour of carrots and many other vegetables). Its cholesterol is only a fraction that of eggs, and its fat is high in polyunsaturates. Although it cannot create a whole poached or boiled egg, it can be used to make omelettes, scrambled eggs, pancakes and in general cooking.

Polyunsaturated eggs contain a greater proportion of poly-unsaturated fat, but their cholesterol count is similar to ordinary eggs. The chickens are reared on a special feed rich in polyunsaturated seeds, blended from soyameal, sunflower seeds and grains, which alters the composition of the eggs they lay.

3 Key steps to eating for a healthy heart

Make your favourite recipes lighter and lower

Eating for a healthy heart doesn't mean giving up all your favourites. Cut back and keep the essential flavour with small changes to ingredients and cooking methods.

Reduce fats

1 Use as little oil, butter or margarine as possible when cooking. Cook in a non-stick pan or use a non-stick food spray. When stir-frying it is easy to cook 2 or 3 cups of chopped vegetables with just one tablespoon of oil in a preheated wok. Try lighter sauces or no-oil commerical salad dressings. Avoid snacks and keep to three meals a day. Biscuits, cakes, chocolates and packet snack foods are 'hidden' sources of fat (usually saturated).

Reduce salt intake

2 Gradually reduce the amount of salt you use in cooking and your taste buds will adapt after 2 to 3 weeks. Add extra flavour with double quantities of herbs and spices. Chilli, basil, garlic, coriander, rosemary and nutmeg are good choices for full flavour without salt. Beware salty sauces, they raise the salt content of your cooking (even if you're not actually adding salt) and should not be splashed on liberally. Shop for no-added-salt or salt reduced ingredients like canned tomatoes, cheese, margarine, sauce mixes, canned salmon and tuna.

Increase fibre

3 Switch to less refined foods such as brown rice, wholemeal bread and wholegrain or bran cereals rather than the more refined ones. Do not peel vegetables and fruit unless really necessary, instead just scrub them with a vegetable brush. Increase the serve size of vegetables, salads, grains and pasta on your plate and give more modest serves of meat. Create your own fresh fruit desserts in place of the sweet treats you're now indulging in.

STOCK TAKING

Homemade stocks are easy to make and contain none of the preservatives and salt of commercially prepared products.

CHICKEN STOCK

To make 2 litres of chicken stock you will require the carcass of one chicken, with all visible fat and any remaining skin removed. Place carcass in a large saucepan with 1 diced carrot, 6 stalks sliced celery, 2 large diced onions, herbs of your choice and $^1/2$ teaspoon of peppercorns. Pour over 3 litres of water and bring to the boil, reduce heat and simmer for 2 hours, stirring occasionally. Strain stock and refrigerate overnight. Skim any fat from the surface and use as required.

VEGETABLE STOCK

To make 2 litres of vegetable stock you will require 1 head celery, 2 large onions, 2 carrots, a bunch of parsley and $^1/2$ teaspoon peppercorns. Peel onions and chop. Wash and chop the celery, carrots and parsley, do not discard the celery leaves or the parsley stalks but keep them to use in the stock. Place all ingredients in a large saucepan with 2.5 litres of water. Bring to the boil, reduce heat and simmer for 30 minutes, stirring occasionally. Remove from heat and allow to cool. Puree the cold vegetable mixture, push through a sieve and use stock as required.

BEEF STOCK

Beef stock is made in much the same way as chicken stock but instead of using a chicken carcass use 500 g diced shin beef and 500 g marrow bones cut into pieces then make up as for chicken stock.

FREEZE IT

Make a quantity of stock and freeze it in $^1/2$ cup (125 mL) or 1 cup (250 mL) portions, to use as required. It is also a good idea to freeze some in ice cube containers for those times when you may only require one or two tablespoons of stock.

Make your own stock for natural goodness and flavour

SIMPLE SUBSTITUTES
Low fat, low cholesterol

IF A RECIPE CALLS FOR:	USE:
Sour cream	Unflavoured non fat yoghurt, buttermilk, or soft tofu
Cream	Soft tofu, unflavoured non fat yoghurt, or canned evaporated skim milk
Cream cheese	Ricotta cheese blended with vanilla essence, a little caster sugar and grated lemon rind
Melted cheese on top	Half grated cheese, half breadcrumbs, half grated cheese, half crushed cornflakes or a fine sprinkle of sesame seeds
Butter	Polyunsaturated margarine, low fat spread or half butter, half oil
Coconut milk, coconut cream	One tablespoon desiccated coconut plus evaporated skim milk or unflavoured non fat yoghurt
Bacon	Lean ham
Shortcrust or puff pastry	Filo pastry or make a one crust pie

Essential Essences

Most desserts and sweets are loaded with fat and sugar. These are not only a danger to your heart, but also to your waistline and teeth, especially chewy sweet foods that cling around teeth for hours after eating. Here we present a selection of lighter, healthier alternatives, that we've flavoured with essences. They create a luscious flavour and aroma, needing only a touch of sugar or honey to taste perfect.

❖

APRICOT ALMOND DELIGHT

The delicate flavour and interesting texture of juicy apricots and toasted almonds complement each other beautifully in this light and fluffy dessert – perfect after any main course.

Serves 4

☐ **250 g dried apricots**
☐ **1 tablespoon gelatine, dissolved in 4 tablespoons hot water**
☐ **1 cup (250 mL) evaporated skim milk**
☐ **3 tablespoons caster sugar**
☐ **1 teaspoon almond essence**
☐ **1 tablespoon finely chopped toasted almonds**

1   Place apricots in a bowl, pour in sufficient water to cover and leave to soak overnight.
2   Drain apricots and place in a food processor or blender with gelatine mixture, skim milk, sugar and almond essence. Process until smooth. Pour into individual glasses. Refrigerate until firm. To serve sprinkle with almonds.

1105 kilojoules (260 calories) per serve

Fat	1.4 g	low
Cholesterol	2 mg	low
Fibre	18 g	high
Sodium	109 mg	low

❖

COFFEE MERINGUES

Who would believe that these delicious morsels are free of fat and cholesterol? They are perfect to serve with coffee or as an afternoon tea treat.

Makes 30

☐ **³/₄ cup (185 g) raw sugar**
☐ **3 tablespoons water**
☐ **1 egg white**
☐ **1 teaspoon white vinegar**
☐ **2 teaspoons cornflour**
☐ **2 teaspoons coffee essence**

1   Place sugar and water in a small saucepan, over a medium heat, stirring until sugar dissolves. Bring to the boil and boil for 1–2 minutes. Brush any sugar grains from sides of pan with a wet pastry brush.
2   Beat egg white until stiff peaks form. Continue beating while pouring in hot syrup in a thin stream, a little at a time. Beat until meringue is thick. Fold in vinegar, cornflour and coffee essence.
3   Place mixture in a large piping bag fitted with a fluted tube. Pipe 4 cm stars onto greased and lined oven trays. Bake at 140°C for 1 hour or until firm and dry. Cool in oven with door ajar.

162 kilojoules (38 calories) per serve

Fat	0 g	low
Cholesterol	0 mg	low
Fibre	0 g	low
Sodium	3 mg	low

❖

STRAWBERRY AND RICE CREAM

A creamy fruit dessert that will be a hit with all the family. For something different you might like to try apricots with almond essence.

Serves 4

☐ **¹/₂ cup (100 g) short grain rice**
☐ **200 g fresh strawberries, hulled and halved**
☐ **¹/₂ cup (125 mL) low fat unflavoured yoghurt**
☐ **³/₄ cup (190 mL) evaporated skim milk**
☐ **1 tablespoon caster sugar**
☐ **¹/₂ teaspoon strawberry essence**

1   Cook rice in a saucepan of boiling water for 10–12 minutes or until just tender. Drain and rinse under cold running water.
2   Combine rice, strawberries, yoghurt, milk, sugar and essence. Spoon rice cream into four individual dishes. Refrigerate until well chilled.

631 kilojoules (150 calories) per serve

Fat	3.0 g	low
Cholesterol	4 mg	low
Fibre	1.9 g	med
Sodium	114 mg	low

THE ESSENCE

✧   Essences can be produced in one of three ways: by steeping the ingredient in water or alcohol; by distillation; or by synthetic chemical compounds. By far the best are those made naturally, the flavour is truer and while you will find them a little more expensive the end result is well worth it.

✧   Essences should be purchased in small quantities and are best if used within three months.

✧   Always store essences in tightly stoppered bottles in a cool, dark place, this will ensure that the maximum flavour is retained.

✧   It is believed that rosewater – one of the sweet smelling essences – was originally brought to India by the Moguls. It became a fashionable flavouring in England during the 16th Century and remained a staple ingredient until Victorian times.

✧   One of the first uses for rosewater in the Western world was to scent the finger bowls of the wealthy.

✧   As the name implies rosewater is extracted from roses.

✧   Rosewater and orange flower water are essential ingredients in Indian and Middle Eastern cooking, where they are used in both savoury and sweet dishes.

✧   Other popular essences include peppermint, almond and vanilla.

Apricot Almond Delight, Coffee Meringues, Strawberry and Rice Cream

Fish

Fish – light, appetising and nutritious – plays a key role in lowering your cholesterol. It is low in fat and cholesterol, it helps with weight control, being so low in kilojoules (calories), and it is rich in omega-3 fats, which are now believed to protect the heart against disease.

Omega-3 fats reduce the tendency for the blood to clot and so lessen its 'stickiness'. They can lower blood pressure and reduce the fatty build up on blood vessel walls. They occur in all fish but are particularly rich in oily fish like herring, salmon, tuna, mackerel, sardines and ocean trout. Aim to eat fish at least three times a week, including fresh, frozen and canned for variety. Follow the ideas in our recipes for new and interesting ways to prepare fish.

FAT FIGHTERS

Forget frying fish in fat. Instead, try one of the many methods of cooking fish without fat.

✧ Microwave in a little skim milk and chopped herbs. Cook 500 g fish fillets covered on HIGH (100%) for 4–5 minutes.

✧ Poach in a flavoursome stock.

✧ 'Dry fry' in a pan that has been sprayed with non-stick spray or lined with a silicon-coated paper liner.

✧ Barbecue whole fish wrapped in foil. Squeeze lemon juice into the cavity of the fish and fill with lemon slices and sprigs of dill or mint. Wrap in two layers of foil and cook on barbecue for 25–30 minutes, or until flesh flakes when tested with a fork.

Fish and Basil Vermicelli Soup, Salmon Cutlets with Basil Sauce, Thai Flavoured Whole Chilli Fish

24

THAI FLAVOURED WHOLE CHILLI FISH

For this delicious fish dish we used baby bream but you might like to use small snapper or similar small fish.

Serves 4

- ☐ **4 small whole fish**
- ☐ **1 red chilli, seeded and finely sliced**

MARINADE

- ☐ **1 tablespoon chopped fresh coriander (including root and stem)**
- ☐ **1 teaspoon grated fresh ginger**
- ☐ **1 clove garlic, crushed**
- ☐ **¹/₂ teaspoon chilli paste (sambal ulek)**
- ☐ **1 teaspoon sugar**
- ☐ **2 teaspoons ground turmeric**
- ☐ **1 tablespoon peanut oil**
- ☐ **1 tablespoon vinegar**
- ☐ **1 tablespoon water**

1   Clean fish and rinse under cold running water. Pat dry with absorbent kitchen paper and arrange in a deep tray.
2   To make marinade, combine coriander, ginger, garlic, chilli paste, sugar, turmeric, oil, vinegar and water. Pour over fish and rub well into the skin and flesh. Cover and refrigerate for 2 hours.
3   Barbecue or grill fish for 3–4 minutes each side or until flesh flakes when tested with a fork. Serve fish with any remaining marinade. Top with chilli slices.

945 kilojoules (224 calories) per serve

Fat	8.4 g	med
Cholesterol	120 mg	med
Fibre	0.3 g	low
Sodium	240 mg	med

SALMON CUTLETS WITH BASIL SAUCE

Serves 4

- ☐ **4 x 125 g salmon cutlets**
- ☐ **freshly ground black pepper**

BASIL SAUCE

- ☐ **1 bunch fresh basil, leaves removed**
- ☐ **2 tablespoons lemon juice**
- ☐ **1 tablespoon olive oil**
- ☐ **1 clove garlic, crushed**
- ☐ **4 tablespoons grated Parmesan cheese**
- ☐ **3 tablespoons pine nuts, toasted**

1   Place fish cutlets in a glass dish and season with pepper to taste.
2   To make sauce, place basil leaves, lemon juice, olive oil, garlic, Parmesan and pine nuts in a food processor or blender and process until smooth.
3   Spoon half the basil sauce over fish. Cover and refrigerate for 30 minutes. Grill or barbecue fish for 4–5 minutes each side or until flesh flakes when tested with a fork. Serve fish with remaining sauce.

963 kilojoules (230 calories) per serve

Fat	14.2 g	high
Cholesterol	84 mg	med
Fibre	0.7 g	low
Sodium	274 mg	high

FISH AND BASIL VERMICELLI SOUP

Serves 6

- ☐ **1 tablespoon olive oil**
- ☐ **1 onion, finely chopped**
- ☐ **2 cloves garlic, crushed**
- ☐ **800 g canned tomatoes (no added salt), undrained and mashed**
- ☐ **3 tablespoons tomato paste (no added salt)**
- ☐ **¹/₂ teaspoon sugar**
- ☐ **3 cups (750 mL) water**
- ☐ **1 kg fish cutlets, such as mackerel or groper**
- ☐ **2 teaspoons grated lemon rind**
- ☐ **2 tablespoons finely chopped fresh basil**
- ☐ **100 g vermicelli**
- ☐ **freshly ground black pepper**

1   Heat oil in a large saucepan. Cook onion and garlic for 2–3 minutes or until onion softens. Stir in tomatoes, tomato paste, sugar and 1 cup (250 mL) water. Bring to the boil, reduce heat and simmer covered for 10 minutes.
2   Poach fish cutlets in remaining 2 cups (500 mL) of water, drain and reserve cooking liquid. Remove skin from fish and flake into large pieces.
3   Add lemon rind, basil, vermicelli and reserved liquid. Cover and simmer for 5–6 minutes or until vermicelli is cooked. Season to taste with pepper. Stir in fish and cook 2–3 minutes to heat through.

938 kilojoules (183 calories) per serve

Fat	6.9 g	med
Cholesterol	100 mg	med
Fibre	1.8 g	med
Sodium	216 mg	med

MARINATED CITRUS FISH SALAD

Serves 4

- ☐ **500 g white fish fillets, cut into strips**
- ☐ **2 teaspoons pink peppercorns**
- ☐ **2 teaspoons orange rind**
- ☐ **400 g canned lychees, drained**
- ☐ **1 orange, peeled and segmented**
- ☐ **1 grapefruit, peeled and segmented**
- ☐ **¹/₂ bunch fresh watercress**

MARINADE

- ☐ **1 tablespoon grape seed oil**
- ☐ **¹/₂ cup (125 mL) orange juice**
- ☐ **1 tablespoon grapefruit juice**
- ☐ **1 tablespoon lime juice**
- ☐ **1 tablespoon tarragon vinegar**
- ☐ **1 teaspoon grated fresh ginger**

1 Place fish in a glass bowl with peppercorns and orange rind.

2 To make marinade, combine oil, orange, grapefruit and lime juices, vinegar and ginger. Pour marinade over fish, cover and refrigerate overnight.

3 To serve, remove fish with a slotted spoon to a bowl. Add lychees, orange and grapefruit segments to fish mixture. Toss lightly to combine. Arrange watercress on a plate and top with fish salad. Spoon over a little of the marinade.

1104 kilojoules (262 calories) per serve

Fat	*7.1 g*	*med*
Cholesterol	*75 mg*	*med*
Fibre	*3.4 g*	*high*
Sodium	*177 mg*	*med*

❖

TUNA PATE

Serves 4

- ☐ **200 g canned tuna in springwater, drained**
- ☐ **1 small Lebanese cucumber, peeled, seeded and chopped**
- ☐ **1 cup (250 mL) tomato juice (no added salt)**
- ☐ **1 ¹/₂ tablespoons gelatine dissolved in ¹/₂ cup (125 mL) hot water**
- ☐ **1 tablespoon chopped fresh dill**
- ☐ **1 teaspoon grated lemon rind**
- ☐ **1 teaspoon lemon juice**
- ☐ **2 teaspoons finely chopped capers**
- ☐ **1 teaspoon horseradish relish**
- ☐ **3 tablespoons low fat unflavoured yoghurt**
- ☐ **freshly ground black pepper**

1 Place tuna, cucumber, tomato juice, gelatine mixture, dill, lemon rind, lemon juice, capers, horseradish relish and yoghurt in a food processor or blender. Process until smooth.

2 Season to taste with pepper. Pour tuna mixture into four individual dishes. Refrigerate until firm.

371 kilojoules (88 calories) per serve

Fat	*5.8 g*	*low*
Cholesterol	*23 mg*	*low*
Fibre	*0.8 g*	*low*
Sodium	*108 mg*	*low*

SATAY SALMON PATTIES

Serves 6

- ☐ **440 g canned red salmon, no-added-salt, well drained and flaked**
- ☐ **3 medium potatoes, cooked and mashed**
- ☐ **2 tablespoons plain flour**
- ☐ **1 clove garlic, crushed**
- ☐ **1 teaspoon grated fresh ginger**
- ☐ **1 teaspoon grated lemon rind**
- ☐ **1 small red chilli, seeded and finely chopped**
- ☐ **2 teaspoons low salt soy sauce**
- ☐ **1 teaspoon curry paste (vindaloo)**
- ☐ **pinch of chilli powder**
- ☐ **1/4 teaspoon ground cumin**
- ☐ **2 tablespoons finely chopped unsalted roasted peanuts**
- ☐ **1/2 cup (60 g) dry breadcrumbs**
- ☐ **1/2 cup (60 g) sesame seeds**
- ☐ **1 tablespoon peanut oil**

1 Combine salmon, potatoes, flour, garlic, ginger, lemon rind, chilli, soy sauce, curry paste, chilli powder, cumin and peanuts in a large mixing bowl.

2 Combine breadcrumbs and sesame seeds. Shape salmon mixture into twelve patties. Roll in sesame seed mixture and refrigerate for 30 minutes. Brush the base of a non-stick frypan with oil and heat. Cook patties for 3–4 minutes each side or until golden brown. Remove from pan and drain on absorbent kitchen paper.

1635 kilojoules (389 calories) per serve

Fat	*19.1 g*	*high*
Cholesterol	*66 mg*	*med*
Fibre	*2.1 g*	*med*
Sodium	*161 mg*	*med*

FISH KEBABS WITH BANANA SAUCE

Serves 6

- ☐ **750 g white fish fillets, cut into 5 cm cubes**
- ☐ **1 tablespoon peanut oil**

BANANA SAUCE
- ☐ **20 g polyunsaturated margarine**
- ☐ **3 tablespoons brown sugar**
- ☐ **3/4 cup (190 mL) evaporated skim milk**
- ☐ **3/4 cup (185 g) low fat unflavoured yoghurt**
- ☐ **4 medium bananas, sliced**
- ☐ **2 tablespoons chopped nuts, toasted**

1 Thread fish onto twelve oiled wooden skewers. Brush with oil and grill or barbecue for 3–4 minutes each side.
2 To make sauce, melt margarine in a frypan. Remove pan from heat.
3 Dissolve brown sugar in evaporated milk. Stir evaporated milk mixture and yoghurt into melted margarine. Add bananas and nuts and cook gently over low heat for 1–2 minutes.
4 Arrange kebabs on a serving plate, spoon over sauce and serve immediately.

1523 kilojoules (362 calories) per serve

Fat	*12.3 g*	*med*
Cholesterol	*78 mg*	*med*
Fibre	*2.3 g*	*med*
Sodium	*256 mg*	*high*

Above: Satay Salmon Patties, Tuna Pate
Left: Marinated Citrus Fish Salad, Fish Kebabs with Banana Sauce

NUTRITION TIPS

When using tuna and salmon canned in brine, drain off as much liquid as possible and add some cold water to the can. Drain off again and use fish as specified in the recipe. This removes over half the salt content and is handy when no added salt or salt reduced products are not available.

❖ Fish can actually be a good source of bone-building calcium, an essential mineral mainly derived from milk! The edible bones of tiny fish like whitebait, canned salmon and sardines can be consumed with the flesh and provide substantial amounts of calcium.

FISH CUTLETS WITH ITALIAN SAUCE

Serves 4

- ☐ **4 x 150 g white fish cutlets**
- ☐ **2 tablespoons lemon juice**
- ☐ **6 shallots, finely chopped**
- ☐ **1 clove garlic, crushed**
- ☐ **400 g canned tomatoes (no added salt)**
- ☐ **200 g button mushrooms, sliced**
- ☐ **$^1/_2$ cup (125 mL) red wine**
- ☐ **2 teaspoons finely chopped fresh basil**
- ☐ **$^1/_2$ teaspoon dried oregano**
- ☐ **freshly ground black pepper**
- ☐ **2 tablespoons grated Parmesan cheese**

1 Brush fish cutlets with lemon juice. Place under a preheated griller and cook for 4–5 minutes each side. Remove from griller and keep warm.

2 Place shallots, garlic, tomatoes, mushrooms, wine, basil, oregano and pepper to taste in a saucepan. Bring to the boil. Reduce heat and simmer gently for 8–10 minutes.

3 Arrange fish cutlets on serving plates. Spoon sauce over and top with Parmesan cheese.

876 kilojoules (206 calories) per serve

Fat	4.5 g	low
Cholesterol	92 mg	med
Fibre	1.8 g	med
Sodium	225 mg	med

Left: Fish Cutlets with Italian Sauce
Right: Salmon Souffles

FISHY TALES
A guide to buying fresh fish

	LOOK FOR	WATCH OUT FOR
Fillets	Fillets should be shiny and firm with a pleasant sea smell	Fillets that are dull, soft, discoloured or 'ooze' water when touched indicate fish that is past its best.
Whole Fish	Whole fish should have a pleasant sea smell and a bright lustre to the skin. Gills should be red and the eyes bright and bulging. When touched, the flesh should be firm and springy.	Dull-coloured fish with sunken eyes should be avoided at all costs.

SALMON SOUFFLES

Serves 4

- ☐ **220 g canned red salmon, no added salt, drained and flaked**
- ☐ **100 g bottled oysters, drained, rinsed and chopped**
- ☐ **2 teaspoons finely chopped capers**
- ☐ **1 teaspoon finely chopped fresh dill**
- ☐ **2–3 dashes Tabasco sauce**
- ☐ **1 cup (250 g) low fat cottage cheese**
- ☐ **freshly ground black pepper**
- ☐ **4 egg whites**

1   Combine salmon, oysters, capers, dill, Tabasco and cottage cheese in a bowl. Season to taste with pepper.

2   Beat egg whites until stiff peaks form and fold lightly through salmon mixture. Spoon into four lightly greased individual souffle dishes and bake at 200°C for 30–35 minutes.

550 kilojoules (132 calories) per serve

Fat	*2.2 g*	*low*
Cholesterol	*54 mg*	*med*
Fibre	*0.2 g*	*low*
Sodium	*385 mg*	*high*

COOK'S TIP

When incorporating egg whites into a mixture, firstly mix in 1 tablespoon of the beaten egg whites, this loosens the mixture and makes it easier to fold in the remaining egg whites.

FINISHING TOUCHES

Fruit

Fresh fruit – juicy, sweet and luscious – is one of the nicest and healthiest ways to end a meal. With fruit, you can satisfy a sweet tooth, and keep your heart healthy too. And for day-to-day sweets, nothing can compare with a beautiful ripe peach, a crunchy apple or a juicy pear for nutrition, convenience and flavour.

Fruit is good for your heart because it has negligible amounts of fat and lots of fibre. Its fibre is rich in gums and pectins, which are known to lower blood cholesterol and slow the absorption of food. The fibre also creates 'bulk' and makes fruit a filling snack between meals.

Dried fruits are a useful addition to your diet. Sultanas, raisins, dried apricots, dates, prunes and figs, have a natural sweetness (being high in fruit sugars), no fat, and an excellent fibre content. Yoghurt and desserts are enlivened with a handful of dried fruit; meat and poultry team particularly well with apricots, currants and prunes; salads take on a new air with a touch of fruity sweetness.

We've devised a collection of fruity recipes to inspire and delight you and your family.

All recipes are sweetened subtly, with a little sugar or honey, sometimes with a dash of liqueur. This allows the fruit's delectable flavour to come through, enhanced with the help of spices or grated rinds.

Blueberry Mousse, Mango Raita, Hot Bananas and Oranges

BLUEBERRY MOUSSE

This pretty dessert is the perfect way to finish any dinner party. When fresh blueberries are in season they are the ideal garnish.

Serves 8

- ☐ **400 g canned blueberries, drained and liquid reserved**
- ☐ **3 tablespoons caster sugar**
- ☐ **2 tablespoons gelatine**
- ☐ **1 cup (250 mL) evaporated skim milk, chilled**
- ☐ **1 cup (250 g) low fat unflavoured yoghurt**

1   In a food processor or blender puree blueberries and sugar. Strain and discard skins. Dissolve gelatine in ³/₄ cup (185 mL) of warmed reserved blueberry liquid. Whip evaporated milk until thick and beat in yoghurt. Mix in gelatine mixture and fold through blueberry puree.
2   Spoon mousse into a wet mould, or eight individual moulds, cover and chill until set. Unmould and serve.

657 kilojoules (154 calories) per serve

Fat	0.5 g	low
Cholesterol	4 mg	low
Fibre	2.2 g	med
Sodium	116 mg	low

MANGO RAITA

Raitas are soothing yoghurt-based relishes. Traditionally served with curries, they act as a palate cooler. We have used mangoes and bananas in our raita, you might prefer to use only mangoes or bananas.

Serves 6

- ☐ **2 cups (500 g) low fat unflavoured yoghurt**
- ☐ **1 mango, diced**
- ☐ **1 banana, diced**
- ☐ **2 tablespoons finely chopped fresh mint**
- ☐ **¹/₂ teaspoon ground cumin**
- ☐ **pinch chilli powder**

Beat yoghurt until smooth. Fold in mango, banana, mint, cumin and chilli powder.

373 kilojoules (89 calories) per serve

Fat	1.0 g	low
Cholesterol	6 mg	low
Fibre	1.3 g	med
Sodium	68 mg	low

NUTRITION TIPS

Most fruit provide vitamins, but some stand head and shoulders above the rest. Citrus fruit, berries, guava, kiwi fruit and pawpaw are the fruit richest in vitamin C, and worth eating on a daily basis. Orange-coloured fruit like apricots, mangoes, and rockmelon are rich in beta-carotene (the precursor of vitamin A).

✧   If your children refuse to eat vegetables, remember that fruit is the ideal substitute. Fruit supplies the same nutrients as vegetables, notably vitamins A and C, fibre and essential minerals such as potassium. Most children will happily tuck into a piece of fruit or cut-up portions with no worries.

✧   Beware of too much fruit juice! Fruit juice is fruit in concentrated form, with its fibre removed. Drinking a glass of orange juice takes no effort. Eating your way through the equivalent of two or three oranges is much harder. The kilojoules (calories) are the same!

HOT BANANAS AND ORANGES

Barbecuing is the perfect way to cook this easy dessert. But it is just as good baked in the oven.

Serves 4

- ☐ **1 teaspoon polyunsaturated oil**
- ☐ **4 bananas, peeled and sliced in half lengthways**
- ☐ **4 tablespoons orange juice**
- ☐ **1 orange, segmented**
- ☐ **1 tablespoon brown sugar**

1   Cut four pieces of aluminium foil large enough to wrap around the bananas. Brush foil very lightly with polyunsaturated oil. Place two banana halves side by side on each piece of foil. Sprinkle 1 tablespoon orange juice over each banana. Divide orange segments and sugar into four portions and spoon over bananas.
2   Wrap foil around bananas and oranges to form a parcel. Cook on the barbecue for 15–20 minutes or in the oven at 180°C.

681 kilojoules (163 calories) per serve

Fat	1.2 g	low
Cholesterol	0 mg	low
Fibre	4.3 g	high
Sodium	3 mg	low

BERRY STRUDEL

For our strudel we use a little polyunsaturated oil instead of butter and in this way provide the perfect dessert for any cholesterol watcher.

Serves 8

- ☐ **6 sheets filo pastry**
- ☐ **1 tablespoon polyunsaturated oil**
- ☐ **2 tablespoons icing sugar, sifted**

FILLING

- ☐ **200 g fresh raspberries**
- ☐ **250 g fresh strawberries, halved**
- ☐ **1 tablespoon caster sugar**
- ☐ **3 tablespoons ground almonds**

1 Brush two sheets of pastry with oil and stack alternately with unoiled sheets.

2 Combine strawberries, raspberries and sugar, toss to combine.

3 Sprinkle pastry with almonds, top with berry mixture, leaving 2.5 cm around all edges. Fold in the long edges of the pastry. Starting from the short edge roll up the strudel. Place on an oven tray lined with baking paper. Bake at 200°C for 20–25 minutes or until golden. Just before serving sprinkle with icing sugar.

581 kilojoules (138 calories) per serve

Fat	6.1 g	med
Cholesterol	0 mg	low
Fibre	4.0 g	high
Sodium	77 mg	low

> ## COOK'S TIP
> It is easy to lower fat intake when using filo pastry. Instead of brushing every sheet of pastry with oil, just brush every second sheet, the result will still be crispy filo pastry but you have reduced fat content by half!

Berry Strudel, Watermelon and Strawberry Sorbet

Fruit Cake

❖

WATERMELON AND STRAWBERRY SORBET

Sorbets or water ices are light and refreshing. The perfect dessert to serve at a summer luncheon or as a palate cleanser during the meal. We have made our sorbet with watermelon and strawberries, you might like to try other favourite fruits.

Serves 8

- ☐ **1 cup (250 mL) water**
- ☐ **2 tablespoons caster sugar**
- ☐ **300 g watermelon, skinned, seeds removed and chopped**
- ☐ **250 g strawberries, hulled**
- ☐ **$^3/_4$ cup (190 mL) dry champagne (optional)**

1   Combine water and sugar in a saucepan and bring to the boil. Remove from heat and allow to cool completely.
2   In a food processor or blender puree watermelon flesh and strawberries.
3   Mix puree into sugar mixture and freeze in a stainless steel bowl. Whisk from time to time during freezing to give a smooth even texture. To serve, spoon into elegant glasses and at the last minute pour a tablespoon of champagne into each glass.

220 kilojoules (52 calories) per serve

Fat	*0.1 g*	*low*
Cholesterol	*0 mg*	*low*
Fibre	*0.9 g*	*low*
Sodium	*4 mg*	*low*

NUTRITION TIPS

❖   Dried fruit needs to be carefully counted by anyone with a weight problem. During drying, the fruit's water is largely removed which concentrates the kilojoules (calories) remaining.
❖   Remember: two dried apricots were originally one fresh apricot; one prune is equivalent to one plum; a handful of raisins is equivalent to a bunch of grapes.
❖   Apricots have the most concentrated dietary fibre of all dried fruit and supply vaulable amounts of iron, potassium, carotene, niacin and other B vitamins.

❖

FRUIT CAKE

No one would ever guess that our fruit cake has no eggs and so little fat. Yet it's a beautifully moist cake that's perfect for afternoon tea or lunch boxes.

Serves 16

- ☐ **$^3/_4$ cup (60 g) rice bran**
- ☐ **1 kg mixed dried fruit**
- ☐ **$^3/_4$ cup (130 g) brown sugar**
- ☐ **1 tablespoon grated orange rind**
- ☐ **4 tablespoons fresh orange juice**
- ☐ **6 tablespoons stout or beer**
- ☐ **$^3/_4$ cup (190 mL) hot water**
- ☐ **90 g melted polyunsaturated margarine (salt reduced)**
- ☐ **2 cups (270 g) wholemeal self-raising flour, sifted**
- ☐ **$^1/_2$ teaspoon ground cinnamon**
- ☐ **$^1/_2$ teaspoon ground ginger**
- ☐ **$^1/_2$ teaspoon ground nutmeg**
- ☐ **$^1/_2$ teaspoon ground cardamom**

1   Combine rice bran, dried fruit, brown sugar, orange rind, orange juice, 4 tablespoons of stout, and water in a bowl. Cool slightly, cover and stand overnight.
2   Stir in margarine, flour, cinnamon, ginger, nutmeg and cardamom. Spoon mixture into a lightly greased and lined 23 cm round cake pan. Bake for 1 $^1/_2$ hours at 150°C, or until cooked. Remove from oven, pour over remaining stout and wrap in aluminium foil until cool.

1295 kilojoules (295 calories) per serve

Fat	*5.1 g*	*med*
Cholesterol	*0 mg*	*low*
Fibre	*6.7 g*	*high*
Sodium	*223 mg*	*med*

Almond Fruit Bread, Fruity Cookies

❖

FRUITY COOKIES

As a treat these light fruity cookies will satisfy even the sweetest tooth.

Makes 16

☐ **60 g polyunsaturated margarine (salt reduced)**
☐ **4 tablespoons brown sugar**
☐ **2 tablespoons plain flour, sifted**
☐ **1 teaspoon mixed spice**
☐ **60 g finely chopped pecans**
☐ **1 tablespoon finely chopped glace cherries**
☐ **1 tablespoon currants**
☐ **1 tablespoon mixed peel**

1   Place margarine in a mixing bowl and beat until light and fluffy. Gradually add sugar and beat until just combined.
2   Fold in flour, mixed spice, pecans, cherries, currants and mixed peel. Place spoonfuls of mixture onto lightly greased oven trays, leaving 5 cm between each spoonful. It is best to cook only four biscuits at a time.
3   Bake at 180°C for 15 minutes or until golden brown. Remove from oven and using a spatula, push biscuits into a round shape and allow to cool on trays for 1–2 minutes. Transfer to a wire rack to cool.

296 kilojoules (71 calories) per serve

Fat	*5.0 g*	*low*
Cholesterol	*0 mg*	*low*
Fibre	*0.3 g*	*low*
Sodium	*28 mg*	*low*

❖

ALMOND FRUIT BREAD

Perfect to serve with coffee, this adaptation of an old favourite is the ideal finish to any dinner party.

Serves 30

☐ **3 egg whites**
☐ **1 teaspoon almond essence**
☐ **$^1/_2$ cup (110 g) caster sugar**
☐ **1 cup (125 g) plain flour, sifted**
☐ **60 g slivered almonds**
☐ **125 g glace cherries, chopped**
☐ **60 g glace pineapple, chopped**
☐ **60 g glace apricots, chopped**
☐ **60 g glace ginger, chopped**

1   Beat egg whites and almond essence until soft peaks form. Add caster sugar, a spoonful at a time, beating well after each addition.
2   Fold in flour, almonds, cherries, pineapple, apricots and ginger. Spoon mixture into a lightly greased and lined 25 cm x 8 cm loaf pan. Bake at 180°C for 35–40 minutes or until firm.
3   Turn out onto a wire rack to cool completely. Wrap in aluminium foil and set aside for 1–2 days. Using a very sharp serrated knife, cut bread into wafer thin slices. Place slices onto an oven tray lined with baking paper and bake at 150°C for 35 minutes or until dry and crisp. Remove from oven and cool on wire rack.

227 kilojoules (54 calories) per serve

Fat	*1.1 g*	*low*
Cholesterol	*0 mg*	*low*
Fibre	*0.6 g*	*low*
Sodium	*9 mg*	*low*

D ID Y OU K NOW ?

❖   Raisins and apricots are the oldest dried fruits and have been enjoyed by man since ancient times.
❖   Mention is made in the Old Testament of raisin cakes.
❖   It is known that apricots were being cultivated in China as long ago as 2205 BC.
❖   The Romans made a wine called Acinatisius from raisins and they were also a popular fruit at their banquets.

Garlic

Although scientific debate continues, more and more people are turning to garlic to keep their heart healthy. Large amounts of garlic, far in excess of that normally used in everyday cooking, have been shown to reduce the build up of fats in the blood after a fatty meal. Adding a little garlic to your cooking gives a wonderful flavour and aroma.

❖

TABBOULEH FILLED TOMATOES

Serves 4

- ☐ **4 large tomatoes**

TABBOULEH FILLING
- ☐ **3 tablespoons burghul (cracked wheat)**
- ☐ **boiling water**
- ☐ **8 shallots, finely chopped**
- ☐ **3 cloves garlic, crushed**
- ☐ **3 tablespoons finely chopped fresh parsley**
- ☐ **2 tablespoons finely chopped fresh mint**
- ☐ **1 tablespoon olive oil**
- ☐ **freshly ground black pepper**

1   Remove tops from tomatoes with a sharp knife. Scoop out pulp using a spoon, chop and reserve.
2   To make filling, place burghul in a bowl and pour over boiling water to cover. Set aside to soak for 10 minutes. Drain burghul and combine with tomato flesh, shallots, garlic, parsley, mint and oil. Season to taste with pepper. Spoon mixture into tomato shells and place on an oven tray. Bake at 200°C for 10 minutes or until heated through.

437 kilojoules (104 calories) per serve		
Fat	4.9 g	low
Cholesterol	0 mg	low
Fibre	6.0 g	high
Sodium	13 mg	low

Tabbouleh Filled Tomatoes, Garlic Sesame Ginger Prawns

GARLIC SESAME GINGER PRAWNS

This spicy stir-fry makes a delightful entree for a dinner party. As it is high in cholesterol, save it for special occasions.

Serves 8

- ☐ **1 teaspoon sesame oil**
- ☐ **1 kg uncooked prawns, shelled and deveined, tails left intact**
- ☐ **2 cloves garlic, crushed**
- ☐ **1 teaspoon grated fresh ginger**
- ☐ **2 tablespoons dry sherry**
- ☐ **³/4 cup (190 mL) beef stock**
- ☐ **2 teaspoons low salt soy sauce**
- ☐ **60 g canned pimento, finely chopped**
- ☐ **2 tablespoons finely chopped fresh chives**
- ☐ **1 tablespoon barbecue sauce (no added salt)**
- ☐ **3 teaspoons cornflour blended with 3 tablespoons water**
- ☐ **2 tablespoons toasted sesame seeds**

1   Heat oil in a non-stick frypan. Stir-fry prawns, garlic and ginger over high heat until prawns have just changed colour.
2   Stir in sherry, stock, soy sauce, pimento, chives and barbecue sauce. Simmer gently for 2–3 minutes. Add cornflour mixture and cook until sauce boils and thickens. Serve sprinkled with sesame seeds.

703 kilojoules (167 calories) per serve		
Fat	4.5 g	low
Cholesterol	250 mg	high
Fibre	0.3 g	low
Sodium	528 mg	high

> ### COOK'S TIP
> To neutralise garlic's strong odour from your breath, try chewing fresh parsley. Cooked garlic is less offensive than raw.

Grains

Grains such as wheat, rice, oats, rye, barley, maize, millet and buckwheat have been the staple food of many people for centuries and for good reason: all are high in complex carbohydrate and fibre, with a good protein content and very little fat or salt. They are nourishing, satisfying foods that we should all include in generous quantities in our diet. Choosing from our flavoursome versions of favourite recipes, you'll have no difficulty enjoying these delicious foods each week.

❖

VEGETABLE SOUP

Hearty, delicious and nourishing, this soup is a complete meal in itself.

Serves 6

- ☐ 6 cups (1.5 litres) chicken stock
- ☐ ¹/₂ cup (100 g) pearl barley
- ☐ 2 tablespoons tomato paste (no added salt)
- ☐ 1 teaspoon mixed dried herbs
- ☐ 1 large onion, chopped
- ☐ 2 cloves garlic, crushed
- ☐ 2 stalks celery, sliced
- ☐ 2 large carrots, diced
- ☐ 1 parsnip, diced
- ☐ 1 small turnip, diced
- ☐ 200 g green beans, sliced

1 Place stock, barley, tomato paste and herbs in a large saucepan. Bring to the boil, reduce heat and simmer for 30 minutes.
2 Add onion, garlic, celery, carrots, parsnip, turnip and beans and cook for 20–25 minutes or until vegetables are tender.

496 kilojoules (111 calories) per serve

Fat	0.5 g	low
Cholesterol	0 mg	low
Fibre	5.3 g	high
Sodium	48 mg	low

❖

TUNA RICE RING

Quick and easy to prepare, this rice mould makes an attractive main course.

Serves 4

- ☐ 1 tablespoon olive oil
- ☐ 6 shallots, chopped
- ☐ 1 stalk celery, chopped
- ☐ 150 g button mushrooms, sliced
- ☐ 1 red capsicum, chopped
- ☐ 2 tablespoons chopped fresh parsley
- ☐ 3 cups (540 g) cooked brown rice
- ☐ 425 g canned chunk style tuna in spring water, drained
- ☐ 1 cup (45 g) rice bran
- ☐ 1 teaspoon chilli sauce
- ☐ 2 tomatoes, peeled and chopped
- ☐ freshly ground black pepper

1 Heat oil in a large frypan. Add shallots, celery, mushrooms and capsicum and cook for 2–3 minutes.
2 Stir in parsley, rice, tuna, rice bran, chilli sauce and half the tomatoes. Toss until heated through. Season to taste with pepper.
3 Spoon mixture into a lightly greased ring pan. Press down well. To serve, turn out onto a plate and top with remaining tomatoes. Serve hot or cold.

1902 kilojoules (458 calories) per serve

Fat	17.8 g	high
Cholesterol	35 mg	low
Fibre	7.2 g	high
Sodium	111 mg	low

DID YOU KNOW?

❖ Buckwheat is botanically a grass, but is usually included with the cereal grains because it is cooked and eaten in the same way. A part of the cuisines of Poland and Russia, buckwheat has a nutty flavour and is prepared in the same way as barley.

❖ Wild rice is not really rice at all but a grain from an aquatic grass which grows in North America. It has been a favourite food of North American Indians for hundreds of years. Wild rice has a pleasant nutty flavour and requires about 30 minutes' cooking, by which time the cooked grains should have burst.

SPINACH GNOCCHI

Gnocchi is an Italian favourite. It is easy to make yourself and our version has a herb sauce, which makes it a marvellous main course.

Serves 4

- ☐ 3 large potatoes, peeled and quartered
- ☐ 2 egg whites, lightly beaten
- ☐ 1 cup (170 g) semolina
- ☐ 250 g spinach, shredded and cooked
- ☐ freshly ground black pepper
- ☐ 2 tablespoons grated Parmesan cheese

SAUCE
- ☐ 1 ¹/₂ cups (375 mL) chicken stock
- ☐ 3 tablespoons dry white wine
- ☐ 1 cup (250 mL) evaporated skim milk
- ☐ 1 teaspoon French mustard
- ☐ 3 tablespoons grated Parmesan cheese
- ☐ 2 teaspoons polyunsaturated mayonnaise
- ☐ 1 teaspoon mixed dried herbs
- ☐ 2 tablespoons cornflour blended with ¹/₂ cup (125 mL) water
- ☐ freshly ground black pepper

1 Boil, steam or microwave potatoes. Drain well and mash. Add egg whites, semolina, spinach and pepper; mix to combine. Set aside to cool completely.
2 Turn out on a lightly floured board and knead briefly. Break off portions and roll into a sausage 1 cm diameter. Cut into 3 cm pieces. Press each piece lightly with a fork. Drop into a large saucepan of boiling water. Cook for 5 minutes or until gnocchi rises to the surface. Remove with a slotted spoon and keep warm.
3 To make sauce, bring stock, wine and evaporated milk to the boil. Mix in mustard, cheese, mayonnaise and herbs. Stir in cornflour mixture and bring back to the boil, stirring constantly. Simmer for 5 minutes and season to taste with pepper. To serve, place gnocchi on a warm serving plate, spoon over sauce and sprinkle with Parmesan cheese.

2025 kilojoules (483 calories) per serve

Fat	4.6 g	low
Cholesterol	10 mg	low
Fibre	11 g	high
Sodium	394 mg	high

Vegetable Soup, Spinach Gnocchi, Tuna Rice Ring

PUMPKIN WITH LEEK AND BEANS

Pumpkin with a difference, golden nuggets filled with a Middle Eastern flavoured stuffing.

Serves 4

☐ 2 golden nugget pumpkins

FILLING
☐ 15 g burghul (cracked wheat)
☐ 1 tablespoon olive oil
☐ 2 cloves garlic, crushed
☐ 1 small leek, thinly sliced
☐ 50 g button mushrooms, sliced
☐ 310 g canned red kidney beans, drained and rinsed
☐ 1 tablespoon tomato sauce (no added salt)
☐ 2 teaspoons Worcestershire sauce
☐ 1/2 teaspoon chilli sauce
☐ 3/4 cup (90 g) grated mozzarella cheese

1   Cut tops from pumpkin and scoop out seeds. Bake or microwave pumpkin until just tender. Drain and pat dry with absorbent kitchen paper. Transfer to a lightly greased tray.
2   To make filling, soak burghul in water for 30 minutes. Drain and set aside. Heat oil in a large frypan. Add garlic, leek and mushrooms, and cook over medium heat for 2–3 minutes.
3   Stir in beans, tomato sauce, Worcestershire sauce, chilli sauce and burghul. Toss to heat through.
4   Divide filling evenly between pumpkins. Sprinkle with cheese and bake at 180°C for 10 minutes or until cheese melts.

991 kilojoules (232 calories) per serve
Fat	9.9 g	med
Cholesterol	16 mg	low
Fibre	1.2 g	med
Sodium	88 mg	low

VEGETABLE AND RICE PATTIES

Serves 8

☐ 2 1/2 cups (450 g) cooked brown rice
☐ 3/4 cup (30 g) unprocessed bran
☐ 3/4 cup (90 g) plain flour
☐ 1 onion, grated
☐ 1 clove garlic, crushed
☐ 1 teaspoon grated fresh ginger
☐ 1 cup (250 g) drained corn kernels
☐ 1 carrot, grated
☐ 1 zucchini, grated
☐ 3 tablespoons toasted pine nuts
☐ 2 tablespoons peanut butter
☐ 2 teaspoons salt reduced soy sauce
☐ 3 tablespoons low fat unflavoured yoghurt
☐ 2 egg whites
☐ 1 1/2 cups (185 g) dry breadcrumbs
☐ 2 tablespoons olive oil

1   Combine rice, bran, flour, onion, garlic, ginger, corn, carrot, zucchini and pine nuts. Blend together peanut butter, soy sauce, yoghurt and egg whites and add to rice mixture.
2   Shape mixture into 16 patties. Coat with breadcrumbs. Heat a non-stick frypan and brush lightly with oil. Cook patties turning frequently until golden brown and cooked through.

1478 kilojoules (353 calories) per serve
Fat	11.1 g	med
Cholesterol	0 mg	low
Fibre	4.6 g	high
Sodium	240 mg	med

WILD RICE SALAD

Serves 6

☐ 100 g wild rice
☐ 1/2 cup (100 g) long grain white rice
☐ 1/2 cup (100 g) quick cooking brown rice
☐ 3 tablespoons chopped fresh mint
☐ 1/2 cup (60 g) toasted sunflower seeds
☐ 2 tablespoons chopped glace ginger
☐ 2 kiwi fruit, peeled and sliced
☐ 1/2 cup (90 g) sultanas

KIWI FRUIT DRESSING
☐ 2 kiwi fruit, peeled and chopped
☐ 1 tablespoon polyunsaturated oil
☐ 1 clove garlic, crushed
☐ 1 teaspoon grated fresh ginger
☐ 2 teaspoons honey
☐ 1 teaspoon lemon juice

1   Cook wild rice in a large pan of boiling water for 20–25 minutes or until grains burst. Add white and brown rice during last 12 minutes of cooking. Drain and set aside to cool.
2   Combine rice, mint, sunflower seeds, ginger, kiwi fruit and sultanas in a bowl.

3   To make dressing, place kiwi fruit, oil, garlic, ginger, honey and lemon juice in a food processor or blender. Process until smooth. Pour dressing over salad, toss and refrigerate until well chilled.

1051 kilojoules (250 calories) per serve
Fat	7.8 g	med
Cholesterol	0 mg	low
Fibre	3.4 g	high
Sodium	25 mg	low

THIRST QUENCHER

Barley water is a favourite summer time drink and is very easy to prepare. To make 1 litre of barley water, place 100 g pearl barley and 5 cups (1.25 litres) water in a saucepan with the rind of 2 large lemons. Bring to the boil and simmer for 20 minutes. Strain and stir in 3 tablespoons of caster sugar and the juice of 2 lemons. Chill before serving with a sprig of mint.

MICROWAVE RICE

✧   While you do not really save time cooking rice in the microwave, you are assured of a perfect result and no messy pot.

✧   To cook white rice, place 1 cup (210 g) rice and 2 cups (500 mL) water or stock in a large microwave-safe dish. Cook, uncovered, on HIGH (100%) for 12–15 minutes or until all the liquid is absorbed.

Pumpkin with Leek and Beans, Vegetable and Rice Patties, Wild Rice Salad

Honey

Many people believe honey to be superior to sugar, as it is a 'natural' sweetener with supposedly therapeutic benefits, such as the ability to ward off colds, arthritis and heart problems. Unfortunately, such claims do not always hold true. Honey consists of around 75 per cent sugars (half of which are glucose, half fructose), with small quantities of plant acids, gums, pigments and oils. It makes a pleasant alternative sweetening agent to sugar but has no medical advantages. It does contain small amounts of B vitamins and some minerals, but not in significant amounts. Like sugar, it supplies kilojoules which must be counted by anyone watching their weight. One tablespoon of honey supplies about 370 kilojoules (87 calories), which is about the same as one tablespoon of sugar. Enjoy it if you like its taste, but don't expect any miracles!

Ice Cream

With its saturated fat and cholesterol, ice cream is generally restricted on cholesterol-lowering diets. But there are several categories of 'ice cream' and in warm climates there is nothing more refreshing than a scoop of this icy cold smooth confection.

Water ices, gelato and low fat 'ice confections' have the least fat and are the best choices.

Standard ice cream (as sold in tubs in supermarkets) has around 10 percent of milk fat and is acceptable occasionally. Three scoops of a standard vanilla ice cream supply 574 kilojoules (137 calories) and 7 grams of fat.

Premium ice creams, sold by exclusive confectionery outlets, have the highest fat content of 15–16 per cent and are denser which is why they taste richer and smoother.

Try our Watermelon and Strawberry Sorbet (page 33), which is also delicious made using 500 g of apricots in place of the watermelon and strawberries.

Jelly

For a delicious low cholesterol dessert that children will love don't forget jelly. It can be a refreshing fat free dessert, whether you use a commercial packet or make your own from pureed fruit or juices and gelatine. While a packet mix is largely sugar, gelatine and flavouring, it has no fat, is convenient and appreciated by children. There are low kilojoule jelly mixes for those wishing to avoid sugar or cut kilojoules.

All you need to do to make your own fresh fruit jelly is dissolve 4 teaspoons gelatine in 4 tablespoons water and mix with 600 mL fresh fruit juice. Do not use fresh pineapple or pawpaw juice because enzymes present in these juices prevent the jelly from setting.

Kilojoules
(Calories)

Kilojoules are units used to measure the energy of foods or diets. As metric units, kilojoules are replacing kilocalories (often called simply calories) in research and teaching. To convert kilojoules to calories, divide by 4.186 (4.2 or just 4 is accurate enough for a quick conversion). Most women eat an average of 7500 kilojoules (1800 calories) a day and a sensible weight loss plan should be no less than 4000 to 5000 kilojoules (1000 to 1200 calories) a day.

Spicy Vegetable Loaf, Vegetables with Almond Curry

Legumes

Lentils, dried peas, and beans (known collectively as pulses or legumes) are excellent foods to include in a cholesterol-lowering diet. They have very little fat, no cholesterol, and substantial amounts of protein, which is useful for vegetarians. Most importantly, they offer a good fibre content, high in water-soluble fibre, which helps remove cholesterol from the body, in a similar way to oat bran.

The initial step of presoaking beans often deters people from using dried beans. Lentils are the most convenient, requiring no pre-soaking to soften before cooking. Alternatively, canned beans are quick and nutritious. There is some loss of B vitamins during canning, but this is not significant. A couple of cans of beans in your cupboard is always handy for an easy, no-fuss high fibre meal.

SPICY VEGETABLE LOAF

Serves 6

- ☐ **1 tablespoon olive oil**
- ☐ **1 clove garlic, crushed**
- ☐ **1 onion, finely chopped**
- ☐ **$^1/_2$ teaspoon chilli powder**
- ☐ **$^1/_2$ teaspoon ground cumin**
- ☐ **$^1/_2$ teaspoon ground coriander**
- ☐ **$^1/_2$ teaspoon ground turmeric**
- ☐ **2 $^1/_4$ cups (450 g) red lentils**
- ☐ **1 carrot, grated**
- ☐ **1 large potato, grated**
- ☐ **400 g canned tomatoes (no added salt), undrained and mashed**
- ☐ **2 cups (500 mL) vegetable stock**
- ☐ **1 $^1/_2$ cups (135 g) rolled oats**
- ☐ **3 egg whites**
- ☐ **freshly ground black pepper**

1   Heat oil in a large frypan and cook garlic, onion, chilli powder, cumin, coriander and turmeric for 4–5 minutes or until onion softens.

2   Add lentils, carrot, potato, tomatoes and stock. Bring to the boil, cover and simmer for 30 minutes or until lentils are tender. Remove from heat and set aside to cool slightly. Beat egg whites until stiff peaks form and fold into lentil mixture.

3   Stir in rolled oats and mix well to combine. Season to taste with pepper. Spoon into a lightly greased and lined 15 cm x 25 cm loaf pan. Bake at 180°C for 1 hour or until cooked.

918 kilojoules (219 calories) per serve

Fat	5.0 g	low
Cholesterol	0 mg	low
Fibre	5.0 g	high
Sodium	27 mg	low

VEGETABLES WITH ALMOND CURRY

Serves 4

- ☐ **1 tablespoon olive oil**
- ☐ **1 onion, sliced**
- ☐ **1 clove garlic, crushed**
- ☐ **1 teaspoon ground cumin**
- ☐ **1 teaspoon ground coriander**
- ☐ **1 teaspoon ground turmeric**
- ☐ **2 carrots, peeled and sliced**
- ☐ **$^1/_2$ cup (110 g) red lentils**
- ☐ **440 g canned peeled tomatoes (no added salt), undrained**
- ☐ **1 $^1/_2$ cups (375 mL) vegetable stock**
- ☐ **1 teaspoon chilli sauce or according to taste**
- ☐ **500 g pumpkin, peeled and cut into 2 cm cubes**
- ☐ **$^1/_2$ cauliflower, cut into florets**
- ☐ **2 tablespoons blanched almonds**
- ☐ **freshly ground black pepper**
- ☐ **4 tablespoons unflavoured low fat yoghurt**

1   Brush a large saucepan with olive oil, heat and cook onion, garlic, cumin, coriander, turmeric and carrots for 5 minutes or until onion softens.

2   Stir in lentils, tomatoes and stock. Bring to the boil, reduce heat, cover and simmer for 15 minutes.

3   Add chilli sauce, pumpkin and cauliflower. Cook for 15–20 minutes longer or until pumpkin is tender. Mix in almonds and season to taste with pepper. Ladle curry into bowls and top with a spoonful of yoghurt.

818 kilojoules (194 calories) per serve

Fat	6.6 g	med
Cholesterol	0 mg	low
Fibre	5.2 g	high
Sodium	62 mg	low

LENTIL SALAD

Serves 6

- ☐ 1 cup (200 g) red lentils
- ☐ 1 cup (200 g) yellow lentils
- ☐ 6 cups (1.5 litres) vegetable stock
- ☐ 1 teaspoon cumin seeds
- ☐ 2 tomatoes, diced
- ☐ 2 stalks celery, sliced
- ☐ $1/2$ small green capsicum, diced
- ☐ $1/2$ small red capsicum, diced
- ☐ 1 small onion, finely chopped
- ☐ 1 small avocado, chopped
- ☐ freshly ground black pepper
- ☐ 2 tablespoons chopped chives

1 Place lentils, stock and cumin seeds in a saucepan and bring to the boil. Reduce heat and simmer for 20 minutes or until lentils are tender. Drain and allow to cool.

2 In a large salad bowl place cold lentils, tomatoes, celery, green and red capsicum, onion and avocado.

3 To make dressing, in a screwtop jar combine coriander, turmeric, chilli powder, garlic, vinegar and oil. Shake well to combine and pour over salad. Toss and season to taste with pepper. Sprinkle with chives to serve.

526 kilojoules (126 calories) per serve

Fat	8.2 g	med
Cholesterol	0 mg	low
Fibre	3.2 g	high
Sodium	20 mg	low

Below: Lentil Salad, Red Hot Beans

Knowing Your Legumes – from top left:

borlotte beans
red lentils
lima beans
kidney beans
green split beans
chick peas
cannellini beans
brown lentils

NUTRITION TIPS

✧ Legumes are often avoided because they cause embarrassing flatulence (wind). This can be considerably reduced by discarding the soaking water, rinsing beans, and adding fresh water for cooking. The flatulence is caused by certain food components in legumes, which are not fully digested, and end up being broken down to gases in the bowel.

✧ Legumes supply valuable amounts of B group vitamins, especially vitamin B, B6, niacin, and folic acid. They are also a good source of the minerals calcium, potassium and phosphorus. Their iron content is fairly high, but occurs in an inorganic form, not well absorbed by the human body. Eating a food high in vitamin C (like orange juice or a salad) at the same meal as legumes, increases the absorption of the iron.

RED HOT BEANS

The hotness of these Red Hot Beans can be altered according to taste. If you are unsure, carefully add a little chilli sauce, tasting until it is right. Serve with bowls of unflavoured low fat yoghurt. These beans make a wonderful main course.

Serves 4

- ☐ **³/₄ cup (125 g) dry red kidney beans**
- ☐ **1 eggplant, diced**
- ☐ **1 red capsicum, cut into strips**
- ☐ **1 large onion, sliced**
- ☐ **1 clove garlic, crushed**
- ☐ **4 large tomatoes, skinned and roughly chopped**
- ☐ **2 tablespoons tomato puree (no added salt)**
- ☐ **2 teaspoons chilli sauce**
- ☐ **¹/₂ cup (125 mL) water**
- ☐ **freshly ground black pepper**
- ☐ **2 tablespoons chopped fresh coriander**

1 Soak beans in water overnight, then drain well.

2 In a large saucepan place beans, eggplant, capsicum, onion, garlic, tomatoes, tomato puree, chilli sauce and water. Bring to the boil and boil rapidly for 10 minutes. Reduce heat and simmer, stirring occasionally, for 1 hour or until beans are tender.

3 Season with pepper and sprinkle with coriander to serve.

1245 kilojoules (293 calories) per serve		
Fat	1.7 g	low
Cholesterol	0 mg	low
Fibre	27.4 g	high
Sodium	60 mg	low

TIMESAVERS

❖ When cooking beans, cook extra as these can be frozen and added to dishes as required.

❖ While pulses are usually soaked overnight and this is preferable there is a way to speed up the soaking process if necessary. Place pulses in unsalted water, bring to the boil and simmer for 5 minutes, remove from heat and stand for 1 hour. Drain, rinse and use as required.

10 WAYS TO LOW FAT COOKING

One of the easiest ways to reduce the amount of fat you eat is to use less fat when you cook.

1 Avoid frying in oil, butter, margarine or ghee. Instead stick to grilling, roasting on a rack, steaming or microwave cooking. Try wrapping in foil and baking, or stir-frying in stock for a change.

2 Always trim all visible fat from meat; remove fat and skin from chicken. At the butcher's or supermarket, look for lean meat with the least fat and marbling. Limit the amount of sausages, luncheon meats and salamis you eat.

3 Use a non-stick frypan and simply brush with a little oil (don't pour oil in) for browning and sauteing.

4 Change the emphasis of your meals. Eat more pasta, rice, vegetables, bread and fruit, and less meat and fatty sauces.

5 Cook casseroles and soups one day ahead and chill. Any fat will rise to the surface and can be easily removed once it solidifies.

6 Experiment with vegetarian recipes. Replace some meat in casseroles with lentils and dried beans.

7 Baste foods with wine, oil free marinade, stock or fruit juice – not oil.

8 Use low fat or skim milk in cooking whenever possible. Switch to cottage cheese or ricotta in place of cream cheese and sour cream. Experiment with less butter and margarine in cake and biscuit recipes.

9 Indulge in gelato or fruit sorbets instead of ice cream.

10 Try non fat, unflavoured yoghurt in place of sour cream to finish casseroles. Do not reboil, as the yoghurt will look curdled.

Meats

Lean meats, whether red or white, can be part of a healthy low cholesterol way of eating provided that all visible fat is trimmed away and the cooking method does not add extra fats. Recent analyses show that if meat is not 'marbled' almost all the fat lies between muscles and is easy to remove. Hence lean beef, lamb and pork can now all be incorporated into family meals and provide all-important nutrition and flavour. Fat-trimmed meat is an excellent source of protein (containing all the amino acids needed for growth and health), iron and B vitamins. Sample our mouth-watering meat dishes and you'll be surprised at how easy and tasty lean meat cooking can be.

BEEF WITH MUSTARD AND ROSEMARY

Great for mid-week entertaining this easy main course dish takes next to no time to prepare.

Serves 4

- ☐ **600 g whole lean beef fillet**
- ☐ **2 teaspoons French mustard**
- ☐ **2 tablespoons cracked peppercorns**
- ☐ **1 tablespoon polyunsaturated oil**

SAUCE
- ☐ **1 clove garlic**
- ☐ **2 teaspoons chopped fresh rosemary**
- ☐ **1 teaspoon grated lemon rind**
- ☐ **1/2 cup (125 mL) dry white wine**
- ☐ **1/4 cup (60 mL) evaporated skim milk**
- ☐ **1 teaspoon cornflour**

1   Trim all visible fat from meat. Spread mustard over all surfaces of meat. Coat with peppercorns.

2   Heat oil in a roasting pan. Add meat and sear well on all sides. Transfer pan to oven and bake at 180°C for 20–25 minutes. Remove meat from pan. Set aside and keep warm.

3   To make sauce, skim any fat from pan. Place pan on stove top and stir in garlic, rosemary and lemon rind. Cook for 1–2 minutes.

4   Pour in wine and cook over high heat, stirring frequently to lift sediment from base of pan. Reduce wine by half. Combine skim milk and cornflour, stir into wine mixture. Cook over medium heat until sauce thickens slightly. Slice beef and spoon over sauce to serve.

1078 kilojoules (258 calories) per serve

Fat	10.5 g	med
Cholesterol	101 mg	high
Fibre	0 g	low
Sodium	163 mg	med

FAT FIGHTER

Cook meat with as little extra fat as possible. Do not fry or roast in fat. Instead grill, dry-bake on a rack, barbecue, microwave or cook in a non-stick pan brushed with a little oil. For casseroles, brown meat first in a touch of oil, then remove from pan and continue cooking other ingredients. Sour cream can often be replaced with plain yoghurt, but remember not to boil or the casserole will look curdled.

STEAKS WITH GARLIC TOMATO CONCASSE

For a change try our concasse with lamb chops or chicken fillets.

Serves 6

- ☐ **6 x 120 g boneless rib-eye steaks (scotch fillet)**

GARLIC TOMATO CONCASSE
- ☐ **4 large tomatoes, peeled and chopped**
- ☐ **2 cloves garlic, crushed**
- ☐ **2 tablespoons finely chopped chives**
- ☐ **freshly ground black pepper**

1 To make concasse, place tomatoes, garlic and chives in a saucepan. Cook over medium heat for 8–10 minutes or until tomatoes are just soft. Season to taste with pepper.

2 Trim all visible fat from meat. Heat a non-stick frypan and cook steaks over medium-high heat for 4–5 minutes each side. Spoon sauce over steaks and serve immediately.

799 kilojoules (192 calories) per serve

Fat	5.3 g	med
Cholesterol	80 mg	med
Fibre	3.3 g	high
Sodium	62 mg	low

LOW FAT ROASTS

To enjoy the full flavour of a traditional roast cook the roast on a rack. In this way the meat does not absorb the fat that is released during cooking. To avoid splattering during cooking, place a cup of water in the pan. To make gravy, use the pan juices and at the end of cooking, throw a handful of ice cubes into the pan and stir until melted. You will see the fat solidify on the surface, remove it using a slotted spoon and make your gravy as usual.

Above: Athenian Lamb Kebabs
Left: Beef with Mustard and Rosemary, Steaks with Garlic Tomato Concasse

ATHENIAN LAMB KEBABS

Our Mediterranean-flavoured kebabs will quickly become a family favourite.

Serves 6

- ☐ **750 g lean lamb, cubed and trimmed of fat**
- ☐ **12 bay leaves**
- ☐ **1 large onion, cut into eighths**
- ☐ **12 cherry tomatoes**
- ☐ **1 green capsicum, cubed**

MARINADE
- ☐ **1 tablespoon olive oil**
- ☐ **3 tablespoons lemon juice**
- ☐ **1 teaspoon finely chopped fresh rosemary**
- ☐ **3 tablespoons finely chopped fresh parsley**
- ☐ **fresh ground black pepper**
- ☐ **dash Tabasco sauce**

1 To make marinade, combine oil, lemon juice, rosemary, parsley, pepper to taste and Tabasco sauce in a glass bowl. Add meat, toss to coat and marinate for 30 minutes.

2 Remove meat from marinade and thread on to twelve oiled wooden skewers, alternating with bay leaves, onion, tomatoes and capsicum.

3 Barbecue or grill kebabs slowly, turning and basting frequently with remaining marinade, until well browned and cooked.

798 kilojoules (192 calories) per serve

Fat	7.2 g	med
Cholesterol	83 mg	med
Fibre	0.9 g	low
Sodium	103 mg	low

PORK WITH ORANGE AND CRANBERRY

Butterfly pork steaks with their lean meaty quality, are excellent with this tasty sauce.

Serves 4

- ☐ 4 x 125 g lean butterfly pork steaks
- ☐ cracked black peppercorns
- ☐ 1 teaspoon grape seed oil

MARINADE
- ☐ 1 cup (250 mL) fresh orange juice
- ☐ 2 teaspoons grated orange rind
- ☐ ¼ teaspoon ground cloves
- ☐ 3 tablespoons cranberry sauce

1   Trim all visible fat from meat. To make marinade, combine orange juice, orange rind, cloves and cranberry sauce in a glass bowl. Add meat and marinate for 1–2 hours.
2   Remove steaks from marinade and coat with peppercorns. Heat oil in a non-stick frypan. Cook steaks for 4–5 minutes each side or until cooked. Set aside and keep warm.
3   Strain remaining marinade and pour into a saucepan. Bring to the boil and boil rapidly to reduce slightly. Spoon sauce over steaks and serve.

911 kilojoules (218 calories) per serve

Fat	*2.4 g*	*low*
Cholesterol	*68 mg*	*med*
Fibre	*0 g*	*low*
Sodium	*70 mg*	*low*

NUTRITION TIP

Red or white meat? It seems that the colour of cooked meat has no bearing on its fat and cholesterol content. Some of the leanest meats such as venison, buffalo and kangaroo are deep red in colour and their very lack of fat has made them more difficult to cook without becoming tough!

MOUSSAKA WITH CRUNCHY TOPPING

Great for casual entertaining. Prepare and cook this tasty moussaka in advance, then all you need do is reheat when you are ready to serve.

Serves 4

- ☐ 1 onion, chopped
- ☐ 2 cloves garlic, crushed
- ☐ 500 g lean minced beef
- ☐ 1 teaspoon chopped fresh rosemary
- ☐ 400 g canned tomatoes (no added salt), undrained and mashed
- ☐ 2 tablespoons tomato paste (no added salt)
- ☐ 2 teaspoons low salt soy sauce
- ☐ ½ cup (125 mL) dry red wine
- ☐ 1 teaspoon sugar
- ☐ ¼ teaspoon ground nutmeg
- ☐ 1 eggplant, thinly sliced
- ☐ 6 slices wholemeal bread, crusts removed
- ☐ 1 tablespoon polyunsaturated margarine
- ☐ 2 tablespoons finely chopped fresh basil
- ☐ 1 tablespoon grated Parmesan cheese

1   Heat a non-stick frypan. Cook onion, garlic, mince and rosemary over medium heat for 4–5 minutes, stirring constantly.
2   Stir in tomatoes, tomato paste, soy sauce, wine, sugar and nutmeg. Cook, uncovered, over medium heat for 20–25 minutes or until mixture reduces and thickens slightly.
3   Steam or microwave eggplant for 2–3 minutes. Arrange layers of eggplant and mince mixture in a 16 cm x 28 cm lightly greased ovenproof dish, finishing with a layer of mince.
4   Spread bread slices with margarine and cut into large cubes. Place on top of moussaka. Sprinkle with basil and Parmesan cheese, bake at 180°C for 30–35 minutes.

1534 kilojoules (367 calories) per serve

Fat	*10.6 g*	*med*
Cholesterol	*64 mg*	*med*
Fibre	*5.1 g*	*high*
Sodium	*423 mg*	*high*

Left: Pork with Orange and Cranberry
Right: Moussaka with Crunchy Topping, Hungarian Ragout.

HUNGARIAN RAGOUT

In our tasty ragout the meat is gently simmered giving a hearty and wholesome dish.

Serves 4

- ☐ **500 g lean stewing veal**
- ☐ **1 tablespoon polyunsaturated oil**
- ☐ **1 large onion, finely chopped**
- ☐ **1 clove garlic, crushed**
- ☐ **125 g button mushrooms, sliced**
- ☐ **2 teaspoons ground paprika**
- ☐ **$^1/_2$ teaspoon dried caraway seeds**
- ☐ **2 large tomatoes, peeled and chopped**
- ☐ **1 tablespoon tomato paste (no added salt)**
- ☐ **$^3/_4$ cup (190 mL) chicken stock**
- ☐ **3 tablespoons dry white wine**
- ☐ **freshly ground black pepper**
- ☐ **1 tablespoon cornflour blended with $^1/_2$ cup (125 g) low fat unflavoured yoghurt**

1   Trim meat of all visible fat. Cut into 2.5 cm cubes and set aside.
2   Heat oil in a large saucepan. Cook onion, garlic and mushrooms for 2–3 minutes. Add meat and cook for 3–4 minutes, tossing until browned on all sides.
3   Add paprika and caraway seeds and toss through meat mixture. Combine tomatoes, tomato paste, stock and wine and pour into pan. Season to taste with pepper. Bring to the boil, reduce heat and simmer covered for 1$^1/_2$ hours or until meat is tender.
4   Remove pan from heat and whisk in cornflour mixture. Cook over low heat for 3–4 minutes or until sauce thickens.

897 kilojoules (215 calories) per serve

Fat	6.0 g	med
Cholesterol	93 mg	med
Fibre	3.9 g	high
Sodium	127 mg	low

LIVER

✧ Liver and other offal or organ meats (kidney, heart, brains, tongue, tripe and sweetbreads) have a very high cholesterol count and are often excluded when trying to reduce blood cholesterol levels. However, provided you keep your saturated fat intake low and you do not have a 'cholesterol sensitive' biochemistry, offal meats can be eaten occasionally (say, once a week).

✧ All offal is nutritious, being an excellent food for iron, zinc, B vitamins, vitamin A and protein. Liver was once regularly fed to pregnant women and people suffering anaemia, for its exceptionally rich iron content. Brains have the highest cholesterol content (three times as concentrated as eggs) followed by liver and kidneys. The others are much lower.

Milk

One of our basic foods, milk, has excellent nutritional benefits, being rich in bone-building calcium and phosphorus and high in protein and B vitamins (particularly riboflavin or vitamin B2). Full cream milk, however, contributes much saturated fat and cholesterol, so skim and fat reduced 'modified' milks are recommended for those trying to lower their blood cholesterol.

Honey Banana Smoothie , Strawberry Flip

HONEY BANANA SMOOTHIE

Sure to last you until lunchtime, our thick smoothie is great for a quick breakfast. Try it with your favourite fruits.

Serves 4

- [ ] **2 large ripe bananas, chopped**
- [ ] **2 ¹/2 cups (625 mL) skim milk**
- [ ] **1 cup (250 mL) evaporated skim milk, chilled**
- [ ] **¹/2 teaspoon cinnamon**
- [ ] **1 ¹/2 tablespoons honey**

Place bananas, both milks, cinnamon and honey in a food processor or blender. Process until thick and smooth.

919 kilojoules (217 calories) per serve

Fat	0.4 g	low
Cholesterol	5 mg	low
Fibre	2.0 g	med
Sodium	146 mg	low

STRAWBERRY FLIP

Feeling hungry? Our flip is the ideal snack and you can use any berries you like.

Serves 2

- [ ] **100 g fresh strawberries, hulled**
- [ ] **1 cup (250 mL) skim milk**
- [ ] **2 tablespoons orange juice**

Place strawberries, skim milk and orange juice into a food processor or blender. Process until smooth. Serve immediately.

247 kilojoules (58 calories) per serve

Fat	0.2 g	low
Cholesterol	3 mg	low
Fibre	1.2 g	med
Sodium	69 mg	low

WHICH MILK?

Most milks carry a nutrition information label on the side of their package which can help you decide the best type to buy, as there are differing names for similar types of milk in different areas.

Skim milk has had virtually all fat and cholesterol removed, while retaining a full complement of calcium, protein and minerals. It has the least fat and kilojoules of all milks, but has a thin 'watery' feel in the mouth.

Modified low fat milks have a fat content similar to skim milk but with added calcium, protein and lactose. This gives them a 'richer' taste than skim milk.

Modified reduced fat milks have around half the fat and cholesterol of regular milk, but with a creamy taste, which most people find quite acceptable.

Soya bean milks are suitable for children who have an allergy to the protein in cow's milk or for people unable to digest lactose (milk sugar), but are not always a good substitute. Although they are free of cholesterol, they can contain just as much fat as full cream milk and, unless fortified with added calcium, are not as rich in calcium.

MILK FATS

MILK TYPE	FAT CONTENT
Full cream	4%
Reduced fat modified	1.5 – 2%
Low fat modified	0.15%
Skim	0.1%

CREAMY ASPARAGUS SOUP

A swirl of unflavoured natural yoghurt and freshly chopped chives make a wonderful garnish for this flavoursome soup.

Serves 4

☐ **420 g canned asparagus cuts (no added salt)**
☐ **1 1/2 cups (375 mL) chicken stock**
☐ **2 tablespoons chopped fresh chives**
☐ **1 clove garlic, crushed**
☐ **pinch ground nutmeg**
☐ **1 cup (250 mL) skim milk**
☐ **freshly ground black pepper**

1 Drain asparagus reserving 1/2 cup (125 mL) of liquid. Place asparagus cuts, reserved liquid, stock, chives, garlic and nutmeg in a food processor or blender. Process until smooth.
2 Transfer mixture to a saucepan. Bring to the boil, reduce heat and stir in skim milk. Heat gently, without boiling. Season to taste with pepper.

139 kilojoules (33 calories) per serve

Fat	*0.4 g*	*low*
Cholesterol	*0 mg*	*low*
Fibre	*0.8 g*	*low*
Sodium	*38 mg*	*low*

Creamy Asparagus Soup

Nuts

In small amounts, nuts add a wonderful flavour and aroma to your cooking. They are restricted because their high natural content of oil makes them high in fat and kilojoules (calories). Also, they are so "more-ish", it's often difficult to stop crunching, which creates a problem for anyone trying to shed excess weight. Certain nuts are preferred because of their richer content of unsaturated fats. We have used these to create the following deliciously nutty recipes. They're sure to be winners with your family and friends.

CONSUME WITH CARE

✧ To increase the flavour of nuts, try them roasted – but not in fat! Simply place on a baking tray and heat in the oven at 180°C for 5 minutes, shaking the tray once or twice. Take care not to burn – remove when just golden. Sesame, sunflower and pumpkin seeds can also be roasted in the same way.

✧ Try roasting nuts in the microwave. Place 250 g nuts in a microwave-safe glass or ceramic dish and cook on HIGH (100%) for 2–3 minutes. Do not add any oil or fat or they will burn.

✧ Nuts contain around half their weight as fat, which means they carry more fat than fatty meat or even cream! Make sure you use them cautiously. Coconut has the highest content of saturated fat (94%), followed by cashews at 20%, the rest are predominantly polyunsaturated or monounsaturated. Nuts contain no cholesterol.

PEANUT SAUCE

Peanut sauce is great served with vegetables, meat, chicken or fish. We have served ours with vegetable crudites making a great nibbles tray for a party.

Makes 1 cup (250 mL)

- ☐ **1 clove garlic, crushed**
- ☐ **1 onion, chopped**
- ☐ **1 teaspoon chilli sauce**
- ☐ **5 tablespoons crunchy peanut butter (no added salt)**
- ☐ **1/2 cup (125 mL) water**
- ☐ **1/2 cup (125 mL) low fat yoghurt**
- ☐ **freshly ground black pepper**

Cook garlic and onion in a non-stick frypan until onion softens. Add chilli sauce, peanut butter and water. Mix well to combine and bring to a gentle boil. Stir in yoghurt and season to taste with pepper.

271 kilojoules (65 calories) per serve

Fat	4.7 g	low
Cholesterol	0 mg	low
Fibre	0.3 g	low
Sodium	10 mg	low

SPICED ALMONDS

Serves 6

- ☐ **1/2 teaspoon chilli powder**
- ☐ **1/4 teaspoon ground cumin**
- ☐ **1/2 teaspoon ground coriander**
- ☐ **1 cup (160 g) blanched almonds**

1 Place chilli, cumin and coriander in a non-stick saucepan. Cook over low heat for 1 minute. Add almonds and toss with spices and cook for a further 3–5 minutes or until golden.

2 Remove pan from heat and set aside to cool. Serve as a snack or with drinks.

623 kilojoules (151 calories) per serve

Fat	14.3 g	low
Cholesterol	0 mg	low
Fibre	3.8 g	high
Sodium	2 mg	low

Left: Knowing your nuts – from top left:

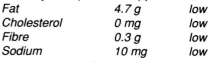

macadamia pecans cashews walnuts brazils pistachios peanuts almonds pinenuts sesame seeds

Peanut Sauce, Spiced Almonds

NUTTY NUTRITION			
NUT	POLY-UNSATURATED %	MONO-UNSATURATED %	SATURATED %
Almonds	22	68	10
Brazil nuts	38	36	10
Coconut, desiccated	1	5	94
Cashews	18	62	20
Chestnuts	42	39	18
Hazelnuts	10	81	8
Macadamias	2	82	16
Peanuts	33	52	15
Pecans	26	66	8
Pinenuts	44	40	16
Walnuts	66	24	9
Expressed as % of total fatty acids			

Oats

In recent years, oats have risen in prominence after nutrition research showed that they have a natural ability to lower blood cholesterol. From their humble beginnings as a peasant food, they are today considered a valuable 'health' food to eat daily, whether as porridge (rolled oats), muesli, oat muffins or in many other tempting dishes.

Oat bran is oat fibre in concentrated form, being the outer layers of the oat grain. It is high in soluble fibre, which nutritionists presently believe to be responsible for removing cholesterol from the body as well as delaying absorption of food (especially helpful for diabetics). Rolled oats also contain oat bran, as it is part of the oat grain, but in smaller quantities.

Three tablespoons (30 g) of oat bran gives you 5 grams of dietary fibre and 445 kilojoules (105 calories).

To have a significant effect on cholesterol you need to consume 60 to 100 g per day as well as modifying the fats in your diet.

❖

BANANA AND PINEAPPLE MUFFINS

Makes 12

- [ ] 1 ¹/₄ cups (165 g) wholemeal self-raising flour
- [ ] 1 teaspoon baking powder
- [ ] 1 teaspoon mixed spice
- [ ] 4 tablespoons brown sugar
- [ ] 1 cup (45 g) oat bran
- [ ] 1 small banana, mashed
- [ ] 150 g canned crushed pineapple, drained
- [ ] 3 egg whites, lightly beaten
- [ ] 2 tablespoons polyunsaturated oil
- [ ] ¹/₂ cup (125 mL) pineapple juice

1   Sift flour, baking powder and spice into a mixing bowl. Add sugar and oat bran.

2   Make a well in the centre of the dry ingredients. Combine banana, pineapple, egg whites, oil and juice. Stir into flour mixture and mix to combine all ingredients.
3   Spoon mixture into lightly greased muffin pans. Bake at 200°C for 12–15 minutes or until golden brown.

505 kilojoules (120 calories) per serve

Fat	3.2 g	low
Cholesterol	0 mg	low
Fibre	2.5 g	med
Sodium	139 mg	low

❖

FRESH HERB AND OAT SCONES

Make these delicious scones in advance. Freeze them and reheat just before serving.

Makes 9

- [ ] 1 ¹/₂ cups (185 g) self-raising flour, sifted
- [ ] ¹/₂ cup (45 g) instant oats
- [ ] ¹/₂ teaspoon baking powder
- [ ] 30 g polyunsaturated margarine
- [ ] 2 teaspoons chopped fresh parsley
- [ ] 2 teaspoons chopped fresh basil
- [ ] 2 teaspoons chopped fresh rosemary
- [ ] ³/₄ cup (190 mL) skim milk

1   Place flour, oats and baking powder in a bowl. Rub through margarine until mixture resembles fine breadcrumbs. Stir in parsley, basil and rosemary.
2   Make a well in the centre of mixture and pour in milk. Mix lightly with a knife until all ingredients are just combined. Turn mixture out onto a lightly floured board and knead lightly.
3   Press dough out evenly to 2 cm thickness. Cut into rounds using a 5 cm cutter dipped in flour. Arrange scones side by side in a lightly greased 18 cm round shallow cake pan. Brush tops with a little extra milk and bake at 220°C for 15–20 minutes or until scones are a golden brown.

486 kilojoules (115 calories) per serve

Fat	3.6 g	low
Cholesterol	0 mg	low
Fibre	2.3 g	med
Sodium	211 mg	med

CHEESY APPLE MUFFINS

Makes 12

- ☐ 1 ¼ cups (165 g) wholemeal self-raising flour
- ☐ ¼ teaspoon ground cinnamon
- ☐ ¼ teaspoon ground nutmeg
- ☐ ¼ teaspoon ground ginger
- ☐ ¼ teaspoon ground cloves
- ☐ 1 teaspoon baking powder
- ☐ 1 cup (45 g) oat bran
- ☐ 3 tablespoons brown sugar
- ☐ 1 green apple, peeled and grated
- ☐ 125 g ricotta cheese
- ☐ 2 tablespoons polyunsaturated oil
- ☐ ¾ cup (190 mL) apple juice

1   Sift flour, cinnamon, nutmeg, ginger, cloves and baking powder into a mixing bowl. Add oat bran and sugar.

2   Make a well in the centre of the flour mixture. Stir in apple, ricotta, oil and apple juice. Mix until just combined. Spoon mixture into lightly greased muffin pans.

Bake at 200°C for 25 minutes or until golden brown.

495 kilojoules (118 calories) per serve

Fat	4.4 g	low
Cholesterol	5 mg	low
Fibre	2.4 g	med
Sodium	147 mg	low

FAT FIGHTER

Most muesli consists of one half rolled oats, the other half dried fruit, nuts and seeds. Plain non-toasted muesli is a nutritious easy breakfast and can be made at home from your own ingredients. Take care with toasted muesli, much of which has twice as much fat from the oil used during toasting. It is usually saturated and not good for your heart.

❖   Look for 'low in fat' brands with no saturated fat.

DID YOU KNOW?

❖   Oats were first cultivated in Europe in about 1000 BC and became well established in cold damp climates such as Scotland and Scandinavia, where other grains could not survive. They have long been used as a feed for animals and were often considered a 'poor man's food' as they were cheap and filling.

❖   Muesli was first first developed by a Swiss doctor, Dr Bircher-Benner, in his Zurich sanatorium in the 1890s. Rolled oats were soaked in water overnight and then a whole apple grated over the top. It was served with chopped nuts and yoghurt or cream. A far cry from today's muesli mixes!

Left: Banana and Pineapple Muffins, Cheesy Apple Muffins
Right: Fresh Herb and Oat Scones

Oils

Oils play a vital part in a cholesterol-lowering diet as they can influence the proportion of saturated, monounsaturated and polyunsaturated fat you eat. In a stir-fried vegetable dish the only fat is derived from whichever oil is selected for cooking. If it is peanut oil, the dish will be predominantly mono-unsaturated; if it is safflower, the result is polyunsaturated.

WHICH OIL?

✧ Safflower and sunflower oils are both light in colour, with a neutral taste, and are interchangeable in recipes. They are ideal for salad dressings, sauteing and baking. Sunflower oil is frequently used in the manufacture of polyunsaturated margarines.

✧ Soya bean oil is light and bland tasting and is the world's leading oil, a major ingredient of blended vegetable oils and polyunsaturated margarines.

OILS AND OILS	
TYPE OF FAT	OILS
Polyunsaturated	Safflower, sunflower, walnut, maize (corn), soya bean, wheatgerm, cottonseed, sesame, grapeseed
Monounsaturated	Olive, canola (rapeseed), peanut, avocado
Saturated	Coconut, palm, palm kernel

All oils are mixtures of the three types of fats.
The type occurring in greatest proportion gives the oil its classification.

✧ Peanut oil has a slightly nutty flavour and is preferred in Asian cookery, especially for stir-frying.

✧ Olive oil is enjoying a resurgence in popularity since studies showed that it helps lower blood cholesterol levels. It contains 77% mono-unsaturated fats, the highest proportion among all vegetable oils, which are thought partly responsible for the lower incidence of heart disease in Mediterranean countries.

✧ Maize or corn oil is derived from the heart of corn kernels and popular in the USA where maize is widely grown. It has a somewhat spicy flavour which develops during cooking, and is predominantly polyunsaturated.

✧ Sesame, walnut, grape seed and avocado are speciality oils which are sold at health food shops and are valued for their exotic flavour.

A few drops of sesame or walnut oil in a salad dressing change its character dramatically and gourmets have long appreciated these expensive oils.

✧ Blended oils are mixtures of several oils. Some are poly-unsaturated and this is clearly marked on the label.

✧ Palm and palm kernel oils are derived from an oil palm cultivated in tropical countries. Palm kernel oil, almost 90% saturated, is similar to coconut oil.

✧ Coconut oil is an ingredient in commercial shortenings, biscuits, pies, confectionery and couvertures. It has unique physical characteristics and keeps well without becoming rancid.

HEALTHY LIFESTYLES

Cholesterol and heart disease have become intertwined over recent years, yet it must be stressed that high cholesterol is just one of many risk factors influencing the development of heart problems. A healthy lifestyle, in combination with a low fat, low cholesterol diet, can do much towards minimising personal risk.

WEIGHT

Reducing excess weight almost always reduces your blood cholesterol and is a key step in controlling cholesterol.

EXERCISE

Regular moderate exercise is essential for a healthy heart. It can raise the levels of the protective HDL-cholesterol and lower the dangerous LDL-cholesterol. It also has another benefit. It burns up kilojoules (calories) and helps eliminate another serious risk factor – being overweight.

To be beneficial, exercise does not have to be vigorous and sweaty, but it does have to be aerobic. This means any activity that increases the oxygen needs of the body, thus working the heart and lungs. Choose an exercise that you enjoy, that uses the legs, torso or arms, and gets your breathing going; do it for 30 minutes three times a week. Walking, swimming, bicycling, skipping and running are good choices. Start at a modest level and gradually increase your time and intensity. Avoid sudden bursts of fast exercise which can strain an unfit heart.

Weight loss diets are generally low in fat, so what is good for your figure will be good for your heart. Anyone trying to shed weight will find the recipes in this book perfect for both goals.

STRESS

Some Cardiologists designate certain personality types as 'Type A': perfectionist, highly competitive, impatient, always in a hurry and striving to achieve goals. Research has shown that people with marked Type A are especially prone to developing heart disease at an early age. By contrast, 'Type B' people are relaxed and easygoing.

If you recognise tendencies in yourself towards Type A behaviour, start to relearn your 'hurried' way of thinking and give up trying to be a superperson. Learn to say 'no' and to begin to cultivate your spiritual side through activities you find enjoyable.

Long term unrelieved emotional stress is a potential risk factor in many illnesses, not just heart disease. When tension and worries mount up it is important to find ways of 'letting go'. Physical exercise helps lower stress, as does meditation, yoga and Tai Chi.

RISK FACTORS

- ◇ High blood pressure
- ◇ High blood cholesterol
- ◇ Cigarette smoking
- ◇ Excess weight
- ◇ Lack of physical activity
- ◇ Family history (heredity)
- ◇ Diabetes
- ◇ Stress

ALCOHOL

A modest intake of alcohol (one or at most two drinks a day) was once considered to confer 'protection' against heart disease. Population studies showed that moderate drinkers suffered fewer heart attacks and lived longer than total abstainers or people who regularly drank more than three drinks daily.

Now, however, new findings reveal that alcohol is detrimental to your heart. A high proportion of abstainers, far from being lifelong teetotallers, were former heavy drinkers who had been forced to give up alcohol because of ill-health such as existing heart trouble, high blood pressure, diabetes and gout. They suffered more heart disease than moderate drinkers, not because they abstained, but because they were a much less healthy group to start with. The message for alcohol now seems clear: less is best.

Pasta

Pasta (spaghetti, macaroni and noodles) is a wonderful food for the heart. It has very little fat, no cholesterol (except for egg noodles) and is high in complex carbohydrates, which makes it a satisfying meal when you're really ravenous. Best of all, it is quick and easy to cook and has endless variations depending on what sauce you serve with it. Remember that cheese, oil or cream in a sauce significantly increase the fat level so try to use lighter sauces based on tomato or vegetables. You'll find more than a little inspiration with our healthy pasta dishes presented here.

❖

GINGERED NOODLES AND VEGETABLES

The flat Oriental noodles that we have used in this recipe are different from egg noodles; they are made from flour and water and are available from Chinese food stores.

Serves 6

- ☐ **1 tablespoon peanut oil**
- ☐ **2 teaspoon grated fresh ginger**
- ☐ **1 clove garlic, crushed**
- ☐ **1 onion, sliced**
- ☐ **1 carrot, sliced diagonally**
- ☐ **2 stalks celery, sliced diagonally**
- ☐ **100 g bean sprouts**
- ☐ **200 g snow peas, trimmed**
- ☐ **500 g flat Oriental noodles, cooked**
- ☐ **freshly ground black pepper**

1   Heat oil in wok or large frypan. Add ginger and garlic, and stir-fry for 1–2 minutes. Stir in onion and carrot, and stir-fry for 4–5 minutes.
2   Add celery, bean sprouts and snow peas, and stir-fry for 2–3 minutes.
3   Stir in noodles, and stir-fry 3–4 minutes or until noodles are heated through. Season to taste with pepper and serve immediately.

619 kilojoules (146 calories) per serve

Fat	3.3 g	low
Cholesterol	0 mg	low
Fibre	3.2 g	high
Sodium	28 mg	low

❖

HERBY TOMATO AND PASTA SALAD

As a luncheon, this salad only needs crusty bread to accompany it.

Serves 6

- ☐ **250 g fresh spinach tagliatelle**
- ☐ **250 g fresh tagliatelle**
- ☐ **2 zucchini, cut into matchsticks**
- ☐ **1 small red capsicum, sliced**
- ☐ **1 small green capsicum, sliced**
- ☐ **200 g green beans, cooked**

TOMATO AND BASIL DRESSING
- ☐ **4 ripe tomatoes, peeled and roughly chopped**
- ☐ **1 clove garlic, crushed**
- ☐ **2 teaspoons olive oil**
- ☐ **2 teaspoons red wine vinegar**
- ☐ **2 tablespoons finely chopped fresh basil**
- ☐ **1 tablespoon finely chopped fresh parsley**
- ☐ **1 tablespoon finely chopped fresh chives**
- ☐ **freshly ground black pepper**

1   Cook both tagliatelles together in boiling water in a large saucepan following packet directions. Rinse under cold running water, drain and set aside to cool completely.
2   Place cold tagliatelles, zucchini, capsicums and beans in a large salad bowl.
3   To make dressing, place tomatoes, garlic, oil and vinegar in a food processor or blender. Process until smooth. Stir in basil, parsley and chives, season to taste with pepper. Spoon dressing over pasta and vegetables. Toss lightly to coat all ingredients with dressing.

622 kilojoules (146 calories) per serve

Fat	2.1 g	low
Cholesterol	0 mg	low
Fibre	5.0 g	high
Sodium	14 mg	low

Gingered Noodles and Vegetables, Herby Tomato and Pasta Salad, Hot Pasta and Mushrooms

PERFECT PASTA

PERFECT PASTA

The secret of cooking perfect pasta is to bring a large pot of water to a rolling boil. Add a splash of oil to prevent the pasta from sticking together (do not add salt, as it only toughens the pasta). Immerse your pasta, bring back to the boil, then cook 2–3 minutes for fresh or 5–8 minutes for dried. Pasta should taste 'al dente' – just cooked, but with no hard core in the centre. Drain and place in bowls, ready for the sauce.

❖

HOT PASTA AND MUSHROOMS

Creamy mushroom sauce and hot pasta – the food that dreams are made of! A green salad and crusty bread will complete your meal.

Serves 4

- ☐ **2 cups (300 g) macaroni**
- ☐ **3 tablespoons finely chopped fresh parsley**
- ☐ **2 tablespoons grated Parmesan cheese**

MUSHROOM SAUCE
- ☐ **2 teaspoons polyunsaturated oil**
- ☐ **1 onion, sliced**
- ☐ **500 g mushrooms, sliced**
- ☐ **1 teaspoon paprika**
- ☐ **2 tablespoons tomato paste (no added salt)**
- ☐ **1 cup (250 mL) evaporated skim milk**
- ☐ **freshly ground black pepper**

1   Cook macaroni in boiling water in a large saucepan following packet directions. Drain, set aside and keep warm.
2   To make sauce, heat oil in a non-stick frypan. Cook onion and mushrooms until they soften. Blend together paprika, tomato paste and milk. Stir into mushroom mixture and cook gently over low heat for 5 minutes. Season to taste with pepper.
3   Place pasta in a heated serving dish and spoon over sauce. Toss gently to combine. Sprinkle with parsley and Parmesan to serve.

945 kilojoules (223 calories) per serve

Fat	3.9 g	low
Cholesterol	7 mg	low
Fibre	4.4 g	med
Sodium	155 mg	med

RAVIOLI WITH TUNA SAUCE

Serves 4

- ☐ **375 g fresh or frozen ravioli with spinach filling**
- ☐ **2 tablespoons grated Parmesan cheese**
- ☐ **fresh dill sprigs**

TUNA SAUCE
- ☐ **2 teaspoons olive oil**
- ☐ **1 onion, finely chopped**
- ☐ **1 clove garlic, crushed**
- ☐ **440 g canned tomatoes (no added salt), undrained and mashed**
- ☐ **1 tablespoon tomato paste (no added salt)**
- ☐ **1 tablespoon dry red wine**
- ☐ **1 teaspoon sugar**
- ☐ **425 g canned tuna in spring water, drained and flaked**
- ☐ **1 tablespoon finely chopped fresh parsley**
- ☐ **1 tablespoon finely chopped fresh dill**
- ☐ **freshly ground black pepper**

1   Cook ravioli in boiling water in a large saucepan following packet directions. Drain and keep warm.

2   To make sauce, heat oil in a frypan. Cook onion and garlic for 4–5 minutes or until onion softens. Stir in tomatoes, tomato paste, wine and sugar. Bring to the boil. Add tuna, parsley and dill, reduce heat and simmer for 10 minutes.

3   Place pasta on a warmed serving platter. Spoon over sauce, sprinkle with Parmesan cheese and garnish with dill sprigs.

1187 kilojoules (283 calories) per serve

Fat	16.0 g	high
Cholesterol	40 mg	low
Fibre	2.5 g	med
Sodium	165 mg	med

SPAGHETTI WITH ASPARAGUS SAUCE

Serves 6

- ☐ **500 g spaghetti**
- ☐ **2 tablespoons grated Parmesan cheese**

ASPARAGUS SAUCE
- ☐ **500 g fresh asparagus spears, trimmed**
- ☐ **1 tablespoon olive oil**
- ☐ **1 thick slice wholegrain bread, crumbed**
- ☐ **1 cup (250 mL) evaporated skim milk**
- ☐ **60 g grated mozzarella cheese**
- ☐ **freshly ground black pepper**

1   Cook spaghetti in boiling water in a large saucepan following packet directions.
2   To make sauce, steam, boil or microwave asparagus until tender. Drain and refresh under cold running water. Cut into 3 cm pieces and set aside. Heat oil in a frypan, add breadcrumbs and cook over low heat for 2 minutes, stirring all the time. Stir in milk and asparagus, and cook over medium heat for 5 minutes. Mix in cheese and continue to cook until melted. Season to taste with pepper.
3   Place spaghetti on a warmed serving platter, spoon over sauce and toss gently to combine. Sprinkle with Parmesan cheese and serve immediately.

1000 kilojoules (237 calories) per serve

Fat	6.7 g	med
Cholesterol	11 mg	low
Fibre	2.4 g	med
Sodium	188 mg	med

TASTY TOMATO AND MACARONI BAKE

Serves 6

- ☐ **2 cups (300 g) wholemeal macaroni**
- ☐ **2 teaspoons grape seed oil**
- ☐ **2 large onions, sliced**
- ☐ **1 red capsicum, sliced**
- ☐ **1 green capsicum, sliced**
- ☐ **1/2 cup (125 mL) tomato paste (no added salt)**
- ☐ **2 large tomatoes, peeled and sliced**
- ☐ **2 tablespoons finely chopped fresh basil**
- ☐ **3 cups (750 mL) Cheese Sauce (see page 17)**

TOPPING
- ☐ **2 teaspoons olive oil**
- ☐ **1 tablespoon finely chopped fresh chives**
- ☐ **3 tablespoons grated mozzarella cheese**
- ☐ **1 tablespoon grated Parmesan cheese**

1   Cook macaroni in a large saucepan of boiling water following packet directions. Drain, rinse under cold running water and spread over the base of a 16 cm x 28 cm shallow ovenproof dish.

2   Heat oil in a non-stick frypan. Cook onions and red and green capsicums for 5 minutes or until they soften. Drain off any liquid and mix in tomato paste.

3   Spread over macaroni, top with tomato slices, sprinkle with basil and spoon over cheese sauce.

4   To make topping, mix together oil, chives, mozzarella and Parmesan cheeses. Sprinkle on top of macaroni mixture and bake at 180°C for 20 minutes or until topping is golden and macaroni bake is heated through.

811 kilojoules (192 calories) per serve

Fat	5.0 g	low
Cholesterol	7 mg	low
Fibre	3.7 g	high
Sodium	10 mg	low

Quark

Quark or quarg is a continental-style cottage cheese which is packed in a solid mass and is not separate curd particles usually seen in cottage cheese. It has a sharper, more acidic taste, making it less popular for sweet dishes and more suitable for savoury ones.

Quark is usually made from skim milk and so has a very low fat content of around 1 per cent – ideal for a healthy heart diet. Be sure to check the label before buying, as it can also be made from full cream milk which gives it a high fat content. The label will give an indication of this as 'full cream quark'. It is generally packaged in a soft plastic envelope or a sausage-shaped pack and is available through many delicatessens or specialty shops. A 20 gram serving has 63 kilojoules or 15 calories.

Ricotta
(see Cheese)

Ricotta is a soft unriped curd cheese. It is similar in food value to cottage cheese, but its fat content can be higher if whole milk or cream is added, so check the label if you are uncertain. Ricotta makes an excellent substitute for cream, cream cheese and sour cream.

Top left: Spaghetti with Asparagus Sauce, Ravioli with Tuna Sauce
Bottom left: Tasty Tomato and Macaroni Bake

Shellfish

Shellfish are frequently avoided by people trying to lower cholesterol as they have heard that shellfish are high in cholesterol. Readings are not as high as was once thought, because earlier analyses measured a number of sterols as well as cholesterol, giving a false high reading. Apart from prawns, all shellfish contain low to moderate amounts and can be safely included in your meals. Recent Australian tests show that shellfish are extremely low in fat and what little fat they carry is high in the unique omega-3 fats which can improve our blood profile and immune system.

❖

FRUITY SEASIDE SLAW

Serves 4

- ☐ 20 scallops
- ☐ 4 cooked large prawns, peeled and deveined
- ☐ 1/4 red cabbage, shredded
- ☐ 250 g seedless green grapes
- ☐ 400 g canned mango slices, drained and liquid reserved
- ☐ 3 tablespoons low fat unflavoured yoghurt
- ☐ 1 tablespoon chopped fresh chives
- ☐ 1 tablespoon chopped fresh dill
- ☐ 1 teaspoon grated fresh ginger
- ☐ 1/4 teaspoon curry powder
- ☐ pinch chilli powder

1   Poach scallops in water for 3–4 minutes. Drain and set aside to cool.
2   Combine scallops, prawns, cabbage, grapes and mango slices in a salad bowl.
3   Blend together yoghurt, 2 tablespoons of reserved mango liquid, chives, dill, ginger, curry and chilli powders. Fold lightly through salad. Refrigerate until required.

994 kilojoules (234 calories) per serve

Fat	1.9 g	low
Cholesterol	81 mg	med
Fibre	6.0 g	high
Sodium	301 mg	high

❖

SEAFOOD PAELLA

Serves 6

- ☐ 1 1/2 tablespoons olive oil
- ☐ 2 spanish onions, finely chopped
- ☐ 4 cloves garlic, crushed
- ☐ 1 green capsicum, thinly sliced
- ☐ 1 red capsicum, thinly sliced
- ☐ 1 tablespoon finely chopped fresh tarragon
- ☐ 1/4 teaspoon ground turmeric
- ☐ 2 cups (500 mL) chicken stock
- ☐ 3 tomatoes, peeled and chopped
- ☐ 1 tablespoon tomato paste (no added salt)
- ☐ 1/2 cup (125 mL) dry white wine
- ☐ 3 tablespoons lemon juice
- ☐ 2 cups (420 g) quick cooking brown rice
- ☐ 200g fresh or frozen peas
- ☐ 4 white fish fillets, cut into pieces
- ☐ 18 shelled oysters
- ☐ 150 g scallops
- ☐ 18 mussels in shells, cleaned
- ☐ freshly ground black pepper

1   Heat oil in a large heavy-based frypan. Cook onions, garlic, capsicums and tarragon for 3–4 minutes.
2   Combine turmeric, stock, tomatoes, tomato paste, wine and lemon juice. Add to pan with rice. Cover and simmer for 12 minutes.

CHOLESTEROL IN SHELLFISH

Milligrams per 100 g uncooked shellfish, shell and bone removed	
Scallops	29
Oysters	40
Mussels	45
Crab	68
Lobster	98
Octopus	140
Cuttlefish	160
Squid (calamari)	160
Prawns	170–190
Average	140

Fish Marketing Authority 1989, except for oysters, scallops and mussels from CSIRO Food Research Quarterly 37 (1977), 33–39.

---

3   Remove cover and stir in peas, fish, oysters, scallops and mussels. Season to taste with pepper. Simmer for a further 15 minutes or until rice is tender. Discard any unopened mussels before serving.

1389 kilojoules (332 calories) per serve

Fat	7.9 g	med
Cholesterol	105 mg	high
Fibre	5.0 g	high
Sodium	396 mg	high

❖

SCALLOP AND PRAWN STICKS

Add an exotic touch to your next barbecue with these easy to prepare and tasty kebabs.

Serves 6

- ☐ 6 uncooked king prawns, shelled and deveined
- ☐ 500 g scallops
- ☐ 1 large onion, cut into eighths

MARINADE
- ☐ 1 tablespoon olive oil
- ☐ 2 tablespoons white wine
- ☐ 2 teaspoons finely chopped fresh dill
- ☐ 2 teaspoons finely chopped fresh parsley
- ☐ 2 teaspoons finely chopped fresh chives
- ☐ 2 cloves garlic, crushed
- ☐ 2 teaspoons grated lime rind
- ☐ 2 tablespoons lime juice
- ☐ freshly ground black pepper

1   Thread prawns, scallops and onions onto six wooden skewers.
2   To make marinade, combine oil, wine, dill, parsley, chives, garlic, lime rind and juice in a glass dish. Season to taste with pepper. Add skewered seafood and marinate for 1 hour.
3   Remove seafood from marinade and grill for 2–3 minutes each side, turning and brushing with marinade frequently.

650 kilojoules (154 calories) per serve

Fat	4.4 g	low
Cholesterol	93 mg	med
Fibre	0.8 g	low
Sodium	350 mg	high

Fruity Seaside Slaw, Seafood Paella, Scallop and Prawn Sticks

OYSTER CHOWDER

Serves 4

- [ ] **20 g polyunsaturated margarine (salt reduced)**
- [ ] **1 onion, chopped**
- [ ] **1 stalk celery, sliced**
- [ ] **1 carrot, diced**
- [ ] **2 tablespoons plain flour**
- [ ] **2 potatoes, peeled and diced**
- [ ] **3 cups (750 mL) chicken stock**
- [ ] **2 bay leaves**
- [ ] **6 peppercorns**
- [ ] **16 shelled oysters**
- [ ] **1/2 cup (125 mL) evaporated skim milk**
- [ ] **1 teaspoon Dijon-style mustard**
- [ ] **2 tablespoons chopped fresh chives**

1   Melt margarine in a large heavy-based saucepan. Cook onion, celery and carrot for 3–4 minutes or until tender.

2   Stir in flour and cook for 1 minute. Add potatoes and cook for 1 minute. Remove pan from heat. Combine stock, bay leaves and peppercorns. Blend with vegetables in pan. Bring to the boil, reduce heat and simmer for 20–25 minutes or until potatoes are tender.

3   Remove bay leaves and peppercorns. Add oysters, milk and mustard. Cook for 2–3 minutes over low heat. Ladle soup into individual bowls and sprinkle with chives to serve.

801 kilojoules (156 calories) per serve

Fat	4.8 g	low
Cholesterol	21 mg	low
Fibre	3.4 g	high
Sodium	318 mg	high

DID YOU KNOW?

There is a pearl of truth in the belief that oysters are an aphrodisiac food. Oysters are the richest food source of zinc, an essential mineral needed for sexual maturation in adolescence and for sperm production in adult males. Unfortunately no one has yet discovered how many you need to eat to improve your love life!

PASTA MUSSELS AND WINE SAUCE

Serves 4

- [ ] **250 g wholemeal spaghetti**
- [ ] **2 cloves garlic, crushed**
- [ ] **2 onions, chopped**
- [ ] **1 cup (250 mL) dry white wine**
- [ ] **1/2 cup (125 mL) water**
- [ ] **1 sprig fresh thyme**
- [ ] **2 tablespoons chopped fresh parsley**
- [ ] **1 kg mussels, cleaned and bearded**
- [ ] **fresh thyme sprigs**
- [ ] **fine strips lemon peel**

SAUCE
- [ ] **20 g polyunsaturated margarine (salt reduced)**
- [ ] **2 tablespoons plain flour**
- [ ] **1/2 cup (125 mL) evaporated skim milk**
- [ ] **1 tablespoon lemon juice**
- [ ] **freshly ground black pepper**

1   Cook pasta in a large saucepan of boiling water, following packet directions. Drain and keep warm.

2   Place garlic, onions, wine, water, thyme and parsley in a large saucepan. Bring to the boil and cook for 5 minutes. Drop in mussels, reduce heat and simmer for 5 minutes.

3   Remove mussels from pan with a slotted spoon. Discard any unopened shells. Set remaining mussels aside and keep warm. Strain cooking liquid and reserve.

4   To make sauce, melt margarine in a small saucepan. Stir in flour and cook for 1–2 minutes. Remove from heat and gradually blend in reserved cooking liquid. Cook over medium heat until sauce boils and thickens.

5   Whisk in milk and lemon juice. Season to taste with pepper and heat through gently. Place pasta on a warm serving platter, top with mussels and spoon over sauce. Garnish with shallots and lemon peel.

1386 kilojoules (326 calories) per serve

Fat	7.1 g	med
Cholesterol	126 mg	med
Fibre	2.0 g	med
Sodium	356 mg	high

Pasta Mussels and Wine Sauce, Oyster Chowder

CHOLESTEROL CHECKLIST

Our handy fact finder will sort out the confusion surrounding cholesterol today.

LDL-CHOLESTEROL

Low Density Lipoprotein-Cholesterol. One of the two major forms of cholesterol circulating in the blood. It accounts for most of the cholesterol and contributes to the fatty build-up on artery walls, which encourages heart disease.

HDL-CHOLESTEROL

High Density Lipoprotein - Cholesterol. The second major form of blood cholesterol and the 'good guy', which clears cholesterol from the arteries and protects against heart disease. Athletes and people from long-lived families usually have high levels of this cholesterol. When you have your cholesterol measured, you will receive one figure for the total, plus another set of figures for the two cholesterol forms separately or as a ratio.

LIPIDS

A medical term meaning fats.

TRIGLYCERIDES

Another important type of fat found in food and in the body. Like blood cholesterol, a high reading (over 2 millimoles per litre) increases the likelihood of heart disease, but is not considered as dangerous a risk factor as high blood cholesterol.

OMEGA - 3 FATS

Unique polyunsaturated fats found in fatty fish, which have the ability to reduce blood clotting and to lessen its 'stickiness'. They can lower blood pressure and triglyceride levels (but not cholesterol), and so help protect

CONVERTING CHOLESTEROL

Blood cholesterol can be measured in millimoles per litre (mmol/l) or in milligrams per decilitre (mg/dl or mg%). Here is a handy conversion table for both measurements. In Australia, the National Heart Foundation recommends that your cholesterol be under 5.5 mmol/l.

mg/dL	mmol/L
180	4.66
185	4.78
190	4.91
195	5.04
200	5.17
205	5.30
210	5.43
215	5.56
220	5.69
225	5.82
230	5.95
235	6.08
240	6.21
245	6.34
250	6.47
255	6.60
260	6.72
265	6.85
270	6.98
275	7.11
280	7.24
285	7.37
290	7.50
295	7.63
300	7.76

against heart disease. May also help fight immune-related problems such as asthma, rheumatoid arthritis, and the skin complaint psoriasis.

FISH OIL

A thick, oily liquid extracted from fish flesh, not fish livers. It is a concentrated form of fish, with 2–3 grams of fish oil being equivalent to eating 200 grams of an oily fish. It supplies a high dose of omega-3 fats. Because of its unpleasant taste, it is more popular in capsule form which is tasteless.

EPA

Eicosapentaenoic acid – one of the most common Omega-3 fats. It is a polyunsaturated fat, which remains liquid at very low temperatures, keeping the fish mobile in extreme cold. Found in all fish and shell fish, but especially rich in oily fish such as herring, salmon, tuna, mackerel, sardines, and ocean trout.

P:S RATIO

The ratio of polyunsaturated to saturated fats in a food. Often appearing on the labels of margarines, mayonnaises and oils, a P:S ratio of 2:1 means that there is twice as much polyunsaturated fat present as saturated.

HYDROGENATED FAT

A fat or oil which has been made more solid by the addition of hydrogen to the fat's molecule. Hydrogenation is an important step in the manufacture of margarine, as it allows the use of a range of oils depending on their availability.

Teas

Tea, whether hot or cold, weak or strong, is a wonderfully refreshing drink. If drunk black, without milk or sugar, it has no kilojoules (calories). Herbal teas such as peppermint, rosehip, chamomile and fenugreek are increasing in popularity and make an interesting variation on regular tea. Some contain no caffeine or theophylline, the stimulant compounds of tea and coffee, and this is usually listed on the pack.

Tea has many uses apart from just a drink. It can be an ingredient in dishes as diverse as cakes and chutney and, as our tea recipes show, adds its own unique flavour.

❖

ICED TEA

Icy cool tea served with lemon slices makes the ideal thirst quencher for midsummer.

Serves 4

- ☐ **4 tea bags**
- ☐ **4 cups (1 litre) cold water**
- ☐ **ice cubes**
- ☐ **lemon slices**

1 Place water and tea bags in a large glass jug. Cover and refrigerate overnight.
2 To serve, place ice cubes in long glass, pour in tea and garnish with lemon slices.

5 kilojoules (1 calories) per serve

Fat	*0 g*	*low*
Cholesterol	*0 mg*	*low*
Fibre	*0 g*	*low*
Sodium	*0 mg*	*low*

COOK'S TIP

Using cold water to make iced tea ensures that your tea will be a clear amber and prevents an acid taste. Using hot water and allowing the tea to cool tends to give a cloudy liquid with a bitter taste.

Not Just A Cuppa

Teas and tea leaves have a multitude of uses around the home, here we give you just a few.

❖ Pour spent tea leaves onto pot plants for a natural compost.

❖ Soak cotton wool pads in iced tea and place over eyes to sooth and give them a sparkle.

❖ Turn leftover tea into iced tea or tea punch (with rum or sherry and lime juice).

❖ Soak dried fruit in tea instead of sherry or orange juice when baking puddings or cakes.

❖ Strong black tea makes a wonderful natural dye.

BERRY-FILLED TEA PANCAKES

In these pancakes we replaced milk with tea for a more robust flavour. We have filled our pancakes with a creamy berry fruit filling but you might like to serve them warm with honey and lemon juice, or with a savoury filling of your choice.

Makes 10

PANCAKES
- ☐ **100 g plain flour, sifted**
- ☐ **1 egg, lightly beaten**
- ☐ **1 cup (250 mL) cold tea**
- ☐ **1 tablespoon polyunsaturated oil**
- ☐ **2 tablespoons icing sugar, sifted**

FILLING
- ☐ **1 cup (250 g) ricotta cheese**
- ☐ **1 cup (250 g) low fat unflavoured yoghurt**
- ☐ **2 tablespoons rosewater**
- ☐ **100 g fresh strawberries, hulled and halved**
- ☐ **100 g raspberries**
- ☐ **2 kiwi fruit, sliced**

1 To make pancakes, place flour in a bowl and make a well in the centre. Add egg and work flour in from the sides. Stir in tea a little at a time to make a smooth batter of pouring consistency. Set aside to stand for 30 minutes before cooking.

2 Pour 2 tablespoons batter into a lightly greased non-stick frypan. Cook pancakes until golden brown each side.

3 To make filling, place ricotta, yoghurt and rosewater in food processor or blender. Process until smooth. Transfer to a bowl and fold through fruit. To serve, divide filling between pancakes. Roll up and dust with icing sugar.

559 kilojoules (133 calories) per serve

Fat	5.0 g	low
Cholesterol	31 mg	low
Fibre	1.8 g	med
Sodium	75 mg	low

❖

HOT GINGER TEA

Iced tea in summer, hot ginger tea in winter. It is a particularly comforting drink for a cold.

Serves 4

- ☐ **3 teaspoons black tea leaves**
- ☐ **¹/₂ teaspoon grated fresh ginger**
- ☐ **4 cups (1 L) boiling water**
- ☐ **lemon juice (optional)**
- ☐ **honey (optional)**

1 Place tea and ginger in a warmed teapot. Pour over boiling water, stir and allow to steep for 5 minutes. Stir again and strain before pouring.

2 Flavour tea with lemon juice and honey if desired.

88 kilojoules (20 calories) per serve

Fat	0 g	low
Cholesterol	0 mg	low
Fibre	0 g	low
Sodium	0 mg	low

Did You Know?

❖ Tea is the most popular drink in the world. It has been drunk in ancient China for thousands of years, but did not reach Europe until 1610, when the Dutch began importing samples to Holland.

❖ Tea contains the natural stimulant caffeine, also found in coffee and cocoa. Depending on the variety and length of brewing, a cup of tea has 10–90 milligrams of caffeine, which is about half that of coffee. Tea also contains two other stimulating agents, theobromine and theophylline, which all account for tea's ability to relieve tiredness and act as a 'pick-me-up'.

Hot Ginger Tea, Iced Tea, Berry-Filled Tea Pancakes

Tofu
(Soya Bean Curd)

Tofu, a white soya bean curd, makes a wonderful low fat, cholesterol free substitute for cream, mayonnaise and cheese in cooking. With its bland flavour, it can lend itself to either savoury or sweet dishes, as our recipes illustrate. Although it has been an important food in China and Japan for over two centuries, the West is only now discovering the delights of this ancient food.

❖

SESAME CHICKEN STIR-FRY

Serves 6

- ☐ **250 g tofu, drained, pressed and cubed**
- ☐ **300 g chicken fillets, cut into strips**
- ☐ **2 teaspoons polyunsaturated oil**
- ☐ **2 teaspoons sesame oil**
- ☐ **1 teaspoon grated ginger**
- ☐ **¹/₂ red capsicum, sliced**
- ☐ **¹/₂ green capsicum, sliced**
- ☐ **2 teaspoons cornflour blended with ¹/₂ cup (125 mL) water**
- ☐ **4 shallots, sliced diagonally**
- ☐ **1 cup (50 g) bean sprouts**
- ☐ **1 tablespoon sesame seeds, toasted**

MARINADE
- ☐ **2 tablespoons low salt soy sauce**
- ☐ **1 tablespoon dry sherry**
- ☐ **1 clove garlic, crushed**

1   To make marinade, mix together soy sauce, sherry and garlic. Add tofu and chicken, toss to coat and leave to marinate for 30 minutes. Drain and reserve marinade.

2   Heat oils in a wok or frypan and cook tofu, chicken and ginger for 5 minutes or until chicken is just cooked. Remove tofu and chicken, set aside and keep warm.

3   Toss in red and green capsicums and cook for 3–4 minutes. Return tofu and chicken to pan. Toss to combine. Mix cornflour mixture with reserved marinade. Stir into pan and cook until mixture boils and thickens. Toss in shallots, bean sprouts and sesame seeds. Serve immediately.

576 kilojoules (139 calories) per serve

Fat	7.0 g	med
Cholesterol	34 mg	low
Fibre	0.7 g	low
Sodium	229 mg	med

FAT FIGHTER

Tofu has less than 5% fat, no cholesterol and virtually no sodium (salt). Being extracted from soya beans, it is a good source of protein, minerals and B vitamins. One-third of a cup of tofu (75 g) supplies only 200 kilojoules (48 calories).

❖

FRUITY TOFU SAUCE

Makes 2 cups (500 mL)

- ☐ **250 g tofu, drained and roughly chopped**
- ☐ **250 g strawberries, hulled and roughly chopped**
- ☐ **2 tablespoons honey**

1   Place tofu, strawberries and honey in a food processor or blender and process until smooth.

2   Cover and chill. Stir well before serving.

60 kilojoules (14 calories) per serve

Fat	0.3 g	low
Cholesterol	0 mg	low
Fibre	0.2 g	low
Sodium	2 mg	low

TOFU KNOW HOW

❖ Before using tofu for cooking, place it in a sieve and drain briefly. Sometimes a firmer tofu is required in which case cover and drain in the refrigerator overnight.

❖ A recipe will sometimes say to press tofu, this gives an even firmer texture. To press tofu, place cakes on a board lined with a double thickness of absorbent kitchen paper. Cover with an additional double thickness of paper, and top with a baking tray weighted with a heavy can. Tilt the board towards the sink and leave to drain for 45–60 minutes.

Left: Fruity Tofu Sauce
Below: Sesame Chicken Stir-Fry, Curried Vegetable and Tofu Soup

CURRIED VEGETABLE AND TOFU SOUP

Serves 6

- [ ] **1 tablespoon polyunsaturated oil**
- [ ] **1 large onion, chopped**
- [ ] **1 clove garlic, crushed**
- [ ] **1 teaspoon ground cumin**
- [ ] **1 teaspoon ground coriander**
- [ ] **1 teaspoon ground turmeric**
- [ ] **1/2 teaspoon chilli powder**
- [ ] **1/2 small cauliflower, cut into small florets**
- [ ] **1 carrot, diced**
- [ ] **1 large potato, diced**
- [ ] **1 zucchini, sliced**
- [ ] **4 cups (1 litre) vegetable stock**
- [ ] **250 g tofu, drained, pressed and cut into cubes**
- [ ] **320 g canned corn kernels (no added salt)**
- [ ] **freshly ground black pepper**
- [ ] **3 tablespoons chopped fresh dill**

1   Heat oil in a large saucepan and cook onion, garlic, cumin, coriander, turmeric and chilli powder for 4–5 minutes. Stir in cauliflower, carrot, potato, zucchini and stock. Bring to the boil. Reduce heat, cover and simmer for 15–20 minutes or until vegetables are tender.

2   Using a slotted spoon remove 1 cup of cooked vegetables and puree in a food processor or blender.

3   Stir puree, tofu and corn into soup and heat gently for a further 4–5 minutes. Season to taste with pepper. Sprinkle with dill to serve.

768 kilojoules (184 calories) per serve

Fat	*5.0 g*	*low*
Cholesterol	*0 mg*	*low*
Fibre	*6.1 g*	*high*
Sodium	*91 mg*	*low*

Unrefined Foods

Unrefined foods, sometimes called 'wholefoods', were once the province of health food freaks and vegetarians, but are now very much recommended for their fibre content. Brown rice, wholemeal pastas, lentils, dried beans, grains such as oats, barley and buckwheat are all unrefined foods that are kind to not only to your heart but to your whole body.

Vegetables

There are so many reasons why vegetables are vital to your diet. They add crunch, colour and vitality to your food. They have no cholesterol or fat (except for avocados and olives); they are packed with vitamins, minerals and fibre; they are so low in kilojoules (calories) that you can eat them quite freely; and the type of fibre they contain helps lower cholesterol.

❖
BEETROOT, ORANGE AND HORSERADISH SALAD

Serves 6

- [ ] **4 medium cooked beetroot, peeled and cut into thin strips**
- [ ] **2 teaspoons grated orange rind**
- [ ] **2 oranges, segmented**

HORSERADISH DRESSING
- [ ] **1¹/2 tablespoons olive oil**
- [ ] **3 tablespoons cider vinegar**
- [ ] **1 teaspoon mustard powder**
- [ ] **2 teaspoons horseradish relish**
- [ ] **2 teaspoons sugar**

1   Combine beetroot, orange rind and orange segments. Arrange attractively in a salad bowl. Cover and refrigerate for 1–2 hours.
2   To make dressing, combine oil, vinegar, mustard, horseradish and sugar in a screwtop jar. Shake well to combine. Pour over salad just prior to serving.

260 kilojoules (62 calories) per serve

Fat	0.5 g	low
Cholesterol	0 mg	low
Fibre	3.5 g	high
Sodium	50 mg	low

❖
CANDIED KUMERA

Serve this sweet vegetable with grilled pork chops.

Serves 6

- [ ] **¹/2 cup (85 g) brown sugar**
- [ ] **¹/2 cup (125 mL) water**
- [ ] **20 g polyunsaturated margarine (salt reduced)**
- [ ] **500 g kumera, peeled and thinly sliced**
- [ ] **2 tablespoons toasted slivered almonds**

1   Combine brown sugar, water and margarine in a non-stick frypan. Cook over low heat until margarine melts. Add kumera, cover and continue to cook over low heat for 15–20 minutes or until kumera is tender.
2   Add almonds and toss lightly to combine.

636 kilojoules (151 calories) per serve

Fat	4.4 g	low
Cholesterol	0 mg	low
Fibre	2.3 g	med
Sodium	32 mg	low

NUTRITION TIP

✧ Vegetables of the cabbage family – cabbage, Brussels sprouts, broccoli, cauliflower and turnip – are nutrition 'superstars' and should be included as often as possible. Research has shown that these vegetables contain compounds called indoles and isothiocyanates which can protect against cancer of the bowel. They are also one of the best vegetables for fibre and are high in vitamin C and beta-carotene – and for only a few kilojoules!

✧ Remember to cook vegetables as quickly as possible with the least amount of water to save these valuable vitamins. Steam, boil, microwave or stir-fry for fastest results and try to serve them as soon as cooked - keeping them warm for too long only reduces the heat-sensitive vitamins.

STIR-FRIED BROCCOLI WITH ALMONDS

A colourful stir-fry that is sure to please the whole family.

Serves 4

- ☐ **2 carrots, cut into matchsticks**
- ☐ **500 g broccoli, cut into florets**
- ☐ **2 teaspoons peanut oil**
- ☐ **1 onion, sliced**
- ☐ **1 clove garlic, crushed**
- ☐ **2 teaspoons grated fresh ginger**
- ☐ **2 teaspoons low salt soy sauce**
- ☐ **2 tablespoons toasted almonds**

1 Boil, steam or microwave carrots and broccoli until they just change colour. Drain and refresh under cold running water.

2 Heat oil in wok or frypan. Add onion, garlic and ginger and stir-fry for 4–5 minutes. Add carrots, broccoli and soy sauce, and stir-fry for 3–4 minutes longer, or until vegetables are heated through. Just prior to serving toss through almonds.

390 kilojoules (92 calories) per serve

Fat	4.9 g	low
Cholesterol	0 mg	low
Fibre	7.6 g	high
Sodium	86 mg	low

Beetroot, Orange and Horseradish Salad, Candied Kumera, Stir-Fried Broccoli with Almonds

APPLE, STRAWBERRY AND PECAN SALAD

A variation on the traditional Waldorf salad, with half the fat and no cholesterol.

Serves 4

- [ ] **2 red apples, chopped**
- [ ] **2 stalks celery, sliced**
- [ ] **200 g strawberries, halved**
- [ ] **3 tablespoons sultanas**
- [ ] **60 g chopped pecans**

DRESSING
- [ ] **2 teaspoons finely chopped fresh mint leaves**
- [ ] **3 tablespoons low fat unflavoured yoghurt**
- [ ] **2 tablespoons lemon juice**

1   Combine apples, celery, strawberries, sultanas and pecans in a bowl.
2   To make dressing, blend together mint, yoghurt and lemon juice. Toss with apple mixture and refrigerate until required.

739 kilojoules (176 calories) per serve

Fat	*7.9 g*	*med*
Cholesterol	*0 mg*	*low*
Fibre	*5.0 g*	*high*
Sodium	*43 mg*	*low*

POTATO AND BRUSSELS SPROUTS SOUP

Serves 4

- [ ] **250 g Brussels sprouts, trimmed**
- [ ] **2 large potatoes, peeled and diced**
- [ ] **4 cups (1 L) chicken stock**
- [ ] **1/2 cup (125 mL) skim milk**
- [ ] **freshly ground black pepper**
- [ ] **2 tablespoons chopped walnuts**

1   Place sprouts, potatoes and stock in a saucepan and bring to the boil. Reduce heat, cover and simmer for 20–25 minutes or until potatoes are tender. Remove from heat and set aside to cool slightly.
2   Place in a food processor or blender and puree. Return soup to a clean pan, add milk and season to taste with pepper. Heat gently. To serve, ladle into soup bowls and sprinkle with walnuts.

524 kilojoules (126 calories) per serve

Fat	*4.3 g*	*low*
Cholesterol	*0 mg*	*low*
Fibre	*3.2 g*	*high*
Sodium	*41 mg*	*low*

THE TOP TEN FOR FIBRE

Grams of fibre per average serve of vegetables

Broccoli, 2/3 cup	3.9
Sweetcorn, 1/2 cup kernels	3.5
Potato, unpeeled 1	3.0
Carrot, peeled, 1	2.9
Eggplant, 1/2	2.7
Pumpkin, peeled, 1/2 cup	2.4
Tomato, raw, 1	2.4
Potato, peeled, 1	2.4
Onion, 1	2.2
Cauliflower, 2/3 cup	2.0

All figures refer to cooked vegetables, except tomato which is raw

VITAL VITAMINS

✧ Best vegetables for vitamin C are: capsicum, chilli, parsley, watercress, broccoli, Brussels sprouts, cauliflower and kohlrabi. These have a higher concentration of vitamin C than citrus fruit but are often overlooked as sources of vitamin C.

✧ Remember being told you must eat green and orange vegetables at dinner? Nutritionists today agree! Dark green and orange vegetables contain much beta-carotene (the precursor of vitamin A), which helps protect against cancer and is needed for vision. Carrots are the richest for beta-carotene, followed by orange sweet potato, parsley, pumpkin, spinach, silverbeet, capsicum and chilli.

*Left: Apple, Strawberry and Pecan Salad
Below: Potato and Brussel Sprouts Soup,
Minestrone Soup*

MINESTRONE SOUP

Minestrone is a substantial main meal soup, both tasty and filling. You can vary the vegetables depending on what is available.

Serves 8

- ☐ **2 tablespoons olive oil**
- ☐ **3 cloves garlic, crushed**
- ☐ **1 onion, chopped**
- ☐ **1 large potato, diced**
- ☐ **1 carrot, diced**
- ☐ **2 large zucchini, diced**
- ☐ **100 g green beans, trimmed and sliced**
- ☐ **2 tablespoons finely chopped fresh parsley**
- ☐ **1 tablespoon finely chopped fresh basil**
- ☐ **1 teaspoon finely chopped fresh oregano**
- ☐ **3 tablespoons tomato paste (no added salt)**
- ☐ **6 cups (1.5 litres) chicken stock**
- ☐ **freshly ground black pepper**
- ☐ **440 g canned red kidney beans, drained**
- ☐ **100 g macaroni noodles**
- ☐ **1/2 cabbage, finely shredded**

1 Heat oil in a large heavy-based saucepan. Cook garlic and onion for 2–3 minutes. Stir in potato, carrot, zucchini and beans. Cook for 3–4 minutes, stirring frequently.

2 Combine parsley, basil, oregano, tomato paste and stock. Pour over vegetables in pan. Season to taste with pepper. Cover and simmer for 30 minutes or until vegetables are tender.

3 Add undrained kidney beans. Bring to the boil, drop in macaroni and cook for a further 20 minutes. Add cabbage during last minute of cooking.

753 kilojoules (180 calories) per serve

Fat	4.6 g	low
Cholesterol	0 mg	low
Fibre	4.0 g	high
Sodium	111 mg	low

TOMATO AND SPINACH STUFFED MUSHROOMS

Serves 6

- ☐ **6 large flat mushrooms**
- ☐ **3 tablespoons grated mozzarella cheese**
- ☐ **1 tablespoon grated Parmesan cheese**
- ☐ **1 tablespoon chopped fresh chives**

FILLING
- ☐ **1 tablespoon olive oil**
- ☐ **1 clove garlic, crushed**
- ☐ **3 shallots, finely chopped**
- ☐ **2 spinach leaves, stalk removed and finely shredded**
- ☐ **1 tablespoon tomato paste (no added salt)**
- ☐ **³/₄ cup (45 g) fresh breadcrumbs**
- ☐ **freshly ground black pepper**

1   Wipe mushrooms, remove stalks and finely chop.
2   To make filling, heat 1 teaspoon oil in frypan, cook garlic and shallots for 1–2 minutes. Stir in spinach and tomato paste, cook for 2–3 minutes. Fold through breadcrumbs. Season to taste with pepper.
3   Brush mushroom caps with remaining oil and place on an oven tray. Combine mozzarella and Parmesan cheeses. Spoon filling into mushroom caps, top with cheese mixture and sprinkle with chives. Bake at 200°C for 10–15 minutes.

371 kilojoules (89 calories) per serve

Fat	*4.8 g*	*low*
Cholesterol	*6 mg*	*low*
Fibre	*1.6 g*	*med*
Sodium	*106 mg*	*low*

❖

GIPSY BAKED POTATOES

Serves 4

- ☐ **2 teaspoons polyunsaturated oil**
- ☐ **1 onion, chopped**
- ☐ **1 clove garlic, crushed**
- ☐ **1 teaspoon finely chopped fresh rosemary**
- ☐ **3 large tomatoes, peeled and chopped**
- ☐ **1 green capsicum, diced**
- ☐ **1 teaspoon paprika**
- ☐ **1 cup (250 mL) chicken stock**
- ☐ **freshly ground black pepper**
- ☐ **2 large potatoes, peeled and cut into thick slices**
- ☐ **2 tablespoons finely chopped fresh chives**

1   Heat oil in a frypan and cook onion, garlic and rosemary for 4–5 minutes or until onion softens. Add tomatoes, capsicum, paprika and chicken stock, bring to the boil and simmer for 10 minutes. Season to taste with pepper.
2   Arrange potatoes in layers in a lightly greased ovenproof dish and spoon over tomato sauce. Bake at 180°C for 1¹/₂ hours or until cooked through. Sprinkle with chives just prior to serving.

538 kilojoules (129 calories) per serve

Fat	*2.3 g*	*low*
Cholesterol	*0 mg*	*low*
Fibre	*5.6 g*	*high*
Sodium	*108 mg*	*low*

❖

HERBY VEGETABLE SALAD

Serves 4

- ☐ **¹/₄ cauliflower, broken into florets**
- ☐ **1 head broccoli, broken into florets**
- ☐ **1 large carrot, cut into thin strips**
- ☐ **150 g snow peas, trimmed**
- ☐ **1 red capsicum, cut into thin strips**
- ☐ **3 tablespoons lemon juice**
- ☐ **2 teaspoons finely chopped fresh coriander**
- ☐ **2 teaspoons finely chopped fresh rosemary**
- ☐ **freshly ground black pepper**

LEMON VINAIGRETTE
- ☐ **2 tablespoons lemon juice**
- ☐ **1 tablespoon olive oil**
- ☐ **1 clove garlic, crushed**
- ☐ **1 teaspoon wholegrain mustard**

1   Boil, steam or microwave cauliflower, broccoli, carrot and snow peas until just tender. Drain, refresh under cold water.
2   Drain vegetables well. Toss in a salad bowl with capsicum, lemon juice, coriander and rosemary. Season to taste with pepper. Refrigerate until required.
3   To make vinaigrette, combine all ingredients in a screwtop jar. Shake well to combine. Pour over salad just prior to serving.

348 kilojoules (82 calories) per serve

Fat	*4.5 g*	*low*
Cholesterol	*0 mg*	*low*
Fibre	*5.0 g*	*high*
Sodium	*38 mg*	*low*

Tomato and Spinach Stuffed Mushrooms, Herby Vegetable Salad, Gipsy Baked Potatoes

3   Blend together vinegar and olive oil, pour over beans and refrigerate for 1–2 hours. Sprinkle with sesame seeds and serve.

276 kilojoules (66 calories) per serve

Fat	5.1 g	med
Cholesterol	0 mg	low
Fibre	3.8 g	high
Sodium	5 mg	low

NUTRITION TIP

❖ Frozen vegetables, picked and processed at their peak, retain most of their nutritional value. If cooked when frozen, they will have around the same food value as home-cooked fresh ones.

❖ When compared by weight, the vegetable which is lowest in kilojoules (calories) is celery, then cucumber and lettuce. Three long sticks of celery, 20 lettuce leaves or $1/2$ cucumber contain the same kilojoules as half a slice of bread.

LETTUCE ROLL-UPS

An interesting side dish or light entree, these roll-ups can be prepared several hours in advance.

Serves 6

- [ ] **6 large lettuce leaves**
- [ ] **1 cup (60 g) bean sprouts**
- [ ] **2 mangoes, peeled and chopped**
- [ ] **260 g canned sliced water chestnuts, drained**
- [ ] **2 teaspoons finely chopped preserved ginger**
- [ ] **2 teaspoons finely chopped mint leaves**
- [ ] **3 tablespoons low fat mayonnaise**
- [ ] **1 tablespoon low fat unflavoured yoghurt**

1   Tear lettuce leaves in half lengthways. Toss together sprouts, mangoes, water chestnuts, ginger and mint.
2   Combine mayonnaise and yoghurt. Fold through mango mixture.
3   Place a spoonful of mixture on each lettuce leaf. Roll up tightly and secure with a toothpick.

581 kilojoules (141 calories) per serve

Fat	3.5 g	low
Cholesterol	3 mg	low
Fibre	4.3 g	high
Sodium	80 mg	low

FRENCH BEAN SALAD

Serves 4

- [ ] **500 g green beans, trimmed and sliced**
- [ ] **1 clove garlic, crushed**
- [ ] **1 teaspoon ground fenugreek**
- [ ] **2 tablespoons finely chopped fresh mint leaves**
- [ ] **1 teaspoon red wine vinegar**
- [ ] **1 tablespoon olive oil**
- [ ] **2 teaspoons toasted sesame seeds**

1   Boil, steam or microwave beans until just tender. Drain and place in a salad bowl.
2   Combine garlic, fenugreek and mint. Toss with warm beans. Set aside and allow to cool slightly.

Water

Water is a most wonderful drink. It has no kilojoules, no fat, caffeine or sugar. Icy cold or with a squeeze of lemon or lime, it makes an ideal thirst quencher in hot weather. More and more restaurants are offering water to refresh and cleanse the palate; scores of 'water purifiers' have appeared to meet the desire for cleaner tasting water.

Nutritionists recommend that you drink six to eight glasses of fluid a day, especially if you are in a humid or air-conditioned environment. Try and drink at least half of these in the form of healthy water.

Yoghurt
and Buttermilk

Yoghurt and buttermilk are two cultured dairy products, their tangy slightly acidic flavour being produced by the action of bacteria on milk. Cultured or soured dairy foods are traditional in many parts of the world. They are known to be easier to digest than fresh milk, probably because they contain little lactose (milk sugar), which causes digestive problems for two-thirds of the world's people.

Low fat yoghurt is the best choice for people trying to lower cholesterol and has many culinary uses. It is an excellent substitute for cream, sour cream and mayonnaise and can be used in both savoury and sweet dishes (sweetened fruit yoghurt is the most popular form).

Buttermilk has the same food value as skim milk and makes a refreshing drink in summer. It too is a useful low fat ingredient and you can learn to cook with it by following our delicious recipes.

SPICY CURRY DIP

Yoghurt is the ideal base for many dips. When a recipe calls for sour cream replace it with yoghurt to allow those watching their cholesterol to indulge as well. Serve this dip with vegetables such as blanched asparagus spears, raw carrot and celery sticks and cherry tomatoes.

Makes 1 cup (250 mL)

- ☐ **2 teaspoons polyunsaturated oil**
- ☐ **1 small onion, chopped**
- ☐ **1 teaspoon curry powder**
- ☐ **pinch chilli powder**
- ☐ **1 cup (250 mL) low fat yoghurt**
- ☐ **freshly ground black pepper**

1   Heat oil in a non-stick frypan and cook onion with curry and chilli powders for 4–5 minutes or until onion softens.

2   Whisk into yoghurt and season to taste with pepper. Chill until ready to serve.

77 kilojoules (18 calories) per serve

Fat	0.9 g	low
Cholesterol	2 mg	low
Fibre	0 g	low
Sodium	19 mg	low

❖

BEEF SALAD STROGANOFF

Make this wonderful summer salad from leftover roast beef. For an attractive presentation you might like to serve the salad in lettuce cups garnished with sprigs of coriander.

Serves 6

- ☐ **1 tablespoon polyunsaturated margarine (salt reduced)**
- ☐ **200 g button mushrooms, sliced**
- ☐ **1 tablespoon lemon juice**
- ☐ **500 g lean roast beef, cut into strips**
- ☐ **6 shallots, finely chopped**
- ☐ **2 tablespoons chopped fresh coriander**
- ☐ **1 cup (250 g) low fat unflavoured yoghurt**
- ☐ **freshly ground black pepper**

1   Heat margarine in a non-stick frypan and cook mushrooms with lemon juice for 4–5 minutes. Drain and set aside to cool.
2   Combine mushrooms, beef, shallots and coriander. Add yoghurt and toss lightly to combine. Season to taste with pepper.

761 kilojoules (183 calories) per serve

Fat	7.3 g	med
Cholesterol	58 mg	low
Fibre	1.2 g	low
Sodium	107 mg	low

Beef Salad Stroganoff, Spicy Curry Dip

CREAMY LEMON AND LIME PIE

A light chiffon-style pie that's sure to become an entertaining favourite.

Serves 8

BASE
- ☐ **1 quantity sweet bran pastry (pg 9)**

FILLING
- ☐ **2 tablespoons gelatine dissolved in 4 tablespoons boiling water**
- ☐ **1 cup (250 mL) evaporated skim milk, chilled**
- ☐ **2 tablespoons fresh lime juice**
- ☐ **2 tablespoons fresh lemon juice**
- ☐ **1 teaspoon grated lime rind**
- ☐ **1 cup (250 mL) low fat unflavoured yoghurt**
- ☐ **3 egg whites**
- ☐ **$^1/_2$ cup (125 g) caster sugar**
- ☐ **250 g mixed berries**

1 To make base, roll pastry to a 25 cm circle. Bake on a lightly greased oven tray at 200°C for 30–35 minutes or until cooked through. Remove from oven and using the base of a 20 cm springform pan as guide, cut to fit the pan. Allow to cool completely.
2 To make filling, set gelatine mixture aside to cool. Beat evaporated milk until thick. Blend together lime juice, lemon juice, lime rind and yoghurt. Fold through evaporated milk and gelatine mixture.
3 Beat egg whites until soft peaks form, then continue beating while slowly adding sugar until stiff peaks form. Fold egg white mixture through milk mixture. Place pastry base in a 20 cm springform pan. Top with filling and chill until set. Just before serving top pie with berries.

864 kilojoules (204 calories) per serve

Fat	4.7 g	low
Cholesterol	3 mg	low
Fibre	1.9 g	med
Sodium	75 mg	low

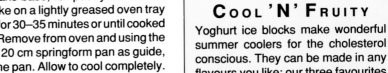

COOL 'N' FRUITY

Yoghurt ice blocks make wonderful summer coolers for the cholesterol conscious. They can be made in any flavours you like; our three favourites are banana, strawberry and pineapple. To make six yoghurt ice blocks you will require 1 cup of mashed or pureed fresh fruit and 1 cup of low fat unflavoured yoghurt. Combine and mix well. Spoon into ice block containers or small plastic cups and freeze. If making banana ice blocks, mix 1 teaspoon of lemon juice into the mashed banana to prevent discolouring.

CHOCOLATE CAKE

Surprise your cholesterol watchers with this chocolate cake.

Serves 16

- ☐ **1 $^1/_2$ cups (180 g) self-raising flour**
- ☐ **1 tablespoon cocoa**
- ☐ **$^3/_4$ cup (190 g) sugar**
- ☐ **1 tablespoon golden syrup**
- ☐ **100 g polyunsaturated margarine, melted**
- ☐ **$^1/_2$ cup (125 mL) buttermilk, warmed**
- ☐ **$^1/_2$ cup (125 mL) skim milk, warmed**

ICING
- ☐ **60 g reduced fat spread (salt reduced), softened**
- ☐ **3-4 tablespoons skim milk**
- ☐ **3 cups icing sugar**
- ☐ **2 tablespoons cocoa**

1 Sift together flour and cocoa into a bowl. Add sugar. Combine golden syrup, margarine, buttermilk and skim milk. Stir into dry ingredients and mix well to combine.
2 Spoon cake into a lightly greased and lined 18 cm round cake pan. Bake at 180°C for 30 minutes. Remove and allow to cool.
3 To make icing, combine spread and milk. Mix in icing sugar and cocoa. Beat for 5 minutes or until mixture is lightly and fluffy. Ice cold cake.

1625 kilojoules (374 calories) per serve

Fat	9.2 g	med
Cholesterol	0 mg	low
Fibre	0 g	low
Sodium	322 mg	high

QUICK WHOLEMEAL AND FRUIT ROLLS

Serves 8

- [ ] **2 cups (270 g) wholemeal flour**
- [ ] **2 cups (250 g) self-raising flour**
- [ ] **1/2 teaspoon ground nutmeg**
- [ ] **1/2 teaspoon ground cinnamon**
- [ ] **1 cup (160 g) dried mixed fruit**
- [ ] **1 1/2 cups (375 mL) buttermilk**

1   Sift together wholemeal and self-raising flours, nutmeg and cinnamon. Mix in dried fruit.

2   Stir in buttermilk a little at a time and beat until dough is firm and leaves the sides of the bowl.

3   Turn out on a lightly floured board and knead briefly. Divide into eight portions and shape into rolls. Place on a lightly greased oven tray. Bake at 200°C for 30-35 minutes or until well risen and golden.

1108 kilojoules (260 calories) per serve		
Fat	2.2 g	low
Cholesterol	0 mg	low
Fibre	5.5 g	high
Sodium	619 mg	high

YOGHURT INSTEAD

❖   If a recipe calls for buttermilk and you do not have any, you can use yoghurt in its place. You will, however, need to thin the yoghurt to about the same consistency as buttermilk. Use 1/2 cup (125 mL) yoghurt to 1 cup (250 mL) water or skim milk.

❖   Yoghurt can also be used to replace sour cream in a recipe. The dish will have a slightly tangier flavour when yoghurt is used. For sweet dishes, add a teaspoon of sugar for each cup of yoghurt if you wish.

Above: Chocolate Cake, Quick Wholemeal and Fruit Rolls
Left: Creamy Lemon and Lime Pie

Zucchini

Zucchini or courgettes are in fact baby marrows. This wonderful vegetable can be eaten cooked or raw. Why don't you try making a zucchini salad using a combination of sliced yellow and green zucchini tossed in our Minty Lemon dressing (page 18). This salad looks particularly pretty if the zucchini is sliced diagonally.

USEFUL INFORMATION

In this book, ingredients such as fish and meat are given in grams so you know how much to buy. A small inexpensive set of kitchen scales is always handy and very easy to use. Other ingredients in our recipes are given in tablespoons and cups, so you will need a nest of measuring cups (1 cup, 1/2 cup, 1/3 cup and 1/4 cup), a set of spoons (1 tablespoon, 1 teaspoon, 1/2 teaspoon and 1/4 teaspoon) and a transparent graduated measuring jug (1 litre or 250 mL) for measuring liquids. Cup and spoon measures are level.

MEASURING UP

Metric Measuring Cups

1/4 cup	60 mL	2 fl.oz
1/3 cup	80 mL	2 1/2 fl.oz
1/2 cup	125 mL	4 fl.oz
1 cup	250 mL	8 fl.oz

Metric Measuring Spoons

1/4 teaspoon	1.25 mL
1/2 teaspoon	2.5 mL
1 teaspoon	5 mL
1 tablespoon	20 mL

MEASURING LIQUIDS

Metric	Imperial	Cup
30 mL	1 fl.oz	
60 mL	2 fl.oz	1/4 cup
90 mL	3 fl.oz	
125 mL	4 fl.oz	1/2 cup
170 mL	5 1/2 fl.oz	2/3 cup
185 mL	6 fl.oz	
220 mL	7 fl.oz	
250 mL	8 fl.oz	1 cup
500 mL	16 fl.oz	2 cups
600 mL	1 pint	

MEASURING DRY INGREDIENTS

Metric	Imperial
15 g	1/2 oz
30 g	1 oz
60 g	2 oz
90 g	3 oz
125 g	4 oz
155 g	5 oz
185 g	6 oz
220 g	7 oz
250 g	8 oz
280 g	9 oz
315 g	10 oz
350 g	11 oz
375 g	12 oz
410 g	13 oz
440 g	14 oz
470 g	15 oz
500 g	16 oz (1 lb)
750 g	1 lb 8 oz
1 kg	2 lb
1.5 kg	3 lb
2 kg	4 lb
2.5 kg	5 lb

QUICK CONVERTER

Metric	Imperial
5 mm	1/4 in
1 cm	1/2 in
2 cm	3/4 in
2.5 cm	1 in
5 cm	2 ins
10 cm	4 ins
15 cm	6 ins
20 cm	8 ins
23 cm	9 ins
25 cm	10 ins
30 cm	12 ins

OVEN TEMPERATURES

°C	°F	Gas Mark
120	250	1/2
140	275	1
150	300	2
160	325	3
180	350	4
190	375	5
200	400	6
220	425	7
240	475	8
250	500	9

GLOSSARY OF TERMS

TERM	MEANING
Baste	To moisten meat or vegetables during cooking
Beetroot	Regular round beet
Bicarbonate of soda	Baking soda
Bottled oysters	Oysters preserved in brine, if unavailable use bottled mussels
Breadcrumbs, fresh	1 or 2 day old bread made into crumbs
Breadcrumbs, packaged	Use commercially packaged breadcrumbs
Butterfly pork steaks	Double pork loin steaks
Butternut pumpkin	Butternut squash
Evaporated skim milk	If unavailable use low fat evaporated milk
Capsicum	Red or green bell peppers
Chilli sauce	A sauce which includes chillies, salt and vinegar
Cholesterol free mayonnaise	A mayonnaise made from polyunsaturated oil without egg yolks
Cornflour	Cornstarch, substitute arrowroot
Ginger	Fresh ginger is ginger root. Preserved ginger is root ginger cooked in syrup
Glace ginger	Crystallised ginger
Golden nugget pumpkin	A summer squash, if unavailable use acorn squash
Grape seed oil	A polyunsaturated oil made from grape seeds, if unavailable use any polyunsaturated oil such as sunflower or safflower oil
King prawns	Scampi or Dublin Bay prawns
Kumera	Orange coloured sweet potato
Lebanese cucumber	Ridge cucumber
Muffin pans	Deep tartlet pans, if unavailable line tartlet pans with paper cake cases
Polyunsaturated oil	A vegetable oil high in polyunsaturated fats such as corn, soya or sunflower
Rice bran	If unavailable substitute oat bran
Shallots	Spring onions
Snow peas	Mangetout
Sour cream	Commercially soured cream
Tomato paste	Tomato puree
White vinegar	Distilled malt vinegar
Yellow lentils	Yellow dhal available from Indian shops
Zucchini	Courgettes

BIG FAT SECRETS

HANDY FAT CHECKLIST

Check the amount of fat contained in 100 grams of each food.

(Expressed as grams per 100 grams or per cent).

Oil	100
Lard, dripping	100
Margarine, butter	80
Mayonnaise, rich	78
Desiccated coconut	63
Bacon	59
Tartare sauce	54
Peanuts, roasted	47
Salami	45
Puff pastry	36
Cream	36
Sour cream	35
Potato chips	33
Cheddar cheese	33
Milk chocolate	31
Corn chips	27
Shortbread biscuits	26
Chocolate eclair	26
Sesame bar	26
Cream-filled biscuits	25
Carob and nut bar	25
Croissant	24
Camembert cheese	24
Avocado	23
Cheesecake	22
Doughnut	20
Sausage roll	20
Beef, lamb, pork, fatty	20–25

INDEX

ACKNOWLEDGEMENTS
The publishers would like to thank The National Heart Foundation of Australia for their assistance during the production.

Admiral Appliances; Black & Decker (Australasia) Pty Ltd; Blanco Appliances; Knebel Kitchens; Leigh Mardon Pty Ltd; Master Foods of Australia; Meadow Lea Foods; Namco Cookware; Ricegrowers' Co-op Mills Ltd; Sunbeam Corporation Ltd; Tycraft Pty Ltd distributors of Braun, Australia; White Wings Foods for their assistance during recipe testing.

Accoutrement, Australia East India Company, China Doll, Classic Ceramics, Country Floors, Dansab, Decor Gifts, Ikea, Inini, Lifestyle Imports, Limoges, Made in Japan, Noritake, Royal Doulton, The Bay Tree, Wedgwood for their assistance during photography.

The Committee of Direction of Fruit Marketing, for supplying Avocado photograph.

C000232433

Garden Styles

AN ESSENTIAL GUIDE

Garden Styles

AN ESSENTIAL GUIDE

Freda Cox

THE CROWOOD PRESS

First published in 2010 by
The Crowood Press Ltd
Ramsbury, Marlborough
Wiltshire SN8 2HR

www.crowood.com

© Freda Cox 2010

All rights reserved. No part of this publication may be reproduced or transmitted in any form or
by any means, electronic or mechanical, including photocopy, recording, or any information
storage and retrieval system, without permission in writing from the publishers.

British Library Cataloguing-in-Publication Data
A catalogue record for this book is available from the British Library.

ISBN 978 1 84797 178 4

PHOTOGRAPHIC ACKNOWLEDGEMENTS
My grateful thanks to the following who kindly supplied photographs and their permission to use
them in this book. P. 14, Japanese garden © Geoffrey Westgate; P. 15, Villa Lante © Rory Stuart;
P. 14, Taj Mahal © Arthur Lees; P. 16, Humphrey Repton © Royal Horticultural Society Lindley
Picture Library; P. 17, Gertrude Jekyll © Royal Horticultural Society Lindley Picture Library; P. 18,
Marjorie Fish © Royal Horticultural Society Lindley Picture Library; P. 18, John Brookes © John
Brookes; P. 18, Beth Chatto © The Beth Chatto Gardens; P. 22, The Exotic Garden © Will Giles;
P. 27, Villa Lante © Rory Stuart; P. 29, Versailles © Rory Stuart; P. 90, Tree house, The Exotic Garden
© Will Giles; P. 92, The Exotic Garden © Will Giles; P. 95, The Exotic Garden © Will Giles; P. 97,
Ensete ventricosum © Will Giles; P. 108, Cherry Blossom © Bill Hammerton; P. 109, Japanese Garden
© Bill Hammerton; P. 110, Japanese Garden © Bill Hammerton; P. 111, Japanese garden (top left)
© Geoffrey Westgate; P. 111, Japanese Garden (bottom left) © Bill Hammerton; P. 113, dry garden
© Bill Hammerton; P. 114, Tsubo Niwa © Bill Hammerton; P. 114, Tea House © Bill Hammerton;
P. 114, Water basin © Bill Hammerton; P. 115, Stone lantern © Bill Hammerton; P. 115, Japanese
bridge © Bill Hammerton; P. 116, Moss garden © Bill Hammerton; P. 118, shrub pruning © Bill
Hammerton; P. 118, Bamboo fencing © Bill Hammerton; P. 119, Tea House © Bill Hammerton;
P. 124, Courtyard © Angus Mackintosh; P. 125, Court of the Lions © Angus Mackintosh; P. 126,
Water canal © Andrew Mackintosh; P. 126, Reflecting pool © Keah Burton; P. 127, Reflecting pool
© D. Chavez, Fotoventures; P. 128, Taj Mahal © Arthur Lees; P. 129, El Bahia Palace © Almidi
Photographic Library; P. 129, Ecclesden Manor © John Brookes; P. 130, Courtyard fountain © Rory
Stuart; P. 131, Decorative paving © Jacqueline Potter; P. 132, Decorative paving © Peter Thompson;
P. 133, Alhambra Palace pools © Jacqueline Potter; P. 134, Moroccan inspired garden, Paris
© Emma Clark; P. 134, Lister Park, Bradford © City of Bradford Metropolitan District Council;
P. 135, Hampstead garden © Emma Clark; P. 146, The Universe Cascade © Charles Jencks; P. 152,
View across contemporary classic garden designed by Charlotte Rowe © Clive Nichols picture
library; P. 156, Serpent Garden © Alnwick Castle Gardens; P. 159, Emperor Fountain © Chatsworth
House Trust; P. 160, Modern cascade © Alnwick Castle Gardens; P. 161, Lister Park, Bradford
© City of Bradford Metropolitan District Council; P. 175, Town garden designed by Charlotte Rowe
© Clive Nichols picture library; P. 187, London garden designed by Charlotte Rowe © Clive Nichols
picture library; P. 196, Green roof ©Rolls Royce Motor Cars Ltd; P. 198, Living wall bridge
© Patrick Blanc.

Typeset by Jean Cussons Typesetting, Diss, Norfolk
Printed and bound in Malaysia by Times Offset (M) Sdn Bhd

Contents

To the new generation of gardeners in style – Matthew, Christopher, Rebekah, Amy, Juliette, Joseph, Mia, Jacob, Douglas – and those I have yet to meet. May your gardens grow in beautiful and abundant profusion.

Acknowledgements

First of all I would very much like to thank my family for their patience and consideration while I have been writing this book. Camilla, Peter and Douglas Stewart; Lorna, Chris, Joseph, Mia and Jacob Hawthorne; John, Elaine, Matthew, Christopher and Rebekah Norton; Mark, Clare, Amy and Juliette Norton; Kathleen Norton and Dominic Marsden; Leslie, Marita and James Rawlins; all the 'Jones' family; Michael Derrett, Sandra Humphries and family; Clive and Veronica Rawlins; love and sincere thanks to you all.

A very special thank you to Camilla Stewart for her hard work and advice in reading, correcting and editing the manuscript; John and Chris Norton, and Dominic Marsden for sorting out numerous computer problems without which the work would never have been finished, and Matthew Norton for his help.

To my friends who have supported me throughout, including: Alisdair Aird; Kathleen Allanson; Andrew and Marianne Beith; Daphne Brown; Albert and Ursula Brunner; Syd Bryan; Heidi Gildemeister; Duncan and Sue Graham; Signe Groos; Colin and Barbara Handy; Caroline Harbouri; Sandra Hawthorne; Tim Longville; Mercedes Maier; Shaunah Murrell; Sally Razelou; Rosemary Rawlins; John and Jay Rendall; Carol Smith; Grace and Norman Stewart; Rory Stuart; Ian and Pauline Tomson; Geoffrey Westgate; Penny Westgate; and all my many other friends – I value your friendship.

Many thanks to all those who helped by supplying photographs for gardens I could not reach, and the garden owners who let me take and use photographs of their beautiful gardens including: Barbara Anderson, Tamarisks; Arley Arboretum and the Trustees of the R.D. Turner Charitable Trust; David Austin and Michael Marriott, David Austin Roses; Andrew Ball and Marco Jahn, Rolls Royce Motors Ltd; Andrew and Marianne Beith, Can Mel; Tony and Mary Benger, Burrow Farm; Tony and Kate Bennett, The Wickets; Patrick Blanc and Jean-Luc Le Gouallec; John Borrett, Docton Mill; Mary Bower, Bridgwalton House; Bradford Council and Simon Drake, Lister Park; Ray Brown, Plant World; Sue Butler, Gladderbrook Farm; Sue Carter and RHS Garden Hyde Hall; Pru Cartwright, Brobury House; Elizabeth Cartwright-Hignett, Iford Manor; Johnny Chambers, Kiftsgate Court; The Chatsworth House Trust; Beth Chatto and the Beth Chatto Garden; Daniel Chavez, Fotoventures; Marcus Chiton-Jones, Curator Dorothy Clive Garden; Emma Clark; John Cope; Charles Cottrell-Dormer, Rousham; Dan Coxon and The Dartington Hall Trust;

Wendy Cunningham, Kingston Maurward College; Michael Edwards, Hillfield House and Cottages; Lord Farringdon and David Freeman, Buscot Park; Gordon Fenn and Raymond Treasure, Stockton Bury; Will Giles, The Exotic Garden; Renata Goldberg, Mallorca; Nick and Marjorie Gouvenot-Gardiner, Mallorca; Peter and Signe Groos, Mallorca; Bill and Marylin Hammerton; Peter and Margaret Hargreaves, Grafton Cottage; Janice Hodgkinson, University of Leicester Botanic Garden; Stella Hore, The Japanese Garden; Martin Hugh-Jones, Holbrook; Heather Jansch, Sedgewell Coach House; Charles Jencks, The Garden of Cosmic Speculation; John and Lesley Jenkins, Wollerton Old Hall; Barry and Joy Jenkinson, The South Pavillion, Morville Hall; Mr and Mrs Simon Kenyon-Slaney, Chyknell; Arthur and Rita Lees; Angus Mackintosh; Dave and Pat McKenna, Little Indonesia; Paul Moir, Painswick Rococo Garden; Sarah Page, Chairman of the Tamar Protection Society, Mary Newman's Cottage; Frances Pardell and Warner Leisure Hotels, Holme Lacey; Keah Pierconti-Burton; Richard Pim, Westonbury Mill; Alex Polizzi and Roland Jaletzke, Hotel Endsleigh; Jacqueline Potter; Oliver Prentice and GMC Publications for permission to reproduce diagrams; Clare Ralph, Alnwick Castle; Mick and Liz Reeve; Joanna Rowe and RHS Garden Rosemoor; Lucy Waitt, Gaynor Messenger, Charlotte Brooks, and the staff at the Royal Horticultural Society Picture Library at the Lindley Library; Lord Sandwich, Mapperton; Lord Strathnaver and Scott Morrison, Dunrobin Castle; Rory Stuart; Katherine Swift, The Dower House, Morville Hall; Peter Thompson; Thornbury Castle Hotel; George Thorpe, Trinity College, Cambridge; Ann Trevor-Jones, Preen Manor; Rob and Jan Wagstaff, North Boreston Farm; Colin and Mary Wells, Applecross House; Mike Werkmeister, East Lambrook Manor; Geoffrey Westgate; Philip White, Hestercombe; and Claire Woodbine, Pinsla. I think I have included everyone but I offer my sincere apologies if someone has been inadvertently left out.

Finally, a sincere and heartfelt 'thank-you' to John Brookes for his Foreword, and to Roy Cheek for botanical editing. Their time, expertise and support are much appreciated.

For plant identification I relied mainly on the *RHS Index of Garden Plants* by Mark Griffiths (MacMillan ISBN 0-333-59149-6), and the *RHS Encyclopedia of Plants and Flowers*, editor-in-chief Christopher Brickell (Dorling Kindersley, ISBN 0-86318-386-7). Any mistakes I have managed entirely on my own.

Preface

We must all examine our environment, always gaining inspiration from existing natural features; we will then enhance rather than overwhelm our surroundings.

Rosemary Verey

When The Crowood Press suggested I write a book on garden styles, it seemed like a good idea. However, it wasn't until I started researching the project that I realized that Chapter 1 on its own could easily fill at least ten books. In one book I can only briefly cover a few main styles, which over the centuries have stamped their mark on this wonderfully inspiring and truly fascinating subject we call gardening.

Where did it all begin? Was it in Mesopotamia, Persia or Egypt? Who was the very first person to decide to turn over a small patch of earth and start growing things rather than scavenging from the wild when anything was needed? Having pushed in a few edible hedgerow plants and medicinal herbs, when did they then decide the area could also become aesthetically pleasing and start arranging things into some sort of order and pattern?

Certainly the Ancient Egyptians had wonderful gardens with formal structure and decorative plants and pools. Chinese gardens stretch far back into history as well. But it all began long before this. Could it be 4,000, 10,000, or even 15,000 years ago? Of course we will never know who that very first person was who ignited the initial spark and grew their own garden.

Paradise is described as a garden in many religions and we all want our own gardens to be a paradise, to give us pleasure and fulfilment whether we are relaxing or working in them. We know what we want to achieve and often spend a lifetime trying to do it, always wanting just that little bit more. A garden is never finished. It can always take just one more plant; something might need moving; a small area or even the whole garden may need redesigning. Gardeners will always find some way of keeping their fingers in the earth.

We put our souls into our gardens and when we have to leave the garden behind, as often happens in this modern age, it can break our hearts. With a jolt you suddenly remember the first cyclamen will have started appearing before August is out in your old garden, and those beautiful snowdrops you coveted for so long before you could afford to buy them will be slowly forcing through frozen earth in January. Your new garden has no cyclamen. It may not even have snowdrops. It almost certainly won't have the special ones with the green tipped outer petals that you loved. But it does have some trees and a few shrubs and a border or two hopefully hiding various delights in the rich soil. You prefer sweeping borders and meandering paths whereas now you have lots of tiny beds scattered around in a rather haphazard fashion with no cohesion to the design; a maze of paths which come to a dead end rather than drawing you round the garden to explore. Something will definitely have to be done about that!

So one starts again, planning ahead, deciding what will go where – a formal corner here, an informal border there, take out that tiny wasted area of grass and fill it with roses, wind a path through, pave a small terrace. And all those straight rows in the vegetable garden – a little companion planting is needed there, and some cutting flowers mixed in, or perhaps a complete change with a decorative potager bordered with low woven hurdles or herbs.

There you go again. Before you know where you are, you are off, planning and planting. Little by little you stamp your own special mark on the new garden, grow the plants you love and develop a style you are comfortable with.

We might not be able to say where it all began, but we do know how history influenced and shaped the different styles, and what may come in the future, a future affected by climate change – although opinions still differ as to whether climate change is really happening or whether it is all a fallacy!

So many questions... and the garden is calling again. The rain has swept through leaving sweetly smelling, warm, moist earth. The roses are shaking off raindrops. A hint of mauve in the far corner beckons. Something new in flower that I haven't noticed before, in that dry corner where I plan to create a Mediterranean garden, approached by a wooden pergola shading the stone-slabbed path…

One carefully and lovingly creates a garden and often sadly has to move on, but hopefully the people who follow will enjoy what you have created, although of course they will want to make their own mark as well, just as you are doing now in this new garden. They may want to entirely redesign the whole area and you will pass in a few years and find it unrecognizable, formal where informal used to flourish – a completely different style.

Our choices are so individual in the styles we choose and what we wish to achieve, and this book aims to give an insight into some of the possibilities available for those starting new gardens or simply seeking fresh inspiration on garden styles. You may discover options you have never considered before, a Japanese or Islamic style perhaps? Gardening enriches our lives and spirits, so relax and enjoy creating your own stylish, paradise garden.

Freda Cox
August 2009

Foreword

I find it difficult to define what style is all about, but in her Preface, Freda Cox has quoted the late Rosemary Verey, who has put her finger on it.

The new gardener, I believe, goes through the process of deciding upon a formal or informal style – dependant often more upon *their* character than that of their site. And then with luck he or she works rationally through the physicals of their garden – its soil, what is sunny and what is in shade. Then over a longer period, he or she works out their necessities – a storage place, where to place the compost, site the herbs and so on down to the decorative. In the smaller garden a style develops through necessity and the materials hard and soft which are selected to realize the plan. Freda, I think, would call it 'the dream'!

After many years of teaching garden design I can say that some people have inherent style and some have not. You can see it in the interior of their homes and in their dress. Some are able to get it together and some are not. For those in the latter category this is their book.

What is important is initial planning – not the scary word *design*. What do you want and what do you not. By all means select a style from photographs but be reasonable. Sissinghurst Castle garden is lovely, but does its scale or style interpret to your plot?

When you eventually get to plants – I write eventually, because they are not the priority, unless you are working in an established site – list those which you like and know, but do not go mad buying what appears to be a charmer, but which turns into a monster in no time at all; check before you buy.

In many locations of the world it is their climate which decides what can and cannot be grown – and subsequently their style as well – too hot, too cold; not enough water and so on. In Britain we have such a benign climate that we have a large range of plant material to choose from. But equally we have a huge range of natural habitats and certainly if you are starting in the country this is what you need to explore, as Rosemary Verey suggests.

If you are starting to revamp an existing garden – try to decide what plants make up the real bones of the garden to be retained. It's probably trees (if they are not too big), and certainly evergreen shrubs for winter containment, then remove the remainder – clear the decks in fact; what is left will begin to define your style.

And of course you can install a formal pool or a rill, or box edge the borders, but get the planning right first so that you start to create a visual progression round the space, as well as a working extension to your home.

Style is not about seeing how many differing plants you can cram in; it's about achieving visual tranquillity. With good proportions to a terrace for instance, to the width of a path and detail of steps through it, the selection of materials hard and soft which should be sympathetic to the house and its period. And lastly creating the three-dimensional aspect of the height and containment with your plant groupings, so that you enjoy time *in* your garden rather than *upon* it.

John Brookes MBE FSGD

1 Introduction to garden style

What exactly is a garden and why do you want one? Is a garden somewhere to show off, escape into, have fun, create a personal paradise, or to be at one with nature? For many gardeners it is the plants that matter. Design and hardscaping are simply foils to exhibit plants to advantage. We set about transforming the landscape, for better or worse. Gardens are a series of designs, effects, materials and plants assembled in diverse formats with reference to personal taste but should incorporate underlying principles of composition, proportion and balance.

Garden styles and fashions come and go, and gardens are as different as the people who create and plant them. They are incredibly personal spaces, and individual style makes them more personal still. We want our gardens to look beautiful, but what one person finds stunning, another abhors. We may have romantic notions of a 'secret garden' that magically recreates itself, unseen, year after year as seasons change. Cocooned behind high walls or trees, bulbs star long grass; roses festoon hedges; fruit hangs ripe from gnarled branches, and there is the soothing murmur of gently trickling water and bird song.

Others have visions of neat, square beds, rectangular borders, straight lines, geometric shapes, clipped hedges, formal pools, and regimented planting. Or cleanly clinical spaces composed of concrete, glass and steel, with carefully sited architectural plants. Not a leaf out of place or a weed in sight. There are huge differences between the various styles and types of garden, from formal to informal, wild or minimalistic.

Gardens often appear exquisitely created with apparent ease. Gardens that make you want to linger and absorb the special atmosphere, returning again at the first opportunity. Other gardens look attractive but lack that defining essence that makes them memorable. Why

Hidden away in the Cornish countryside, Pinsla is truly a secret garden waiting to be discovered. Tranquil and romantic, the garden nestles amidst woodland, a haven of peace and natural beauty.

Chyknell, Shropshire, designed by Russell Page in 1951, is a formal garden surrounded by rolling parkland. Neatly clipped yew hedges create individual rooms with roses, herbaceous borders, magnificent pleached lime trees and a formal pool.

OPPOSITE: *Grafton Cottage, Staffordshire, is an idyllic English cottage garden massed with traditional old-fashioned plants, colour and perfume.*

Walk into the gardens at Wollerton Old Hall, Shropshire, to experience a very special and magical atmosphere, making it a truly memorable experience.

can one attain so much and another fall so short of the ideal? Many of us never quite achieve the effect we are seeking when we have tried so hard, probably because we have simply missed a few basic principles of composition in the style we are trying to fashion. Style is not just a seemingly unattainable image in a glossy magazine created by top-flight designers, or the expensively manicured acres of a country estate. Style is how we visualize our garden dream and what we do with that dream, whether we have a tiny courtyard or an acre or two.

Gardens are spaces we personally live with and must be comfortable with every day. Each has its own plusses and minuses, giving the garden character. It is what we do with our garden that counts. Garden styles are as intransient as sunbeams. They always have and always will constantly change. Present fashion for instance, dictates naturalistic, sustainable gardens, bearing ecological issues and climate change in mind.

Trends swing backwards and forwards across the centuries, but gardens fall into two main categories, formal or informal. Even these are often interwoven. Formal styles encompass classical, Italian, geometric, regular and architectural styles. Informal styles are natural, often irregularly shaped, with softer, freer designs. Over the centuries, these two styles have

Dunrobin Castle Gardens, Sutherland, are grandly formal with beautifully laid out parterres and terraces.

Meandering grass paths wind between curving borders overflowing with an abundance of choice plants in the beautifully designed, informal, Stockton Bury Gardens, Herefordshire.

interacted and been reinterpreted to suit prevailing fashion, or dictates of foremost designers. They have diversified into allied themes, but basically the underlying theme is either formal or informal.

Gardens do not have to be full of grandiose ideas to be effective. Quite often simple gardens are the most stylish. Look at other gardens, parks, stately homes, which are full of ideas waiting to be adapted. See how gardens are balanced, how colours and textures combine, and plants work together. The style of the garden is what gives it atmosphere – whether it has formal straight lines, topiary hedges and classical planting, or is an informal landscape of meandering curves and relaxed planting. A really stylish garden has that extra, indefinable something that you alone add.

Gardens are personal spaces and individual style more personal still. We know how we want gardens to look and feel, and even though most of us inherit ready-made gardens, we set about manicuring them to our liking. When viewing a property we are more likely to be drawn to one that has a garden that appeals to us.

Look at nature and learn. Her beauty, plant and colour combinations, landscape and water effects cannot be bettered, even by the world's best designers. We can manipulate nature but we can never improve on her. Work with nature rather than against her.

The style of the house and building materials are important factors in dictating the garden style. They should merge together harmoniously, whether looking from the house across the garden or from garden back to house. Modern gardens can complement older properties and vice versa. It is a question of choosing the right elements and proportions for the appropriate style. Local landscape and architecture should also be respected and local materials used wherever possible, as they fit in so much better. Present-day conservation and ecological issues are having a big impact on current garden styles as well.

Different combinations of plants, colour and texture set the mood and plants should be in keeping with the style: formal, informal, colourful, wilderness, prairie garden or wildflower meadow. If you are highly organized and like everything in its place, and your garden is flat and evenly shaped, a formal layout is appropriate. An uncluttered approach based on geometric proportions, rectangles, squares and circles will work well, since straight lines and angles break up space and add directional movement. If you prefer relaxed styles with flowing, organic lines, meandering paths, informally shaped beds and softer, natural looking planting, and if your site is uneven, sloping or irregularly shaped, informal is best.

Whatever style you choose, travelling around your garden should be an adventure, an exciting journey enticing you on from one point to another. Frame a beautiful view, enhance a vignette, highlight an attractive garden ornament or plant, discover a romantic arbour, and finally choose a comfortable bench to sit and enjoy your achievement.

History

Mythological gardens are significant in many religions: the Biblical Garden of Eden, Muslim Paradise Gardens of the Qur'an or the Hindu Ida-Varsha. Temple gardens complemented buildings and enhanced the experience of the visit.

Much evidence of the past comes from archaeological excavation, manuscripts, books and paintings. These sources document not only habitations and lifestyle; they also allow glimpses and records of gardens and plants. Travellers, traders and invaders carried plants, seeds and ideas across the globe. Evidence of plant cultivation dates back to 15,000BC, but early Egyptians were amongst the first to create gardens for purely pleasurable and aesthetic reasons, as irrigation techniques developed from around 3500BC. They also recorded the earliest written details of plants in the Ebers Papyrus (1550BC), although this was a compilation of earlier works.

Assyrians and Babylonians created artificial hills, adding interest to flat landscapes, and planted informal parks filled with trees for hunting and pleasure. Ancient Greeks considered private gardens unnecessarily extravagant, but they had public parks, and, outside the cities, 'farm' gardens. In the first century AD, Dioscorides described 600 plants in his De Materia Medica, the standard botanical and medicinal record for the next 1500 years. Romans loved their gardens, which were often imposing, formal affairs with strong distinctions between town and country, and often had small vegetable gardens. Increasing interest and knowledge of horticulture and plants encouraged the spread of ideas. The Roman invasion of Britain in AD43 introduced many new plants and garden developments into the country.

Chinese and Japanese gardens evolved specialized styles. Chinese gardens were probably in existence around 2100BC although the first detailed evidence dates from much later. Japanese gardens probably began to be cultivated around AD200. Both styles were nature based, but carefully contrived, imitating landscapes of mountains, rivers and sea.

Gardens of Islam drew inspiration from the Qur'an, adding new dimensions of spirituality and symbolism in design and planting. Water canals, representing the four rivers of Paradise, divided gardens into quadrants. Gardens had great peace and beauty to nourish the soul, rather than being outward symbols of show.

ABOVE: *Japanese gardens developed their own special and individual style of carefully contrived, nature-based designs.*

BELOW: *The impressive and ethereal Taj Mahal, Agra, created between 1632–54, was based on Islamic and Persian styles carried to India and developed by the great Mughul dynasty.*

Ideas were carried from the Arabian Peninsula to Persia in AD637, absorbing highly sophisticated designs developed by Cyrus the Great in the sixth century BC. The movement spread into Moorish Spain with elegant courtyards shaded by trees and filled with flowers, fruit, reflective pools, cooling fountains and beautiful pavilions, and into India with the great Mughal gardens, which in turn influenced other areas of the Far East.

The Domesday Book (AD1086) recorded ownership of property and land in Britain for the first time. Monarchs, wealthy aristocrats and merchants created extravagant hunting parks and increasingly sophisticated gardens.

Medieval gardens developed along three styles. Monasteries cultivated medicinal and food plants; small cottage gardens grew healing plants and vegetables; and wealthy aristocrats paid for the creation of great pleasure gardens and deer parks. Order was all and plants were set into straight rows in square beds, in square gardens or fields. Privacy and safety were important and gardens enclosed – the *hortus conclusus*. Gardens were for producing food and medicinal herbs, for relaxation and entertaining.

Modern reconstructions of old gardens include Queen Eleanor's Garden in Winchester, a small, enclosed medieval garden recreated from contemporary records. It has a triangular plan with central pool, small canal, raised beds, summerhouse, grassy banks, and a tunnel of trained greenery and vines. Mary Newman's Cottage, in Saltash, Cornwall (said to be the original home of the first wife of Sir Francis Drake) has a beautifully reconstructed Elizabethan garden with raised beds

including plants and herbs used at the period and also an arbour and viewing mount.

External factors affected how gardens developed internally. When lawlessness prevailed, early gardens tended to be small and carefully enclosed, but as a semblance of peace descended, Tudor gardens became more open and intricate, leaning towards classical styles, while Stuart gardens were influenced by French style.

An unprecedented revolution in gardening came with the Italian Renaissance. A period of great cultural change in Europe from the end of the fourteenth century to the beginning of the seventeenth saw reawakened interest in classical style. Gardens had an ordered, structured approach, intended to recreate the landscape as God had intended it to be – and God intended it to be as the Italians created it!

ABOVE: *Well-designed reconstruction of an Elizabethan cottage garden at Mary Newman's Cottage, Cornwall, with plants and herbs of the period.*

BELOW: *The Villa Lante, Italy, designed by Vignola in 1566 as a summer retreat, is a classical Renaissance garden with a grandly structured and ordered design. Here for the first time, paths and fountains are beginning to blend more naturally into the surrounding landscape.*

Renaissance style spread across Europe, triggering the English Renaissance between the early sixteenth and early seventeenth centuries, which incorporated many continental ideas. However, the English Renaissance differed in several ways. For one thing, it began later, and despite sharing similar aesthetics, the British took a more eclectic view, including newer French ideas, but also clinging on to many previous features (such as Gothic) and finding it difficult to relinquish past influences and move forward.

Dutch styles of the late seventeenth century brought highly formal gardens, influencing British design with plants, horticultural skills and knowledge. Hampton Court Palace, London, redesigned in 1685, is a superb example and remains the most important Dutch-influenced garden in Britain.

Plants were being collected together in botanical gardens across Europe and Oxford's Botanic Garden was the first to be established in Britain in 1621. The Tradescants' garden in Lambeth had more than 1,600 named plants in cultivation. Chelsea Physic Garden was founded by the Worshipful Society of Apothecaries in 1673, and William Kent's designs of 1730 developed into The Royal Botanic Gardens at Kew. Wealthy patrons funded expeditions to discover rare and beautiful plants and seeds around the world. Great plant hunters such as John Tradescant The Younger (1608–62) made his first expedition to America in 1637. Joseph Pitton Tournefort (1656–1708) brought plants from Mediterranean

Humphry Repton, 1752–1818, reintroduced terraces, flower gardens and stonework back into picturesque landscapes and incorporated 'Borrowed Scenery' into his designs.

regions, and Sir Joseph Banks (1743–1820) delivered over 3,500 different plants to Kew Gardens and was its President for forty years.

With the development of increasingly sophisticated printing techniques and the advent of printing presses came specialist books, including Master John Gardener's *Feat of Gardening* (*c*.1440); John Gerard's *The Herball or Generall Historie of Plants* (1597); John Parkinson's *Paradisi in Sole Paradisus Terrestris* (1629); Nicholas Culpeper's *Complete Herbal* (1653); and John Rea's *Flora* (1665).

The seventeenth, eighteenth and nineteenth centuries saw renowned designers such as William Kent (1685–1748), who influenced landscape style enormously, developing the 'Picturesque'. Lancelot 'Capability' Brown (1716–83) initially worked with Kent and became the great exponent of the 'Natural' or 'English' garden style, creating vast, manicured landscapes, replicating English countryside. Uvedale Price (1747–1829) preferred a less-manicured approach. Humphry Repton (1752–1818) incorporated 'Borrowed' scenery, viewed from strategic points, and reintroduced terraces, flower gardens and stonework. J.C. Loudon (1783–1843) was passionate about green spaces and city parks, recommending gardens should not replicate nature exactly, but have stylized, abstract designs, emphasizing plants in the 'Gardenesque' style.

Frederick Law Olmsted (1822–1903), founding father of American landscape design, was influenced by his European travels, and considered London's landscape development to represent perfectly balanced urban development and social improvement. His ideas influenced American suburban landscape and parks well into the twentieth century.

Following the highly contrived, 'natural' looking 'Picturesque', nineteenth-century English gardens turned back towards more classical themes again, with revived interest in flowers and plants. The Royal Horticultural Society, founded in 1804, aimed to encourage new developments and collate plant information. The Victorian era incorporated an eclectic mix of previous periods and styles such as Gothic, Tudor, Jacobean, Dutch and Italian. Plants from around the world were ardently collected, and gardens became ostentatious, formal affairs with an over-abundance of plants and ornamentation.

Reaction to this opulence came with William Robinson (1838–1935), a major exponent of wild gardens; his freer design and planting later evolved into the 'cottage garden' style. He spoke strongly against highly formal gardens, promoting natural drifts of perennials and bulbs in meadows, and a mix of native and perennial plants, forerunners to present-day gardens. Robinson's ideas were strongly opposed by Reginald Blomfield (1856–1942), who considered

ABOVE: *Gertrude Jekyll, 1843–1932, was a leading designer in Arts and Crafts-inspired gardens with her firm principles on design and planting, and eye for colour and texture.*

BELOW RIGHT: *Iford Manor, Wiltshire, transformed into Italianate gardens and terraces in the early twentieth century, by Harold Peto who was strongly influenced by Arts and Crafts and Italian Renaissance styles.*

BELOW: *The Grey Walk, Hestercombe Gardens, Somerset, has grey- and silver-leaved plants intermingled with white, blue and mauve in stunning Edwardian gardens designed by Gertrude Jekyll and Edwin Lutyens, now being faithfully restored.*

natural gardening simply a poor attempt at copying nature, and believed that formal design was *the* most important feature of any garden. The two protagonists had long-running and bitter disputes. It took the Arts and Crafts style of the late nineteenth and early twentieth centuries, and Gertrude Jekyll (1843–1932) to show it was possible for both good design and good planting to co-exist as parts of the same ideal. Her work with Edwin Lutyens made an important and lasting impression on the age and everything that followed. Edwin Lutyens (1869–1944) began in the Arts and Crafts style, but later work developed along classical themes. Harold Peto (1854–1933) was strongly influenced by the Arts and Crafts movement and Italian Renaissance gardens, sympathetically ensuring his Italianate designs fitted their English settings.

The Edwardians ushered in neatly manicured lawns, grass walks, large herbaceous borders, formal rose gardens, and features for leisure pursuits such as tennis courts and bowling greens. Styles were slightly less formal in reaction to the rigid Victorian era, and garden owners were beginning to discover the pleasures of working in their own gardens.

The two World Wars had seriously detrimental effects on the garden movement as labour became scarce and more expensive. Importance was placed on food production rather than beauty, and it was some time before gardens re-emerged, with an eclectic mix of styles old and new. Increasing demand for housing led to smaller gardens, while the great gardens and landscaped parks of country estates struggled through lack of labour and resources, and many were lost during this time.

ABOVE: *Marjorie Fish, 1888–1969, had a passion for horticulture and nature and was a prime exponent of the cottage garden style, creating her own garden at East Lambrook Manor, Somerset.*

BELOW RIGHT: *Beth Chatto, renowned garden designer and plantswoman, is justly famous for her gardens at Chelmsford, Essex, which include dry, woodland and water gardens.*

BELOW: *John Brookes is one of the most influential and inspiring garden designers, including creating his own celebrated garden, Denmans, West Sussex.*

Amongst the strongest influencers of twentieth-century style was Vita Sackville West (1892–1962), who bought Sissinghurst Castle, Kent, in 1930, and designed the garden with her husband Harold Nicolson. He provided a strong, architectural framework, which she filled with a romantic profusion of informal planting. Russell Page (1906–1985), one of the foremost designers of his time, combined artistic flair with expert horticultural knowledge, superb taste, meticulous attention to planting detail, and specialist knowledge of relationships between elements. Designs ranged from tiny cottages and town houses to large, corporate parks, and he empathized with Islamic gardens. He worked in Europe and America as well as creating many English gardens.

Sir Geoffrey Jellicoe (1900–96) was strongly influenced by Italian Renaissance gardens, which he combined in classical modern designs, writing many books (including *Italian Gardens of the Renaissance*, 1925). Perhaps his most ambitious project was Sutton Place, Surrey. Water was important in his designs, with rushing torrents, waterfalls, and still, reflective pools.

Other important names included Lawrence Johnston (1871–1958), who created famous gardens at Hidcote, Gloucestershire, and Serre de la Madone, France; Margery Fish (1888–1969) of East Lambrook Manor, who with her passion for plants, horticulture and nature was a prime exponent of cottage garden style; Graham Stuart Thomas (1909–2003), the great rose man; Rosemary Verey (1919–2001), creating gardens in the English Classical Revival style; Sylvia Crowe, distinguished landscape architect; John Brookes, influential garden designer and author; Beth Chatto, garden designer and plantswoman renowned for her

Essex garden; Penelope Hobhouse, garden writer and designer; Christopher Lloyd and his famed Great Dixter garden; and last but certainly not least, Piet Oudolph, well known plantsman and designer. The list is endless and glossy magazines and television programmes have elevated gardeners and designers to cult status.

Clear lines and uncluttered design of the early-twentieth-century Modernist movement, in which materials such as concrete, glass, steel and plastic were fashionable, was closely followed by Postmodernism, which favoured a return to traditional materials and styles. Finally, the latter end of the twentieth century and the early twenty-first century saw more relaxed, increasingly eco-conscious styles, with wildlife-friendly, sustainable gardens.

From Classical, Picturesque, Gardenesque, Art Deco, Art Nouveau, Surrealist, Modernist, Cubist and Abstract styles to present-day, sustainable designs, gardens are inevitably fusions and interpretations of everything that has gone before, one style reacting with another, moving the sequence along. Gardens of the future will continue this theme, incorporating many and varied styles, together with new plants, new materials and new ideas.

Elements of style

COLOUR

Colour enriches garden design, be it harmonious and relaxing muted shades, or strong, vibrant and shocking shades. Love of colour creates gardens filled with an eclectic mix of shrubs, perennials and annuals. If softer shades appeal, try green, single-colour, dry or gravel gardens. In brightly coloured gardens, suddenly coming across a single colour area is a relief.

Monochrome gardens or borders require great discipline. The renowned White Garden at Sissinghurst is a constrained blend of greys, greens and white with strong emphasis on shape and texture. Each single colour has a whole range of shades. Green gardens have infinite tones of green flowers and foliage and are simple and restful. Small touches of yellow or blue, closely related to green, are an advantage. An occasional colour highlight enlivens single-colour themes.

Soft blues and greens have soothing, relaxing properties; white, grey and silver, a cool, calm feel; reds, oranges and bronzes create warmth and richness. Cool colours can lead into vibrant areas for contrast, and placing hot colours against cool, and dark colours against light, creates impact and movement. Hot colours make space appear smaller, while greens and pale blues give a more spacious appearance, beneficial in small gardens. Too much unrelated colour looks cluttered and busy.

Monochrome gardens require great discipline. Wollerton Old Hall, Shropshire has borders of white, green and pale grey, relieved by the odd hint of blue.

Divide borders into single blocks of colour, or limit to one or two main colours, occasionally varied with closely related colours. Large blocks of colour work better than lots of different spots spread everywhere. Choose from opposite sides, or progress around the colour wheel. Light influences colours, strong sunlight diminishing intensity.

Modern gardens also include coloured paint effects, such as white, blue or green, and the overall theme can be extended to include plants, furniture, cushions, mosaics and accessories of the same colour.

CONTRAST

Create contrasts with varying foliage colours as well as flowers; hard materials against soft; and with subtle changes in light, shade, and movement. Gentle contrasts and curving lines draw the eye along and around the garden. Straight lines take the eye immediately to the end of the vista and require a 'full stop'.

In this garden at Wollerton Old Hall, Shropshire, the eye is drawn along the central axis path between neatly clipped hedges while the distant obelisk creates a full stop.

HARDSCAPING

These are the 'hard' elements of the garden, which provide the backbone of the design. Walls, terraces, steps, raised beds, pergolas, concrete, gravel and stone all help to give shape and form.

HARMONY

This is perhaps the most important element of any garden, in sweeping landscape curves, straight lines, plants, light and shade, texture or colour. The garden must be in harmony with itself and its surroundings. The eye can be led along or around the space, and harmony is often best achieved with a simple design. Shapes should interweave creating movement and even though gardens are divided into separate areas they must still all work together. Too many distractions simply confuse, and harmony is lost. However, gardens should never become boring, so it is all a question of balance.

PERFUME

What is a garden without fragrance? Light perfumes add an ethereal touch; heavier scents more exotic, richer notes. Night-time perfumes are pleasant, wafting through open windows. Other scents include earth and moist plants, parched earth after rain, and damp morning dew.

PLANTS

Plants come in infinite variety for every scheme. Architectural plants complement minimalist styles. Colourful annuals and perennials recall cottage gardens. Drought-tolerant species create Mediterranean themes. Exotics inspire tropical jungles. Once you have determined the style, choose plants to complement it.

PROPORTION

Proportion, perspective and scale are paramount in gardens with formal lines or meandering curves. Correct

A path leads through the hedge, between trellised walls, into an adjoining garden – or does it? Deception creates illusions with nothing more than a flat screen and clever use of perspective in the garden at Hunters End, Worcestershire.

use makes space look larger or smaller; it conceals or reveals. Deceptive tricks create illusions with false perspective, limiting or extending views. *Trompe l'œil* suggests there is more than there is, and mirrors give a delusion of space. One feature can dominate, or collective elements work together as one. As in any form of art, the illusion creates the perfect composition so that everything looks in proportion.

SPACE

Spatial composition is fundamental, creating divisions from solid, closed, or open areas. Gardens can be divided into rooms or be open and sweeping.

TEXTURE

All elements in the garden, including plants and hardscaping, have their own texture, from rough to smooth. Textures of water, foliage, flowers, bark, bricks, stone, gravel or steel can be mixed to make constantly changing scenes of interest and variety. Light, airy, open plants add a delicate feel, while large-leaved, dark plants create heavier themes. Texture is also affected by sunlight and shade.

WATER

Water is an essential element in most gardens, with formal or informal pools, streams, cascades, reflective canals, waterfalls, fountains or rills adding life, movement and reflections.

Creating the style

Moving into a newly built house usually presents a completely blank canvas with regard to the garden, while few of us move to an established garden without wanting to change certain aspects. Gardens may need a major overhaul, or simply small sections redesigned, and even introducing favourite plants may be all that is required. The basic outline may be good and easily adapted as time and finance allow. The garden must feel comfortable and relaxing to you, but few of us aspire to be garden designers and we are often frightened of the process.

Water brings light and reflections into the garden, and continually changing movement, as well as creating habitats for wildlife.
(Westonbury Mill Water Gardens, Hampshire)

Well-planned, attractive gardens are always good selling points for a house. If you do not intend staying long, keep plans simple and easily maintained. The next purchaser may not want complicated designs and lengthy maintenance regimes. If you plan to stay long term you can be adventurous and follow your dreams. Every garden owner wants to achieve that perfect balance in the space available.

Take the style of the house into account and important issues such as the fact we look out, and often down, onto gardens from windows, as well as seeing them from ground level. Bold patterns, strong form and clearly defined paths all make impact from above. Take stock before charging in with a spade or bulldozer, unless you have a blank space, and even then careful thought is required. Newly acquired gardens should ideally be left for a year before major work is undertaken. Be patient and allow gardens to reveal what plants and bulbs lie buried beneath the soil; how local climate and prevailing winds affect the site; areas of sun or shade; and the garden's assets as well as its drawbacks.

Beautiful gardens are often destroyed or detrimentally altered by new owners wishing to impose their own style. Given a little patience, they might have realized how fitting the present garden was and what treasures it

held rather than demolishing everything in an avid desire for change. You may deeply regret being too hasty.

Deciding what you want is the first step, which can be achieved while waiting to see what your garden has to offer. Gardens take a long time to develop, and are never really finished, so before putting plans into action take a long, hard look. Enthusiastic gardeners will already have a store of preferences, dislikes, information and plans waiting to be put into place. Keep a notebook and make rough sketches, however basic; gather inspiration from books and magazines; take photographs; visit gardens, garden centres, and reclamation yards; list gardens you find attractive, noting their appealing elements and plants you want; think about interesting layouts and plant combinations, and garden features and ornaments you wish to include in your garden. Gardeners are usually happy to share their knowledge and information.

Little by little a picture develops, together with an increasing awareness of a style. It may be highly formal with neat, ordered geometric beds and straight lines, or something naturalistic with free-flowing curves and meandering paths. It may have manicured, formal borders around an area of neatly mown lawn, overflow with exuberant colours, be a wilderness of wild flowers, an exotic tropical jungle, a Japanese garden, or follow the Italian Renaissance style.

Designing a garden sounds daunting but planning is important, especially in the initial stages. Few of us are experts and we must make the best of what we ourselves create, unless we employ a qualified designer. Many books specialize in the intricacies of garden design and plans. Colleges and mail order supply numerous courses. There is plenty of help out there. Drawing up detailed plans certainly gives an idea of how the finished garden will look, but having to plot precise measurements onto graph paper can be tedious and complicated. However, even the simplest plan helps focus the mind. Things become clearer if you know what must be kept, and where things will go – such as trees, hedges, walls, fences, paths and borders, the garden shed and compost heap.

List what you want: a plantsman's paradise overflowing with flowers, shrubs and trees or low maintenance; areas for entertaining and children's play area; space for animals; utility area; greenhouse; summerhouse; compost heap; washing line; barbecue; ornamental water features; open plan or garden 'rooms'. Consider areas of sun or shade, and soil type; good or bad views and gradients; hardscaped areas such as terraces, steps, walls, paths and raised beds; decorative and practical features such as sculpture, containers and garden furniture; and think about provision for utilities such as water pipes and electricity cables.

Limit the design to a few strong elements at this stage rather than including lots of unrelated plants and objects, which creates a jumble. Leave open spaces as well as secret corners and be prepared to modify designs. Sometimes even the most carefully planned element does not look or feel right when placed in position. The important thing is that everything in the garden works harmoniously together.

Will Giles' Exotic Garden, Norwich, flourishes with an abundance of lush tropical and sub-tropical plants that should not survive the British climate.

Don't worry about minor details and keep things simple. Visualize three-dimensional, rather than flat plans. Take eventual heights of trees and shrubs into account; boundaries to provide privacy and security; and consider views and paths. Introduce layers and height with plants, hardscaping, walls and statues, creating vertical interest as well as horizontal. Ideas can also be marked directly onto the ground using spray paint, string, flexible hosepipe, garden canes or sand, adjusting until you are satisfied.

If you employ a garden designer – and there are hundreds of excellent ones – make sure they fully understand your requirements before beginning. There is no point working hard creating pared-down, clinical constructions of concrete and steel with minimal plants, when you really crave a cottage garden overflowing with bright flowers and roses round the door. Good designers ask loads of questions to discern your requirements before beginning, so consider the same questions before you start.

Whether formal or informal, modern or traditional, small or large, gardens must 'flow'. Elements must work together and the garden should have year-round appeal. Echo shapes, groups of plants and colours, foliage effects and interesting textures. Choose one or two focal points and plan the garden round these. A garden continually evolves but if the basic plan is strong it always looks right.

Begin by dividing the garden into foreground, middle, and distance, giving a feeling of scale. Vistas across the garden are important, drawing the eye to a distant feature or creating pictures that can be seen from particular points. A view from a window in the house makes a good start for creating the first vista, framed with a pair of sculptures, trees or an arch. Place a large pot, sculpture or specimen tree to act as a 'full stop' at the end of the view. Designing gardens is like creating theatrical sets or a series of pictures. Arrange for fresh delights to open up as you move from one to another.

Paths and steps access varying levels, and should be wide enough for comfortable movement. They control directional flow around the garden, revealing focal points and views. Meandering paths in informal gardens direct the eye, while the straight axis of a formal garden can centre on an ornament, urn or statue. The idea is to encourage exploration. Dividing space makes it appear larger, even in small gardens. Different 'rooms' can have different styles and functions, although the garden must still work as a whole.

Consider low-maintenance gardens if you have little time, but if you love plants, love gardens and spend every minute outside, something more complex is appropriate.

Garden design sounds complicated but can be broken down into easy stages.

An attractive stone archway and open door frame the distant view at Burrow Farm Gardens, Devon.

1. Do lots of research and decide on a style.
2. Measure the plot, make a rough plan, and decide what to keep.
3. List elements to include and mark these on the plan.
4. Hardscaping, walls and paths come first, before planting.
5. Consider shape, colour, texture, contrast and plant species.
6. Plant trees and shrubs first, followed by smaller plants.
7. Add final touches such as statues, containers and furniture.

This is over simplified, but by breaking things down into easy stages you remove much of the complex mystique. Take things one step at a time. Everything should flow easily together, be in proportion and fit comfortably into its surroundings. Whatever style you choose, take it and make it your own. Enjoy the process, have fun and don't make things too complicated to begin with. Fine details can come later. Create a mood, an atmosphere. Capture the essence, the *genius loci*, the true spirit of the place. Every garden is a journey – enjoy yours.

2 Formal and classical style

The style

Classical gardens are inspirational with perfect proportions and solid structural design. They can be symmetrical or asymmetrical, with strong axes, straight paths, and geometric shapes. Green predominates with clipped hedges and topiary. Terraces, steps, pergolas, parterres and statuary are important features. Decorative stone pools and fountains can be enormously complex. Symmetrical designs create mirror images, with at least two main axes (from back to front and side to side), dividing the area into matching quarters. Asymmetrical designs have axes at different angles, and patterns are not repeated regularly.

Formal gardens look clean, tidy, ordered and uncluttered. The style dictates strong outlines with ground plan, hedges, paths, beds and borders. Vertical forms create impact, especially when balanced by strong horizontal shapes. The whole garden can be formal, or formal areas can merge with informal. Formal areas work best near the house where architectural lines are reflected in the design. Formal style is easily adapted to any sized garden, even very small gardens, and fits well with traditional houses.

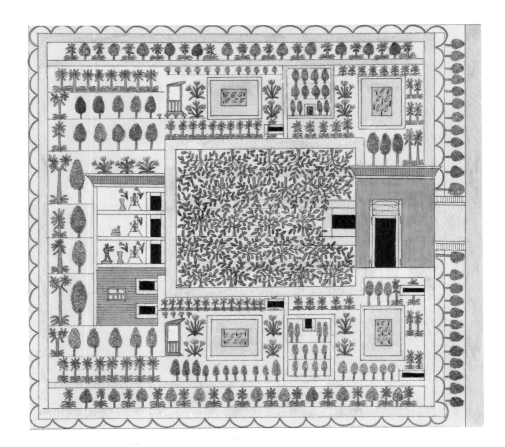

OPPOSITE: *The formal Italianate fountain court at Mapperton Garden, Dorset, a romantic scene of mellow stonework, grass, topiary and water, set into a deep coombe.*

RIGHT: *Drawing of an early Egyptian garden at Thebes showing the formal layout of pools, tree-lined canals and paths, with a shaded central court.*

History

Formal gardens bring to mind great Italian Renaissance gardens with neat, symmetrical lines, carefully clipped hedges, terraces, steps, stone balustrades, sculptures, and grand fountains. But gardens have swung backwards and forwards between formal and informal over the centuries.

Around 3000–2000BC the Egyptians created wonderful gardens in the harsh, desert-like landscape, using geometric designs and proportions that created balance, as well as having mystical significance. Tomb paintings show formal walled gardens with straight paths, canals, square or rectangular pools for fish and water fowl, raised beds, fruit trees, palms, vines, flowers and shaded walks and pavilions. As knowledge of irrigation techniques increased, water was not only utilized for plants but also for water features. Islamic gardens were formal, often based on a quadrilateral design, *'chahar bagh'*, the four squares divided by straight paths or canals and a central fountain.

Ancient Greeks cultivated 'farm' gardens outside city walls with rows of trees, flowers and vegetables. They also created public parks, although private gardens were rare. Some houses had large pots of plants or trees in paved courtyards. Persian influences extended to post-Alexandrian Greece with the gardens of the Athens Academy. Theophrastus was said to have inherited his garden from Aristotle, and Epicurus used his for teaching, philosophizing and relaxation.

The Roman noble, Lucillus, is purported to have begun the gardening tradition in Rome and far more is known about Roman gardens, which began as simple, agriculturally based plots. Romans loved plants and those without gardens often cultivated plants and herbs in pots. Gardens developed in Rome along the River Tiber, and wealthy families had holiday villas and gardens in the countryside, as retreats from city life. Pompeii was buried by volcanic lava and ash in AD79 after Mount Vesuvius erupted, but excavations have revealed beautiful frescoes of gardens, including varying styles, sizes and details. Later gardens were highly formal with strong distinctions between town and country. Town gardens were formal, but it was the grand country villas that inspired impressive classical designs with terraces, arcades, colonnades, sculptures, bathing and ornamental pools, fountains, frescoes and mosaics.

Villas had rooms opening onto a central courtyard, treated as an outdoor space for relaxation, dining or work. Covered walkways or colonnades ran alongside the garden, and sweeping vistas framed glimpses of surrounding landscape. Gardens were outward expressions of prosperity and wealth, and murals and mosaics give pictorial representations of plants and gardens of the time. The engineering of aqueducts

The Privy Garden, the earliest surviving Tudor garden in England, at Thornbury Castle Hotel, Gloucestershire, with clipped yew hedges surrounding a paved court with formal beds.

The exquisite gardens of the Villa Lante, Italy, built around 1566 by Vigonla, have a structured, symmetrical and architecturally-based style, typical of the sixteenth-century Italian Renaissance. They have been variously described as the most beautiful gardens in Italy.

between 27BC and AD14 introduced new possibilities for sophisticated pools and fountains. Vines rambled over stone pergolas, and clipped evergreens were especially popular. Gardens housed shrines sacred to gods and goddesses and the plants associated with them were grown. Fruit trees such as apple, apricot, citrus, fig, mulberry, plum, pomegranate and quince were cultivated, as well as a range of flowering plants. Gardens were for relaxation, but also for philosophical discussion, and learned allusions and mythological imagery were incorporated into designs.

The Roman invasion of Britain in AD43 introduced fresh ideas, and gardens around newly built villas became increasingly grand. Excavations at the first century AD Fishbourne Roman Palace, West Sussex, on the site of a former military base, show massive and lavish buildings, together with impressive formal gardens, parts of which have been beautifully recreated. The remains of planted pots in Romano-British courtyard gardens have also been discovered.

Tudor gardens had formal areas leaning towards the classical Italian style with intricately contrived knot gardens, mazes, pleached lime walks, topiary, pools, fountains, sundials and statues. Heraldic devices were mounted on painted poles interspersed amongst

The Villa Gamberaia, Italy, follows a formal Renaissance style with a later, but very typical, water parterre of four pools divided by paths with a central fountain in the Persian style. Surrounded by clipped cypress, box and yew, the parterre is overshadowed by a semicircular theatre of clipped yew.

A view through to the formal, walled Italianate gardens at Arley Arboretum, Worcestershire. The Italian garden has stone paving and formal pools. Gardens and arboretum date back to the early 1800s and contain many rare trees and plants.

borders. Gardens were intended to be viewed from the windows of the house, rather than at ground level. 'Mounts' were erected at strategic points around the garden, enabling people to view gardens from above. Some mounts were so large they were traversed by wide paths and topped with buildings. Times were affluent and peaceful, allowing a new style of country house and estate to develop rather than the previous, strongly fortified habitations. Consequently gardens became more open and complex, as ideas and craftsmen arrived in Britain from the Continent. Surrounding walls became decorative, rather than protective, features. Tudor gardens can be seen at Montacute House in Somerset, Crossing Temple in Essex, and Thornbury Castle Hotel in Gloucestershire, where the 'Privy Garden' remains the earliest Tudor garden in England.

Stuart gardens were influenced by French style, with rectangular parterres, avenues, carefully clipped and trained trees, and long vistas sweeping away from the house. Blickling Hall in Norfolk and Melbourne Hall in Derbyshire are two fine examples.

It was the Italian Renaissance which most influenced formal style. The early Renaissance began in Italy around

the cultural centre of Florence in the late Middle Ages when Italians yearned to return to their classical roots. Science, art and politics entered a new era, moving away from medieval ways of thinking. It was an expression of Humanism and free will to control one's future rather than being dominated by the Church. People looked again at classical buildings and remains, and developed new ideas based on old villas, gardens and landscapes. Gardens became open rather than enclosed.

Beginning around 1500, the High Renaissance lasted only thirty years or so, but this 'rebirth' inspired a revolution in garden design, which spread throughout Europe. High Renaissance gardens were architecturally based, incorporating rigid, classical ideas of order, proportion and symmetry. Garden design was placed on an equal footing with architecture, and harmony was the governing factor because nature was regulated by harmony, making it perfect. Gardens were sculpted creations styled for maximum theatrical impact with an ordered, structured approach radiating from a central focal point or axis.

Italian landscape that dictated gardens were often on hillsides; the solution was to create terraces with paths and steps connecting different levels. Neatly clipped, evergreen hedges divided gardens into green compartments. Topiary was important. Plants were avidly collected and set into small beds within the formal scheme. Large terracotta or stone pots held specimen trees and lined paths and courtyards, or acted as focal points. Citrus trees were particularly popular, placed outside during summer, and taken indoors during winter. Although flowers were used in Italian gardens, because the season was short, the main emphasis fell on evergreens and dividing beds into geometric compartments and patterns, edged with low, clipped hedges and herbs. Renaissance parterres depicted differing images – as opposed to French styles, which created mirror images. Evergreen trees such as cypress, laurel and holly made enduring contrasts to elegant stonework.

Formal gardens complemented the villa, creating harmonious links between garden and building. They included many architectural features, such as stone walls, colonnades, staircases, balustrades, niches for statues, geometrically shaped beds, straight, shady pergolas and antique statues. In fact many gardens were built simply to house collections of statues. Water was important, symbolizing bountiful nature and fertility. Great formal pools, fountains and water parterres dominated gardens. Rigid lines and strict formality was balanced by landscape views and woodland beyond the garden, including the sacred '*bosco*', or wood.

Many wonderful and outstanding villas and gardens were created in Italy at this time, although many suffered change over the centuries. In 1537 Cosimo

French Baroque was dramatic, sculptural and theatrical and André le Nôtre's seventeenth century design for the gardens at Versailles, France, were all of these things. Landscaped in the classical French symmetrical style, le Nôtre created magnificent parterres and incorporated lavish use of water in lakes, pools, canals and fountains.

Medici, Duke of Florence, began renovating his villa at Castello, Florence. Giorgio Vasari described the gardens as 'the most rich, magnificent and ornamental garden in Europe'. Water was lavishly used with ponds and grand fountains. These, as well as allegorical statues, had a profound influence on the gardens that followed.

The style of the Villa Lante gardens, designed by Vignola around 1566, based on a series of squares and circles, is one of the few gardens not to have undergone radical change over the centuries. These highly formal gardens have a balanced symmetrical plan including water parterres and woodland.

Villa d'Este was constructed on a steeply sloping hillside between 1550 and 1580. It had a garden of lavish stonework, grand statues, nymphs and grottoes where geometric elements combined with symbolism. Harnessing the river created spectacular water features and fountains, including a water organ, establishing the gardens as the wonder of their age.

Villa La Gamberaia, set in the hills above Florence, was constructed around 1610. The garden was destroyed during the Second World War but was later restored. Long and narrow, it is divided into compartments separated by clipped hedges, with a water parterre and famed exedra of carefully trained and clipped cypress.

The elegant Exedra at Painswick Rococo Gardens, Gloucestershire, which are being expertly restored to their former glory. The Rococo style formed part of the transition between highly formal gardens and the 'English Landscape Garden' style that followed.

The Jekyll–Lutyens partnership created many outstanding gardens, including their first great work together, the Formal Gardens at Hestercombe Gardens, Somerset, now being meticulously restored. Soft silver-grey morte slate was complimented by Jekyll's Mediterranean-themed planting palette of silver, grey and white species.

The Great Terrace, Iford Manor, Wiltshire, where Harold Peto designed an Italian-style garden with flights of stone steps and terraces ascending the hillside. The terrace is bordered by an arcade of columns along one side and a small Casita and parterre on the other, while statues line the path.

The great period of cultural change, between the late fourteenth and early seventeenth centuries, swept through Europe, arriving in Britain around the late sixteenth and early seventeenth centuries. Although strongly influenced by Continental ideas and principles of art, architecture and design, the English Renaissance inspired a more eclectic development. The British found it difficult to let go of their past and clung tenaciously to many previous styles such as Gothic, while also embracing ideas and influences from the Dutch, Flemish, German, French and Italian craftsmen who travelled to Britain.

Eventually ideas veered away from severely classical styles into freer designs, which heralded in Mannerism and natural themes with grottoes, rocks and fountains, a return to nature and the sacred '*bosco*'.

In the seventeenth century, Baroque style began in Italy, directly linked to the Catholic Church, expressing dominance of the Church and attempting to inform the illiterate. French Baroque was dramatic, sculptural and theatrical, characterized by a centrally placed building, regular plan, and carefully aligned perspective. The style incorporated elaborate parterres, pools, canals and fountains, using scientific and mathematical principles.

French Baroque peaked with André le Nôtre's design for magnificent gardens at the Château of Versailles, France, created to glorify the Sun King, Louis XIV. Covering many acres, the gardens were landscaped in the classical French style based on symmetry and imposing order on nature. French parterres developed at the end of the sixteenth century but reached their highest perfection with le Nôtre's seventeenth-century designs. Extravagant use of water was highly important, both for movement and reflective qualities in lakes, ponds and canals.

Formal and elegant Dutch gardens had a strong central axis, and elaborate parterres dissected by gravel walks. Gardens were based on a rectangular plan, broken into smaller rectangular or square sections. There were canals, circular pools, fountains, statues, topiary, tubs of evergreen trees, and lots of bulbs.

In 1685 Queen Mary and William of Orange commissioned Christopher Wren to redesign Hampton Court Palace and gardens, London, in the Dutch style. Cardinal Wolsey had developed this country mansion into a magnificent palace. Henry VIII hunted deer in its parkland and created tennis courts and splendid pleasure gardens. Charles I channelled the Longford River eleven miles so water could power fountains in the formal gardens, which were divided into compartments and included knot gardens. Wren's new designs incorporated gilded wrought-iron screens encompassing vast collections of new and exotic plants neatly arranged in formal beds. There were many Dutch influenced gardens in Britain, fuelled by Dutch horticultural skills, knowledge and new plants, but Hampton Court remains the most important.

Between 1720 and 1760 the Rococo style developed. Although never widely adopted in Britain, this flamboyant style with natural curves and intricate patterns, was lighter, more playful than Baroque, and formed an important part of the transition between formal and the increasingly popular informal style. People in Britain generally considered Rococo flamboyance slightly vulgar and it quickly went out of fashion. The restored Rococo Garden at Painswick, Gloucestershire, recreates Benjamin Hyett's 1740s design of geometric patterns and long vistas, meandering paths and architectural follies. The restoration is based on a 1748 painting by Thomas Robins (1716–70), and is highly important in recording this very brief style.

The development of more informal styles heralded the 'Picturesque' movement, which predominated for many years. However, Uvedale Price (1747–1843) designed formal gardens around the house merging into informal areas, before sweeping into parkland and natural landscape beyond, and landscape designer Humphry Repton (1752–1818) reintroduced terraces, stonework and flower gardens, incorporating formal elements back into the 'natural' landscape.

Italian Renaissance style resurfaced strongly again in the mid nineteenth century, influenced by Charles Barry, as a reaction to the previous landscape era with its highly contrived but 'natural' looking gardens and landscape parks.

Victorians incorporated an eclectic mix of past styles including Gothic, Italian, French, Tudor, Jacobean and Dutch, as wealthy industrialists built grand houses and gardens. New plants were ardently collected, and gardens became ostentatious and formal, using an overabundance of plants and ornamentation. Highly intricate, extravagant schemes were devised using bedding plants, often changed on a regular and wasteful basis. Laurel, weeping varieties of trees, monkey-puzzle trees, topiary and formal rose gardens were fashionable. Showy parterres, terraces, balustrades, pergolas, arches, paths, planted urns and jardinières were set amidst immaculate lawns. Collections of tender and exotic plants, housed in large heated conservatories for winter, were carried outside and displayed in summer gardens. Labour was cheap, enabling gardens to become highly elaborate, time consuming, and meticulously maintained.

Reaction to this opulence came with William Robinson (1838–1935), the great exponent of 'wild' gardens. His ideas led to bitter disputes with Reginald Blomfield (1856–1942), who decreed that formal design was the most important feature of any garden. Blomfield published *The Formal Garden in England*, 1892. Designs include Godington House, Kent; Mellerstein House, Scotland; Sulgrave Manor, Oxfordshire; and one of his earlier and best examples, Athelhampton House Garden, Dorset.

When Gertrude Jekyll (1843–1932) arrived on the scene, she showed that good design and good planting could co-exist as parts of the same ideal. Edwin Lutyens

BELOW RIGHT: *Long, formal borders with informal planting in the Four Seasons Walled Garden created by the present Lord Faringdon at his home, Buscot Park, Oxfordshire. The garden is divided into four quadrants with two main axis paths and a central pool and fountain. The borders are edged with clipped box and filled with trees, shrubs, roses, herbaceous perennials, fruit trees and vegetables.*

BELOW: *A simple but highly effective formal garden, with two main axes dividing the garden into four equal parts with a central stone urn.*

(1869–1944), a highly respected architect and garden designer, initially favoured the Arts and Crafts style but later developed classical themes. He designed public buildings and churches as well as gardens and was heavily involved in the redevelopment of Delhi, India, incorporating ideas of Mughal water gardens into his schemes.

The Arts and Crafts movement and Italian Renaissance also strongly influenced Harold Peto (1854–1933). He preferred structured formal styles but ensured his Italian designs fitted sympathetically into English surroundings. Amongst many commissions were Heale Gardens, Wiltshire; water gardens at Buscot Park, Oxfordshire; a magnificent pergola at West Dean, Sussex; and the wonderful garden of his home, Iford Manor, Wiltshire.

Edwardian gardens mixed formal with informal, bound by structured landscaping as Edwardians tried to create country idylls in suburban settings. Pergolas, paths, garden buildings, formal pools, sunken gardens, neat lawns, and locally crafted materials were all features. Long, straight herbaceous borders included drifts of colour after Jekyll's style, and gardens used Italianate themes popularized by Peto.

The Modernist Movement developed in the late 1920s. Gardens were clean and minimal, with straight lines, smooth curves, geometric shapes, rectangular and triangular beds, and lots of white concrete, terraces and paving.

Two World Wars and increasing demand for housing saw gardens become smaller and the next few years developed a range of styles from strictly formal to outrageously wild. Rosemary Verey (1919–2001) created formal modern gardens in the English Classical Revival style. She concentrated on formal structure with informal planting and eclectic mixes of sixteenth- and seventeenth-century designs including parterres, knot gardens, traditional herbaceous borders, and vistas

Beautifully designed, formal parterre at the University of Leicester Botanic Gardens, including box-edged beds set off by patterned brick paths.

of English countryside. She promoted the ornamental kitchen garden or 'potager'. Verey advised and worked on many gardens including HRH Prince Charles's garden at Highgrove, Elton John's Woodside, and her own garden at Barnsley House, Gloucestershire.

Elements of classical style

AXIS

Axes are lines of direction leading the eye around the garden. Basic designs have two main axes, from back to front and from side to side, dividing the area into four equal parts. A main axis can have cross axes radiating from it but these should never dominate the main. Axes can extend or limit the line.

BORDERS

Herbaceous borders had their origins in seventeenth-century Dutch and French gardens, although it wasn't until the late nineteenth and early twentieth centuries that they came into their own. Borders were generally long and rectangular, often in mirror pairs, separated by a central grass path and backed by yew hedges. Deciduous herbaceous perennials could be dug out, divided and replanted in autumn, giving the opportunity to clear all weeds. Borders were bare during winter, but full of colour from early summer onwards, climaxing between June and September in a massive display when everything flowered around the same time. The great borders of Edwardian Britain are prime examples, filled with a wide array of plants including stately delphinium, clouds of gypsophila, white moon daisies, lupins and peonies.

Being costly and time consuming, few private gardens still maintain traditional herbaceous borders, but there are fine examples at Arley Hall, Cheshire. Here, double borders dating from the 1840s claim to be the oldest in continuous cultivation in England. Impressive double borders at Newby Hall, Yorkshire, are also spectacular. Gertrude Jekyll was famed for her stunning, well designed and planted borders. Her many books, including *Colour Schemes in the Flower Garden*, 1911, increased her influence. She was the first to create single-colour borders but also acknowledged the need to be flexible with colour and planting. She made great use of grey foliage, bold leaf shapes, and plant textures, and demonstrated stunning effects of close harmonies with related warm and cool colours in borders. Vita Sackville-West's Sissinghurst Castle Gardens, Kent, combine a formal layout with informal planting, and are one of the best gardens for herbaceous plants.

Sculpture can vary from simply-shaped blocks of stone to large, highly elaborate designs. The Henry Moore statue at Dartingon Hall, Devon, is set above a series of formal grass terraces.

Hidcote Manor, Gloucestershire, another influential garden, was created by Major Lawrence Johnston, around 1903. Hidcote's greatness springs from its strong, structured design and development of hedged 'garden rooms', together with Johnston's introductions of many new plants. Johnston went on to develop a second important garden in Southern France at Serre de la Madone.

Sissinghurst and Hidcote also have spectacular monochrome gardens, and the White Garden at Sissinghurst achieved worldwide acclaim. Both gardens are now under the care of The National Trust. As Gardens Adviser to the National Trust, as well as his writings, Graham Stuart Thomas (1909–2003) was highly influential in the art of planting borders with old roses, perennials and ground cover plants.

DESIGN

Classical gardens are either symmetrical or asymmetrical, demanding strong structure with uncluttered, geometric shapes and straight lines. Formal design is adaptable to any sized garden, and can be incorporated into informal gardens and vice versa. Formal designs work best near the house, reflecting architectural building lines. The style also works with traditional houses, and adapts to modern gardens where clean lines and geometric shapes provide perfect, uncluttered foils for minimal planting.

HARDSCAPING

Stone is traditionally used in formal gardens and the Dutch introduced the fashion for mellow brickwork. From the early twentieth century onwards concrete

The Victorian Terrace, Hestercombe Gardens, Somerset, built between 1873 and 1878, is set out as a formal parterre with four beds surrounding a central fountain, and stone balustrades edging the terrace.

became popular. Stone slabbed terraces, paved and gravel paths, steps, geometrically shaped pool surrounds, stone pergolas and colonnades are all important elements.

PARTERRES AND KNOT GARDENS

Claude Mollet, the French Royal gardener, created the first parterre around 1580 and its popularity spread, with patterns becoming extremely elaborate. Parterres are flat, formal, ornamental gardens of turf or low clipped hedges, sited close to the house to be viewed from windows overlooking the garden. Sophisticated designs were decorative features in larger gardens. There was a great love of detail during the sixteenth and seventeenth centuries and interior decoration, ceilings, tiles, clothing and book covers were all ornate. These complex designs adapted well into gardens.

Knot gardens were features of seventeenth-century gardens. Designs were freer than regimented parterres. In 1618, William Lawson published a book of knot garden designs. Low, evergreen hedges were woven through and around a square plot forming symmetrical patterns. Knot garden hedges rise as they cross, forming the 'knot', whereas parterres have smoothly crossing hedges.

The *parterre à L'Anglais*, popular in the seventeenth century, had outlines of mown grass patterns infilled with gravel or sand. In the early eighteenth century, French influences dictated more complex designs filled with coloured plants, grass, gravel, or crushed glass.

Parterres saw a revival in Britain in the mid nineteenth century, often including pools or fountains. Pots of topiary and evergreen trees were carefully sited to emphasize geometric lines and vistas. Dwarf box hedging traditionally created outlines for knot gardens and parterres. Formal planting schemes included infilling with the same type of plants, such as viola, wild strawberry, cyclamen or roses; using a mix of plants or wild flowers; placing a single specimen plant in each area, surrounded by gravel; or dressing open areas with coloured sand, gravel or marble chippings. Colours ranged from a single shade, or soft pastel shades, to a mix of vivid colours.

SCULPTURE

Sculpture is said to have originated with images of ancient gods and goddesses, and many civilizations created such images. These were important features in Ancient Roman gardens and again in Renaissance gardens. Italian statues were imported into Britain in the sixteenth century and statuary was much in demand again in the nineteenth century. Designs vary from simply shaped blocks of stone, wood or slate in abstract forms, to complex works including animals and figures. Classical sculpture suits formal settings, although abstract pieces by great sculptors such as Henry Moore and Barbara Hepworth fit well into classically landscaped gardens.

Sculpture is not simply a shape dropped in for decoration; it must fit well and enhance the scene. It acts as a focal point to complement gardens, plants and surroundings, providing a strong vertical presence in otherwise horizontal designs. Figures are traditional, but single columns, sundials, urns, finials, stone niches, granite spheres, classical or abstract forms can all be used

Imposing topiary trees and hedges edging the formal water garden at Mapperton Gardens, Dorset, one of the county's most important gardens.

to advantage, depending upon their suitability to the garden. Carefully chosen pieces of natural stone also add a sculptural quality, as do steps, pillars or well-constructed stone pergolas.

TERRACES

Shallow or deep terraces create workable areas on sloping sites, especially practical in hilly landscapes. The Hanging Gardens of Babylon (600BC) in what is now Iraq, were built on massive terraces. One of the original 'Seven Wonders of the World', they were destroyed by earthquakes around the second century BC. Terraces serve the same purpose in gardens and were especially popular in Italian Renaissance gardens, with stone balustrades and steps ascending the hillsides.

TOPIARY

Carefully clipped hedges show off velvet lawns,

sophisticated borders and formal designs to perfection, but hedges do not always have to be smoothly trimmed, two-dimensional forms. The ancient art of topiary creates living sculptures with shaped evergreens such as yew and box. The style has been in and out of fashion for many centuries. Pliny the Elder described cypress trees trimmed into ships and other images in Greece and Rome, and topiary was very popular in Roman gardens. Revived in fifteenth- and sixteenth-century Italian Renaissance gardens, it varied from simple spheres to huge clipped animals and temples. Also popular in formal Dutch gardens, it went out of fashion during the eighteenth-century 'Landscape' period but became popular again in the Victorian era. Twentieth-century cottage gardens included whimsical shapes, in contrast to often highly sophisticated designs of large, formal gardens. Levens Hall, Cumbria is an important topiary garden designed by Guillaume Beaumont, a pupil of le Nôtre. He laid out a formal park, parterre borders and fabulous sculpted topiary of human, animal, and abstract forms.

Topiary creates good structural features, from basic

Striking ancient yew topiary at Holme Lacey House Hotel (Warner Leisure), Herefordshire.

ABOVE: *An unusual and stylish parterre filled with multi-coloured violas, set around a central pool at Hotel Endsleigh Gardens, Devon.*

BELOW: *A simple pansy parterre design that would adapt well to any garden.*

box balls or obelisks in pots, simple bird and animal shapes, to large-scale, complex structures of animals, birds, castles, trains and other wide-ranging designs. Topiary 'lollipops' introduce a sense of formality into small gardens. Although topiary is essentially formal, it can add a fun as well as structural element to gardens. Modern day approaches use pieces in informal, naturalistic landscapes.

WATER

Water was important in formal gardens but took the form of geometrically shaped pools and straight canals rather than meandering streams. Renaissance gardens were renowned for complex, classical fountains, but even small formal gardens should incorporate a pool, a simple channel, a classical wall mask trickling water into a stone basin, or a gently tinkling fountain.

Creating formal style

Straight lines and geometric forms fit well on level ground. Sloping sites can be terraced and accessed by stone steps or paths. Paths have paved or gravelled surfaces, and hedges should be precisely clipped. Square, rectangular, long and formal, or circular beds have neat, straight edges. Water features are formal, structured designs rather than naturalistic.

Modern parterres and knot gardens still favour clipped box but in many areas this has been decimated by box blight (*Cylindrocladium buxicola*), a rapidly spreading fungal disease. Disinfect clippers and secateurs continually to limit spreading the disease round the garden. Other suitable edging plants include berberis, germander, lavender, santolina and yew. Parterres and knots look attractive all year round, whether infilled with coloured gravel, packed with bright flowers, or dusted with frost and snow in winter. They create contrast by adding formal elements to informal gardens. Designs also fit courtyard settings, and may include personal initials or motifs. Carefully measure and peg designs onto the ground before planting. Even simple topiary is extremely effective, especially when viewed

drifting through to the front. Perennial borders are now often planted for all seasons with bulbs, annuals, grasses and winter species such as hellebores, and evergreens. The more you try to extend the flowering period, the more the main impact is lost during the border's climax months.

Original sculpture is expensive and cheap reproductions disappointing. But objects do not have to be costly: large, well-shaped rocks or pieces of slate carefully sited can represent old standing stones; simple obelisks or columns add vertical interest; attractively shaped driftwood and items from architectural salvage yards can be used, as can casual displays of moss-covered terracotta pots. Materials include wood, stone, granite, marble, concrete, reconstituted stones and resins, bronze, cast metal, lead, brushed or polished steel, plastic and woven willow. Simple shapes from crumpled wire netting also look effective and are cheap to make.

Sundials add a historic feel, especially in classical gardens. They represent the illusion of time passing and the transience of life. They can be free-standing, wall mounted, traditional or modern designs, but should be accurately set otherwise they simply become representational ornaments. Place in full sun with the

ABOVE: *Modern stone figure by Helen Sinclair, set against a background of smoothly trimmed hedges.*

BELOW: *Superb Italianate gardens in the 'Grand Manner' at Holme Lacey House Hotel (Warner Leisure), Herefordshire, with lushly planted parterres, ancient topiary yew hedges, pools and fountains.*

against a background of smooth gravel or lawn. Out of fashion for many years, it is again popular and garden centres sell frames as well as clipped shapes.

Once mature, most hedges are clipped once or twice each year. Maintenance depends on complexity. Keeping large, set pieces in order with scaffolding or ladders is very hard work. Bamboo frames placed around pots simplify clipping simple shapes such as cubes and cones. Even ivy can be clipped and trained around frames to create topiary effects. Most hedges and topiary are cut in late summer. They should not be clipped early in the year. as it is illegal to disturb or damage birds' nests (The Wildlife and Countryside Act, 1981). Clip judiciously, as it is better to cut twice rather than wait for over-enthusiastically cut plants to re-grow.

Herbaceous, or as they are now known, perennial borders, mix perennials with shrubs, roses, annuals and bulbs. Plants should work together to create pleasing rhythms. Concentrate on key plants and shapes for unity, and undulating heights with taller sections

shadow falling directly below the arm at noon. Armillary spheres, popular since Renaissance times, depict progression of planets through the universe.

Sculptural elements should be carefully placed to the best advantage. They act as focal points to attract the eye at the end of a long vista; they can peer from between hedges, or fit into niches. Smoothly trimmed hedges make good backgrounds.

Formal, classical gardens are elegant and timeless. Today we are not so determined to prove the cosmos is held together by mathematical ratios, but formal gardens designed along mathematical and geometrical proportions always endure, whatever the current fashion. Uncluttered, regulated, calm, serene and soothing to the eye, precise and considered designs appeal to those who prefer order to informality. They are amongst the simplest designs to execute, as careful division of space creates its own harmony. If you like everything in its place – and a place for everything – you will definitely be inspired by formal gardens.

Formal style

Trees

Trees are the backbone and framework of any garden and are especially important in formal gardens where clear lines and geometric layouts show them off to advantage.

Acer griseum
Acer palmatum
Acer pensylvanicum
Aesculus hippocastanum
Betula papyrifera
Betula pendula
Betula utilis jacquemontii
Camellia japonica
Castanea sativa
Catalpa bignonioides
Citrus limon
Citrus sinensis
Cornus alternifolia
Cornus kousa
Cornus mas
Cydonia oblonga
Eucalyptus gunnii
Eucalyptus pauciflora niphophila
Eucryphia x nymansensis
Euonymus japonicus
Fagus sylvatica
Ficus carica
Ilex x altaclarensis
Ilex aquifolium
Liquidambar styraciflua
Liriodendron tulipifera
Magnolia campbellii
Magnolia x soulangiana
Malus sp.
Morus alba
Morus nigra

Morus rubra
Nyssa sylvatica
Prunus serrulata 'Amanogawa'
Prunus avium
Prunus dulcis
Prunus serrula
Prunus serrulata 'Shirotae'
Prunus subhirtella 'Autumnalis'
Punica granatum
Quercus x hispanica 'Lucombeana'
Salix babylonica
Sorbus aria
Sorbus aucuparia

Coniferous species

Evergreen, low maintenance species are important in formal gardens, providing year round interest.

Araucaria araucana
Cedrus atlantica 'Glauca'
Cedrus C. atlantica 'Pendula'
Chamaecyparisus x Cuproparis leylandii
Chamaecyparis lawsoniana
Chamaecyparis lawsoniana 'Aurea Densa'
Chamaecyparis obtusa 'Nana Gracilis'
Cryptomeria japonica
Cupressus glabra
Cupressus macrocarpa
Cupressus sempervirens 'Green Pencil'
Cupressus sempervirens 'Stricta'
Juniperus communis 'Compressa'
Picea omorika
Picea breweriana
Picea pungens 'Glauca Globosa'
Pinus montezumae
Pinus nigra
Pinus sylvestris 'Fastigiata'
Sequoia sempervirens

Camellia japonica.

Sequoiadendron giganteum
Taxus baccata
Thuja occidentalis 'Smaragd'
Thuja plicata

Hedges

Neatly trimmed, evergreen hedges are synonymous with formal gardens, forming divisions and boundaries.

EVERGREEN

Aucuba japonica 'Crotonifolia'
Berberis darwinii
Buxus microphylla
Buxus sempervirens
Chamaecyparis lawsoniana 'Green Hedger'
Choisya ternata
Cotoneaster lacteus
Elaeagnus x ebbingei
Escallonia sp.
Euomymus japonicus
Griselinia littoralis
Ilex aquifolium

Laurus nobilis
Ligustrum ovalifolium
Ligustrum ovalifolium 'Aureum'
Lonicera nitida
Populus nigra 'Italica'
Prunus laurocerasus
Prunus lusitanica
Pyracantha coccinea
Rhododendron ponticum
Taxus baccata
Thuja plicata
Tsuga heterophylla
Viburnum tinus

DECIDUOUS

Berberis thunbergii 'Atropurpureum'
Carpinus betulus
Fagus sylvatica
Fagus sylvatica purpurea
Hippophae rhamnoides
Prunus cerasifera

Plants for shade

Formal gardens were traditionally very green, with hedges and trees predominating, so shade-loving plants are an asset. Few plants tolerate heavy shade all of the time, but there are a large number that tolerate shade for much of the day or dappled shade beneath trees.

Ajuga reptans
Anemone hupehensis
Arum italicum 'Pictum'
Aucuba japonica
Berberis x stenophylla 'Corolina Compacta'
Bergenia 'Ballawley'
Brunnera macrophylla
Convallaria majalis
Cyclamen hederifolium
Daphne genkwa
Digitalis grandiflora
Doronicum 'Miss Mason'
Dryopteris filix-mas
Epimedium x warleyense
Euonymus fortunei
Euonymus japonicus 'Microphyllus'
Euphorbia amygdaloides robbiae
Filipendula ulmaria 'Aurea'
Geranium maculatum

Magnolia Campbelli.

Geranium phaeum
Geranium sylvaticum
Helleborus orientalis
Hedera helix
Helleborus foetidus
Hosta fortunei
Hosta sieboldiana 'Frances Williams'
Hydrangea paniculato
Hydrangea serrata
Lamium galeobdolon
Lamium maculatum
Lonicera x purpusii
Mahonia aquifolium 'Apollo'
Meconopsis x sheldonii
Osmanthus delavayi
Pachysandra terminalis
Polygonatum x hybridum
Prunus lusitanica
Ruscus aculeatus
Sarcocca confusa
Sarcococca hookeriana var. digyna
Skimmia x confusa 'Kew Green'
Skimmia japonica 'Fragrans'
Skimmia japonica 'Rubella'
Tricyrtis formosana
Viburnum tinus
Vinca major
Viola riviana

Plants for clipping and training

Evergreen species that can be clipped into shapes for topiary are invaluable in formal gardens creating good architectural features, and punctuation marks, while low clipped hedges adorn knots and parterres.

Berberis buxifolia 'Pygmaea'
Berberis x stenophylla 'Corallina Compacta'
Buxus sempervirens 'Suffruticosa'
Euonymus fortunei cvs
Euonymus japonicus 'Microphyllus'
Ilex crenata
Lavandula angustifolia
Myrtus communis
Rosmarinus officinalis
Santolina chamaecyparissus
Taxus baccata
Teucrium fruticans

Climbers

Climbing plants clothe pergolas, arches and walls.

Actinidia kolomikta
Clematis armandii
Clematis x jackmanii
Clematis montana
Humulus lupulus 'Aureus'
Lonicera caprifolium
Lonicera japonica
Trachelospermum jasminoides
Vitis vinifera
Wisteria floribunda
Wisteria sinensis

Roses

Formal rose beds are set into geometric patterns and traditionally contained one type and colour of rose rather than a mixture. Shrub roses form hedges and specimen bushes, while climbing and rambling roses climb over arches, pergolas and walls.

Rosa x alba
Rosa 'Allgold'
Rosa banksiae – clb
Rosa 'Blanc Double de Coubert'
Rosa 'Buff Beauty'
Rosa x centifolia
Rosa 'Cornelia'

Rosa x damascena
Rosa 'Elizabeth Harkness'
Rosa filipes 'Kiftsgate' – clb
Rosa x floribunda
Rosa gallica 'Complicata'
Rosa 'Graham Thomas'
Rosa 'Iceberg'
Rosa 'Lavender Lassie'
Rosa 'Mme Alfred Carriér' – clb
Rosa 'Nevada'
Rosa 'Prima Ballerina'
Rosa 'The Prince'

Borders

The traditional green of formal gardens has diversified over the years and many formal gardens have developed outstanding herbaceous borders.

Acanthus mollis
Achillea filipendulina
Anemone hupehensis
Asphodeline lutea
Campanula glomerata
Campanula portenschlagiana
Cynara cardunculus
Dianthus caryophyllus
Fragaria vesca
Helianthus decapetalus
Leonotis leonurus
Ligularia przewalskii
Lobelia cardinalis
Lychnis coronaria
Monarda didyma
Origanum majorana
Polyonum amplexicaule
Scabiosa caucasica
Tradescantia virginiana

Bulbs, corms, rhizomes and tubers

Bulbs make excellent in-fills for parterres and extend the flowering period of herbaceous borders.

Allium christophii
Allium karataviense
Allium roseum
Alstroemeria sp
Amaryllis belladonna
Anemone blanda
Camassia

Liriodendron tulipifera.

Canna x generalis
Cardiocrinum giganteum
Chionodoxa forbesii
Colchicum sp.
Crinum x powellii
Crocus chrysanthus
Crocus sieberi
Crocus speciosus
Crocus tomasinianus
Cyclamen coum
Cyclamen hederifolium
Dahlia sp,
Erythronium dens-canis
Fritillaria meleagris
Galanthus nivalis
Galtonia candicans
Iris reticulata
Leucojum vernum
Lilium sp
Narcissus sp
Paeonia lactiflora
Tigridia pavonia
Triteleia laxa
Tulipa sp

3 Informal and naturalistic style

The style

As the name implies, 'natural' gardens follow nature in an informal, relaxed style with freedom and looseness in design and planting. Lines are free flowing with meandering paths, curving beds and a lack of rigid symmetry. Informal styles suit uneven slopes and irregularly shaped areas, creating gardens in sympathy with the natural landscape. Rather than geometrically aligned axes, winding paths encourage movement around the garden with ever-changing aspects and views suggesting new, mysterious and inviting surprises around each corner.

Structures are of organic, natural materials rather than man-made, and fit comfortably into their surroundings.

Although gardens are still built on a strong underlying plan, there is a lack of rigidity, harsh lines and formality. More formal areas can be included near the house, and these can merge into informal areas, creating strong contrasts.

Trees, shrubs and plants are grouped in agreeable disorder. Plants and foliage clamber freely up structures, clothe buildings, or tumble from borders, softening path edges. Bulbs naturalize in grassland and beneath trees and shrubs, and wild flowers mingle in meadows. Informal gardens work with nature, rather than against her. Grass does not have to be immaculately manicured, and areas of mown sward merge into longer meadow grasses. Plants self-seed and the whole garden creates a tranquil, relaxed and harmonious atmosphere with rhythm and unity.

OPPOSITE: The naturalistic rockery at Hotel Endsleigh Gardens, Devon, merges into a landscape background.

RIGHT: A picturesquely curving path that flows through the landscape, drawing the eye along at Brobury House, Herefordshire.

A stunning sight in spring, these cyclamen have naturalized over many years, creating a pink carpet beneath the trees.

The thirty-five acre landscape garden at Hestercombe, Somerset, designed by Coplestone Warre Bampfylde between 1750 and 1786, incorporates carefully orchestrated views and Arcadian scenes of waterfalls, cascades and a picturesque, pear-shaped lake.

Sweeping borders burgeon with an abundance of plants, colour, texture, shapes and perfume in informal groups as if nature and not man had planned the scene. Natural gardens include wild landscapes, woodland, wildlife and water gardens, and use exotic plants in jungle gardens as we seek to escape the confines of red brick and concrete creeping across the landscape.

History

Garden styles have swung backwards and forwards between formal and informal over the centuries, as one went out of fashion and the other came back in.

Saxon gardens were small, enclosed patches around tiny cottages for growing food plants and herbs. Medieval plots, roughly rectangular in shape, were more formal and gardens were cultivated in the precincts of fortified castles as well as cottages. Town gardens began to appear for the first time around affluent properties. Gardens were enclosed for safety, surrounded by stone walls, hedges, picket fences, woven willow or hazel hurdles. Because they were secure, they were relaxed areas and as well as beds for plants, gardens often included flowery meads with wild plants growing amongst longer grasses. Medieval gardens contained herbs, fruit and flowers set into formally laid out beds, which were often raised. Vines and climbers clothed trellises, and trees were carefully trained to form natural, shaded archways and walks. Creeper- or rose-clad arbours created private retreats, and raised turf seats provided resting places. There was usually a well, small stream or pond. Medieval books of hours were often exquisitely decorated, showing plants, gardens and scenes of daily life at the time.

Peaceful times saw gardens become more open, flowing into the surrounding landscape. Estates were planted with wooded areas, open rides, and 'wilderness' gardens. Aristocratic owners took an interest in their land and what happened to it. Slowly the new landscape style developed, opening up lakes and creating vistas across idealized landscapes.

John Vanbrugh (1664–1726) was one of the first architects to concentrate on creating gardens which moved away from the strictly formal and symmetrical, into a less controlled, freer, but still architecturally based style. He designed Blenheim Palace, Oxfordshire, and the building and gardens of Castle Howard, Yorkshire. William Kent (1685–1748) had an enormous influence on natural landscape design in the period following the sixteenth-century revival of formal, classical gardens. Originally an artist, he felt landscape design should be seen as a classical painting to create an idealized view of Arcadia as depicted in pictures by Claude and Poussin. He used various ingenious techniques to produce artistic effects of light, colour and form. Kent was the great master of this 'Picturesque' or 'Natural' style of gardening. Although pattern continued as an important element with large parterres and formal paths, Kent introduced informal curving paths and broad walks cut through meadows and swathes of grass. Curving lakes replaced previously geometric pools. These were gardens on the grand scale, with open parkland rather than enclosed, intimate areas. Decorative buildings were incorporated into the scene to attract the eye, together with statues and obelisks. Some of his designs include Shotover House, Oxfordshire; Chiswick House, London; Badminton Park, Gloucestershire; Stowe Landscape Garden, Buckinghamshire; Holkham Hall, Norfolk and Rousham, Oxfordshire – one of the first and most influential landscape gardens, remaining true to its original concept.

Lancelot 'Capability' Brown (1716–83) was accorded the title of 'England's greatest gardener'. He initially worked with Kent and then went on to develop further the 'Natural' or 'English' style of gardening, creating over 170 vast, carefully manicured landscapes in an attempt to improve on nature and its rolling countryside. His designs were epitomized by undulating acres of grass meadows sweeping right up to the house, serpentine curves, gravel walks, follies, temples, fake ruins, grottoes and circular clumps and belts of 'natural' looking woodland. Cascades and bridges connected vast serpentine lakes. Brown destroyed many great, formal gardens in his conquest to reform the landscape, creating massive parks for wealthy aristocratic clients. His work includes Croome Court, Worcestershire; Blenheim Palace, Oxfordshire; Warwick Castle, Warwickshire; and one of his finest parks, Boxwood House, Wiltshire.

The English landscape style was the first major British contribution to garden design. Landscape architects set out to impose man's will on nature, improving the natural scenery by making it look even more 'natural', with rolling parkland, meandering water courses and lakes, and planted areas of beech and oak woodland.

In 1745, Henry Hoare II and architect Henry Flitcroft created imposing parkland around Hoare's Palladian Wiltshire mansion. Stourhead became one of the greatest English landscape gardens, incorporating a massive lake, Chinese water garden, temples, grottoes, follies and bridges which took over eighty years to complete. Uvedale Price (1747–1829) preferred a slightly less manicured approach in achieving the natural landscape. He felt the house must be pivotal to the whole scene and should be surrounded by a formal

William Kent's Arcadian scene at Rousham, Oxfordshire, one of the first and most influential landscape gardens.

garden which blended into less formal areas before finally sweeping off into parkland and the natural countryside beyond. He wrote *Essays of the Picturesque*. Little remains of his garden at Foxley, Herefordshire. The house was demolished and the estate replanted.

The last great English landscape designer of his era was Humphry Repton (1752–1818), who became a landscape gardener at the age of thirty-six. His vistas included 'Borrowed' scenery from the surrounding countryside, viewed to advantage from strategic points on the drives sweeping through the estate. Repton also reintroduced formal elements into the landscape such as terraces, stonework and flower gardens. He considered buildings to be an integral part of the overall scheme and studied how they fitted into the scene. His style developed a natural beauty enhanced by art in his quest to ensure the designs appeared as if created by nature, regardless of how contrived the work had been to establish this effect. Repton wrote *Hints on Landscape*

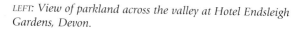

LEFT: *View of parkland across the valley at Hotel Endsleigh Gardens, Devon.*

BELOW: *Humphry Repton reintroduced more formal elements back into his landscapes, including terraces and stonework. His 1811 design for Hotel Endsleigh Gardens, Devon, was one of his last and most favourite designs.*

Gardening in 1795, and created famous 'Red Books' for clients. These were bound volumes of each design including 'before' and 'after' sketches and overlays. Repton worked on many gardens; Ashridge, Hertfordshire, was the first garden for which he advocated the 'Mixed style'. Other works included: Tatton Park, Cheshire; Antony Garden, Cornwall; Clumber Park, Nottinghamshire; Woburn Abbey, Bedfordshire; Longleat, Wiltshire; and Cobham Hall, Kent. Repton also worked on the development of London squares, and Regent's Park, introducing trees and plants to bring landscape into cities. Sherringham Park, Norfolk, remains the most complete project carried out by Repton and his son, and Hotel Endsleigh Gardens, Devon, designed in 1811, was one of his last and most favourite designs.

J.C. Loudon (1783–1843) began his career in agriculture before turning to landscape design. He too was influential in creating green spaces in urban cities. Loudon was responsible for the 'Gardenesque' style in which nature was not exactly represented, but inspired more stylized, abstract designs. He placed strong emphasis on the full appreciation of plants' foliage, colour and texture, as well as their surroundings. He advocated planting exotic species into the natural landscape in such a manner that plants were shown off to their best advantage and could be fully appreciated. There were many new and varied introductions and botanical rarities at the time, which could be displayed to effect. Plants were carefully grouped. Mounds enhanced the appearance of trees and shrubs and carefully positioned island beds were linked by winding paths, meandering through small-scale landscapes so plants could be viewed close to. Sympathetically framed vignettes and other carefully contrived features showed everything off to perfection. Important works include

William Robinson abhorred highly formal designs and advocated naturalizing drifts of bulbs beneath shrubs and trees.

Great Tew, Oxfordshire; Birmingham Botanical Gardens, West Midlands; and the most impressive of his surviving designs, Derby Arboretum, Derbyshire.

In the eighteenth century, vistas incorporated countryside views from outside the garden. Architectural features such as summerhouses, bridges, dovecotes, follies and grottoes became important punctuation marks in the landscape, as well as providing resting places as the gentry rode around the estate.

The Victorian era was notable for its ostentatious and quite formal gardens and a reaction to this opulent style came with William Robinson (1838–1935). Robinson was a gardener and journalist who became a major exponent of the 'wild' garden and a freer, much less formal style of design and planting which later evolved into the cottage garden style. He wrote many books including *The Wild Garden* (1870), in which he spoke out strongly against formal gardens, the Victorian emphasis on greenhouse exotics and big bedding schemes, sham Italian gardens and contrived artifice. Instead he promoted natural drifts of perennials in meadows, in woodland and by water; mixed borders of shrubs, perennials and climbers; bulbs naturalized in grass; ground cover plants; and a groundbreaking style of mixing cultivated perennials together with wild, native plants – a precursor of many of today's gardens. He felt that nature itself represented true and harmonious beauty to which every gardener should aspire. Hardscaping and design might be inevitable but it should be kept to a minimum. Above all, it was the plants and naturalistic approach that were important. He decreed gardens should blend into the natural landscape and the design element should not be developed to the detriment of plants, which must be displayed as naturally as possible.

Robinson's strong views were directly opposed by Reginald Blomfield, who said no gardener could ever hope to compete with nature's wonderful perfection. Blomfield insisted gardens must feature good, strong, classical designs, while Robinson was adamant that natural planting with attention to individual plants was most important, and long and acrimonious discussions ensued. Robinson created his own garden at Gravetye Manor, East Grinstead, Sussex (now a hotel) and also influenced design at Hergest Croft, Herefordshire and at Killerton House, Devon, amongst many others.

The Arts and Crafts style was inspired by William Morris and John Ruskin in the late nineteenth and early twentieth centuries. It was at its height between 1880 and 1910, promoting a return to good craftsmanship and design following the mass production, inferior designs and poor quality that had become by-products of the Industrial Revolution. Traditional values, techniques and plants were epitomized in gardens designed by Gertrude Jekyll. She was an accomplished artist and studied at the South Kensington School of Art in the same year that William Morris founded his company Morris, Marshall and Faulkner. The Arts and Crafts movement exerted a strong influence on her as she associated with so many of its ideals. Deteriorating eyesight turned Jekyll's great talents to designing gardens, and she shared Robinson's enthusiasm for informal gardens. They first met in 1875 when Robinson was editor of *The Garden*, and Jekyll was soon making regular contributions to the magazine. In 1883 Robinson's book *The English Flower Garden* was published and included a chapter on 'Colour in the Flower Garden' by Jekyll. She went on to write many books including: *Wood and Garden*, 1899; *Some English Gardens*, 1904; *Colour Schemes for the Flower Garden*, 1908; and *Annuals and Biennials*, 1916. She also wrote over 1,000 articles for magazines including *Country Life* and *The Garden*. Jekyll applied a structured approach but strongly advocated beauty and harmony in her designs, appreciating both formal and informal styles, and showing that planning and planting were both equally important. She often combined a formal plan with informal planting, packing her large 'hardy flower borders' with either soft, colour-themed plants in simple washes of pale grey, white and green, or radiantly coloured displays which blended into one another and swept across the borders in huge drifts.

She mixed shrubs, perennials, bulbs and annuals in borders and island beds, and advocated growing herbs and vegetables with flowers. Colour and texture were key elements and her meticulous attention to detail was legendary: she would pay as much attention to a tiny garden corner as she would to large-scale plans. Because of this her designs are easily adaptable to small, modern gardens. A garden was not simply a collection of plants, but together with a solid design the combination created a coherent whole, however large or small the site, and it was also important house and garden fitted comfortably together. Jekyll also designed orchards, under-planting fruit trees with bulbs and flowers.

Although Jekyll did not insist on promoting one particular style, and while she realized it was not possible to attain perfection, she worked to achieve the best she possibly could with whatever she was doing. Planning, planting and design were all important elements of the overall scheme, whether it was a woodland walk, bold border, rose garden, or large, complete garden.

When the young Edwin Lutyens came along, the Jekyll-Lutyens combination made a lasting impression on the age, although later Lutyens turned to classical themes. They worked on many schemes ranging from cottages to castles, including Jekyll's own garden, Munstead Wood in Surrey; Folly Farm, Berkshire; Lindesfarne Castle Garden, Northumberland; Castle

The Dorothy Clive Gardens, Staffordshire, have large collections of rhododendrons and azaleas naturalized in the spectacular woodland gardens.

Drogo, Cornwall; and Hestercombe, Somerset. Jekyll's ideas influenced many great gardeners who followed, such as Lawrence Johnston (Hidcote Manor, Gloucestershire), Vita Sackville-West (Sissinghurst Castle, Kent), and Graham Stuart Thomas.

In 1930 Vita Sackville-West and her husband Harold Nicolson bought the ruins of Sissinghurst Castle, Kent and set about creating their dream garden. It developed in the best tradition of the Arts and Crafts Movement. Nicolson's strong, formal layout was complemented by a romantic profusion of plants as his wife filled the various garden 'rooms' with trees, hedges, shrubs, roses, herbaceous plants, colour themed borders including the world famous 'White garden', and pools set against mellow, moss-covered stonework.

Graham Stuart Thomas (1909–2003) also gardened in the Arts and Crafts tradition. As gardens adviser to the National Trust from 1974, he was passionate about roses. He wrote numerous books and designed many gardens including those at Little Moreton Hall and Lyme Park, Cheshire; Lytes Cary Manor, Somerset; and Mottisford Abbey, Hampshire.

As the twentieth century continued to evolve so did gardens and garden design, until in the latter part of the twentieth and into the twenty-first century, gardening became so popular, top designers were elevated to cult status, each with their own enthusiastic following. Now, climate change and ecological awareness have fuelled interest in natural and sustainable gardens, self sufficiency, growing vegetables and fruit, encouraging wildlife, using fewer chemicals, and gardening in harmony with nature. Today's gardens are varied and eclectic mixes of formal, minimalistic, cottage and stylized designs, but overall it is the naturalistic that predominates. Areas of natural grassland; sweeping borders with big drifts of herbaceous perennials and grasses; prairie and wild gardening; naturalized bulbs; and wildflower meadows show informal gardens are back in fashion.

Elements of informal gardens

BOUNDARIES

However natural the garden may be it will still almost certainly require boundaries. Stone walls fit better than man-made brick in informal gardens, although mellow, moss-covered bricks can look very attractive. A small window incorporated into a wall reveals a view beyond. Boundaries can be defined with fences or trellis, clothed with plants, while picket fencing adds a country touch to informal gardens. Hedges are the ideal solution and also provide shelter for birds. Boundaries afford privacy and protection and whereas a 'ha-ha' created an indistinguishable break between garden and farm or parkland in eighteenth-century Britain, they are not generally practical today where boundaries offer security from the outside world.

Willow and hazel are increasingly popular and are often woven into living fences, tunnels, or natural, leafy arbours. Plants are quick growing and easily worked to create anything from simple hedges and boundaries to highly complex structures, and land art.

DESIGN

Flowing lines, irregular shapes and forms, natural planting, meandering curves, informal pools, winding streams, grassland, naturalized bulbs, woodland, wildflower meadows and use of natural materials are all hallmarks of informal design. Straight lines and hard edges are an anathema in such gardens where gently flowing surroundings create relaxing, harmonious and peaceful sanctuaries with abundant plants and flowers growing in an unrestrained fashion.

Informal gardens embrace a wide variety of styles such as cottage, meadows, woodland, alpine, rockery, wildlife, and landscape gardens. Despite their informality, a strong underlying plan binds the structure together, however unrestrained the planting appears. The smallest gardens can have informally shaped beds and natural planting with a small pool. Tiny courtyard gardens can overflow with plants, creating a jungle atmosphere with plants spilling onto paths and patio.

HARDSCAPING

Informal gardens benefit from natural materials, and especially local materials, which harmonize better in the landscape. Gently flowing paths of gravel, shingle, cobbles, wood chip, or bark work well; wood or stone stepping stones weave across lawns; irregularly shaped decking patios and structures created from wood, rustic poles or natural stone are fitting in an informal garden style.

LAWNS AND MEADOWS

Lawns fit well into informal schemes but are high

BELOW RIGHT: *Informal water gardens at Docton Mill, Devon, have extensive plantings of moisture-loving species in natural settings.*

BELOW: *A mixed border for year-round interest, including shrubs, evergreens, herbaceous perennials, roses and bulbs.*

ABOVE: *Nothing is more beautiful than a sea of bluebells spreading beneath delicate boughs of newly opening leaves in springtime.*

RIGHT: *The Forest garden at Dartington Hall, Devon, with layers of trees, shrubs, fruit and vegetables in self-sustaining, organically-managed plant communities that require minimal maintenance and provide food for much of the year.*

maintenance with constant mowing, feeding, aerating and disposing of cuttings. Small areas of lawn near the house can blend into a surround of longer grasses and wild flowers, or merge into a wildflower meadow or prairie garden. Naturalizing plants and bulbs in longer grass means the area only requires mowing once or twice a year. Meadows look stunning filled with native plants in full flower and require limited maintenance once established.

SCULPTURE

Statues can be on the grand scale in classically formal gardens, but more fitting to small, informal gardens are objects created from natural stone and wood. These can be as simple as interestingly shaped, roughly hewn blocks of stone or slate, unpretentious stone sculptures or wood carvings, and found objects which follow the theme of the garden – whether it is woodland, meadow, or coastal.

WATER

The sight and sound of water adds to the relaxed atmosphere of informal gardens, as well as attracting wildlife. Pools, streams, waterfalls, and low rippling or bubbling fountains should have unpretentious shapes, and be constructed of natural materials, with no hard edges, so they blend into their surroundings. Varying

depths of water allow for different species of plants, and boggy areas provide further interesting habitats.

WOODLAND

Nothing is more beautiful than a sea of bluebells spreading beneath delicate boughs of newly opening, spring green leaves. The smallest patch of woodland brings a new environment into the garden, adding a touch of mystery and tranquillity. Layered planting provides many opportunities for unusual and interesting combinations, and plants are available to suit any conditions from damp to dry shade and semi-shade. Larger areas of woodland provide even more exciting opportunities. Gertrude Jekyll used plants sensitively to create many wonderful woodland gardens.

FOREST GARDENING

Over the years there have been increasing developments in Agroforestry and Permaculture, despite this type of cultivation having existed for thousands of years. Two great pioneers were Bill Mollison (Australia) and Robert Hart (England). Agroforestry advocates the importance of trees in the environment for shelter, fuel, conservation and groundwater control. Permaculture emphasizes the wide diversity of plants growing together in harmony in a natural landscape. Plants supply a mix of fruits, nuts,

TOP: *Despite their informality, the design of Stockton Bury Gardens, Herefordshire, still has a strong underlying structure, with curving beds and meandering grass paths that draw the eye along and around the garden.*

MIDDLE: *Borders containing a good mix of shrubs, roses, herbaceous perennials and grasses tumble across the edges of the gravel path at Kingston Maurward College, Dorset.*

BOTTOM: *Hot colours grouped together in formal disarray at Wollerton Old Hall, Shropshire.*

edible leaves, spices, medicinal and culinary herbs, honey, fuel and mulch.

Trees (including fruit and nut trees), shrubs, fruit bushes, climbers, perennial vegetables and herbs grow in layers in closely related plant associations. Taller trees provide the main canopy and other plants grow in zones below. This creates a self-sustaining, organically managed garden requiring minimal maintenance, providing food for much of the year. Systems of companion and compatible planting create a healthy balance, which keeps plant pests and diseases to a minimum. This type of gardening produces one of the most effective and productive forms of land use known. It creates self-sustaining environments that have added health benefits, as well as being naturally beautiful, harmonious and relaxing.

Forest garden layers consist of: a canopy of standard or half-standard fruit trees; fruit and nut trees grown on dwarf rooting stock together with bamboo; shrubs mixed with bushes of gooseberry, currant, and *Rosa rugosa*; herbaceous, perennial vegetables and herbs; ground cover of creeping plants including *Rubus* species; shade-tolerant winter root plants; vertical climbing plants including runner beans, climbing berries, vines, and nasturtium to grow through trees and fences. Most plants are perennial, meaning they regenerate each year, annuals self-seed, and flowers attract insects for pollination.

Once ecosystems are established a wide diversity of plants can be grown in a small area. The scheme will even adapt to containers, with added benefits for plants requiring different soil types. Massive plantings of trees benefit both the environment and climate, and become increasingly necessary, as more and more natural woodland is lost, to the detriment of our environment and the planet.

Creating the style

Despite informality, gardens still have a strong, underlying plan holding the design together. Paths of grass or natural materials meander through lawn and between borders drawing the eye along and around the garden, suggesting hidden surprises. Borders are free flowing and curving, filled with an abundance of plants that merge together and tumble out in drifts of colour and texture so they look natural rather than contrived.

Ornamental grasses have become extremely popular and mix well with herbaceous plants where the slightest breeze brings undulating movement to the border. Plants self-seed, spread between paving, and grow unrestrainedly over garden structures. Mixed borders of trees, shrubs, herbaceous plants, roses and bulbs grow together in harmony. These can be labour intensive, but highly rewarding, providing form and colour throughout the year. Formal areas close to the house including patios, lawns and flower beds, flow into informal areas towards boundaries. Informal gardens and rampant planting schemes benefit from occasional calmer, more formal areas as contrast. Lawns are curving rather than geometric shapes, shorter grass merging into wilder areas of grassland with naturalized bulbs and wild flowers.

The smallest wildflower meadow adds an un-restrained element to the garden. Sow seeds directly into closely cropped turf that has not had fertilizer or herbicide treatments for at least a year. More difficult wildflower perennials can be started in pots, and plug plants are also available. Alternatively, dig or rotovate the area and prepare as for lawn, but without fertilizer, as wild plants prefer impoverished soil. Seed mixtures are available for different situations and soil types. Many contain non-native species, which produce attractive and exuberant displays of colourful flowers, but look slightly out of place in the British countryside. Try to use native British seeds and grasses, grown by British growers, suitable to the area. Meadows require cutting once or twice a year, usually in late summer or early autumn, after plants have seeded and bulb leaves have died back. Remove cuttings, as they enrich the soil when left on the surface. Meadows take time to establish and require maintenance to begin with. Remove perennial weeds such as dock, thistle and ground elder during the first year or two. Although nature appears to do the job effortlessly, some plants are difficult to establish, but it is worth persevering and very rewarding to achieve the wonderful sight of a wildflower meadow in full bloom. The late Christopher Lloyd excelled with meadow gardens and those at Great Dixter, Sussex, are some of the best. One of the most inspired and inspiring gardens of the twentieth century, Great Dixter has stunning plants and plant combinations.

Mow simple paths through grassland to facilitate access to other areas. Paths also form attractive features and create vistas. Simple grasses are beautiful in their own right. Take a look at how nature plans her 'gardens'. Bulbs extend flowering periods of meadows from late winter to summer and autumn, and look very natural in grassland settings. Bulbs also grow well beneath deciduous trees and shrubs.

Create natural transitions between informal gardens and woodland by merging plants gently into wooded areas. Slightly rougher grass and woodland species take over from more traditional garden plants. Woodland

Even the smallest wildflower meadow adds an unrestrained element to the garden; bulbs and wildflowers are beautifully naturalized in grass at Kiftsgate Court, Gloucestershire.

A variety of colourful plants and shrubs border the path leading into the woodland, making a good transition between gardens and wilderness.

A mown path through the wildflower meadow at Morville Hall, Shropshire.

plants are available to suit all situations. Areas of deep woodland have moss, ground cover plants, ferns and naturalized bulbs that bloom before leaf canopies become too dense. Shrubs find one of their most natural habitats along the woodland edge and form a gentle boundary between garden and wood as shrubs mingle with trees. Perennials are also ideal in this situation and white, airy flowers look especially ethereal against dark trees.

Woodland gardens are at their best during spring, complemented by fresh, varied colours of newly opening leaves, and again in autumn with rich and vivid leaf colourings. Woodland gardens also offer varying tones and textures of bark and leaves, as well as patterns of light and shade. In the informal garden, paths move easily through the landscape indicating movement rather than dictating it. Woodland paths are suggested rather than being strictly defined, as they meander and curve between trees. Chipped bark makes a good covering for woodland paths leading to rustic benches beneath trees. Trees and shrubs provide nesting sites for birds, while mossy stumps and fallen, moss-covered branches provide habitats for many insects and small creatures.

Wilderness gardens, however natural and at one with

nature, require the intervention of the gardener. Despite being carefully contrived, informal gardens should give the impression they stay looking at their best with little or no attention from man. Plantings are looser and not rigidly contained with military precision as they are in formal gardens. It is more a question of carefully managing the garden rather than maintaining it.

Wildlife areas in the smallest garden help towards nature conservation as so many habitats are lost in the wild. It is better to concentrate on native species, which fit in better with the local environment, but the suggestion that insects will only feed on native plants is a fallacy, as they will utilize any food and nectar plants they can find. Encourage wildlife into gardens by creating habitats for birds, insects and small creatures such as frogs, toads, newts and hedgehogs. Nectar-rich plants attract insects and butterflies, berried shrubs provide food for birds, and small ponds provide food and habitats for water species.

Try to garden sustainably using organic methods rather than further damaging the environment with harmful pesticides and herbicides. Concentrate on plants that grow with the minimum of intervention, in self-sustaining groups. These are generally tough species that require less water and feeding to flourish. Natural plantings have great aesthetic appeal and are much advocated in today's environmentally friendly gardens.

In the seventeenth century, wilderness gardens were created as part of larger gardens, with paths and vistas running between shrubs and trees. The same effect is achieved today in smaller gardens by delineating an axis using the simple method of mowing a slightly meandering path through long grass to draw the eye along. Frame a view with a pair of trees or creeper-clad arch, and let a 'full stop' arrest the eye with a simple stone ornament, garden seat, or specimen tree. Take inspiration from nature: no-one does it better. See how beautiful patches of simple buttercups are when in flower. Fields filled with the reviled dandelion make stunning displays when golden acres stretch as far as the eye can see, closely followed by a snow of fluffy white seed-heads or dandelion 'clocks'. A mix of red campion and bluebells creates a striking combination. A weed is only a plant growing where we do not want it, and all wild plants provide some benefit as food or nectar plants.

Informal gardens attempt to emulate nature and once established maintenance is kept to a minimum; who will notice if a few flowers or branches are slightly out of alignment, or the odd weeds poke through? Many gardens also incorporate both formal and informal areas creating a good contrast. With ever-increasing awareness of ecological issues, sustainability and wildlife-friendly gardens, the emphasis is very firmly on encouraging a working partnership with nature, creating natural habitats and using native plants in natural settings in a very informal and relaxed manner. Informal and naturalistic gardens are very much at the forefront of today's styles.

Magnificent and sustainable wooden sculptures with innovative use of recycled materials created by Heather Jansch fit perfectly into an informal setting.

Informal style

Trees

Informal gardens benefit from a selection of different species adding vertical interest. Bear in mind future growth and height.

Acer campestre
Acer palmatum
Acer pseudoplatanus 'Brilliantissimum'
Alnus glutinosa
Betula ermanii
Castanea sativa
Cornus mas
Fagus sylvatica
Ficus carica
Ilex aquifolium
Juglans nigra
Malus sp.
Prunus sp.
Quercus robur
Salix alba
Salix babylonica
Salix caprea
Salix pentandra
Sorbus aria
Sorbus aucuparia

Hedges

Informal hedges provide a mix of species, shapes, colours and textures.

EVERGREEN

Berberis darwinii
Berberis x stenophylla
Choisya ternata
Cotoneaster franchetii
Escallonia sp.
Fargesia murielae
Ilex aquifolium
Lonicera 'Teton'
Olearia x haastii
Pyracantha sp.
Rosmarinus officinalis
Viburnum tinus

DECIDUOUS

Berberis thunbergii 'Atropurpurea'

Galanthus nivalis.

Chaenomeles x superba
Corylus avellana
Crataegus monogyna
Euonymus europaeus
Fuchsia 'Riccartonii'
Prunus cerasifera 'Nigra'
Prunus spinosa
Rosa rugosa 'Alba'
Rubus spectabilis 'Flore Pleno'
Sambucus nigra
Vibrunum opulus

Shrubs

Plant in informal groups, with herbaceous perennials, or in sun or dappled shade along woodland edges.

Berberis thunbergii
Brachyglottis 'Sunshine'
Ceanothus thyrsiflorus 'Skylark'
Cornus alba
Cytisus x praecox
Daphne x burkwoodii
Daphne mezereum
Deutzia x elegantissima
Exochorda x macrantha
Forsythia x intermedia 'Spectabilis'
Fothergilla gardenii

Fuchsia magellanica
Hamamelis x intermedia
Hydrangea macrophylla 'Preziosa'
Hydrangea paniculata 'Kyushu'
Hypericum 'Hidcote'
Kerria japonica
Lavandula angustifolia
Lavandula x intermedia
Lupinus arboreus
Mahonia japonica
Magnolia stellata
Osmanthus delavayi
Paeonia suffruticosa
Philadelphus var.
Santolina chamaecyparissus
Spiraea thunbergii
Syringa vulgaris
Vibrnum sp.
Weigela florida var.

Ground cover

Low-growing plants spread beneath trees and shrubs, smothering weeds as well as providing colour and texture.

Cotoneaster dammeri
Epimedium x versicolor
Erica carnea
Erica x darleyensis
Euphorbia amygdaloides var. robbiae
Geranium sp.
Hedera helix var.
Iberis sempervirens
Lamium maculatum 'White Nancy'
Stachys byzantina 'Silver carpet'
Tiarella cordifolia
Thymus 'Doone Valley'
Vinca major
Vinca minor

Climbers

Climbers clothe walls and screens and scramble through trees and garden structures.

Clematis sp.
Hedera helix 'Atropurpurea'
Hedera helix 'Buttercup'
Jasminum officinale
Lonicera caprifolium

Lonicera periclymenum
Passiflora caerulea
Vitis vinifera
Wisteria sinensis

Borders

Curving borders are filled with eclectic mixes of shrubs, roses, perennials and bulbs. Larger plants drift to the fore, and smaller plants tumble onto paths.

Achillea filipendulina var.
Achillea ptarmica
Anchusa azurea 'Loddon Royalist'
Anthemis punctata cupaniana
Aster nova-angliae
Aster novi- belgii
Astilbe x simplicifolia
Campanula sp.
Cephalaria gigantea
Cosmos atrosanguineus
Crambe cordifolia
Cynoglossum nervosum
Delphinium sp.
Dianthus sp.
Diascia rigescens
Dierama pulcherrimum
Doronicum sp
Gaura lindheimeri
Geranium sp.
Geum 'Borisii'
Gypsophilla 'Rosenschleier'
Helenium cvs
Helianthus x multiflorus
Helleborus orientalis
Hemerocallis lilio-asphodelus
Hosta sp.
Incarvillea delavayi
Iris sibirica
Kniphofia cvs.
Lamium maculatum 'Roseum'
Leucanthemum x superbum
Lupinus cvs.
Lychnis coronaria
Primula sp.
Prunella grandiflora
Pulmonaria sp.
Salvia sp.
Sisyrinchium striatum
Thalictrum aquilegiifolium
Thalictrum flavum glaucum
Viola cornuta

LEFT: Hydrangea macrophylla.

RIGHT: Clematis 'Vyvyan Pennell'.

Bulbs, corms, rhizomes and tubers

For borders or naturalizing.

Agapanthus
Anemone blanda
Camassia leichtlinii
Colchicum speciosum
Crocosmia x crocosmiiflora
Crocus sp
Cyclamen coum
Cyclamen hederifolium
Galanthus nivalis
Hyacinthoides non-scripta
Iris pallida
Iris 'Florentine'
Lilium martagon
Muscari armeniacum
Narcissus cvs.
Narcissus obvallaris
Narcissus pseudonarcissus
Ornithogalum umbellatum
Paeonia sp.
Scilla siberica
Tulipa sprengeri
Tulipa sylvestris

Roses

For climbing, as specimen shrubs, or for informal borders.

Rosa 'Albertine' rambler
Rosa 'Bobbie James' rambler
Rosa 'Charles Rennie Mackintosh'
Rosa 'Chianti'
Rosa 'Cornelia'
Rosa 'Felicité et Perpétue' rambler
Rosa 'Frühlingsgold'
Rosa 'Gertrude Jekyll'
Rosa Gloire de Dijon
Rosa 'John Clare'
Rosa 'Nevada'
Rosa 'Rambling Rector' rambler
Rosa rugosa 'Fru Dagmar Hastrup'
Rosa rugosa 'Wild Edric'
Rosa rugosa 'Snowdon'
Rosa 'The Dark Lady'
Rosa 'Wedding Day'
Rosa 'Winchester Cathedral'

Grasses and sedges

These add an ethereal and continuously moving element to the garden with a variety of shapes and colours, many of which look attractive throughout the winter months.

Arundo donax
Calamagrostis x acutiflora 'Karl Foerster'
Carex comans
Carex sp.
Chionochloa conspicua
Cortaderia selloana
Deschampsia cespitosa
Deschampsia flexuosa 'Tatra Gold'
Hakonechloa macra 'Aureola'
Miscanthus sp.
Pennisetum alopecuroides 'Hameln'
Pennisetum setaceum 'Burgundy Giant'

Phyllostachys aureosulcata 'Spectabilis'
Phyllostachys nigra
Pleioblastus pygmaeus var. distichus
Sasa veitchii
Stipa gigantea
Stipa tenuissima

Forest gardens

A wide variety of trees, shrubs, fruit, herbs and vegetables.

Actinidia deliciosa
Alchemilla mollis
Allium cepa
Allium fistulosum
Allium porrum
Allium sativum
Allium schoenoprasum
Allium tuberosum
Allium ursinum
Araucaria araucana
Armoracia rusticana
Arundinaria simonii
Asparagus officinalis
Berberis vulgaris
Beta vulgaris var. flavescens
Borago officinalis
Brassica cvs.
Calendula officinalis
Castanea sativa 'Marron de Lyon'
Chenopodium bonus-henricus
Chusquea culeou
Cichorium intybus
Corylus avellana
Crambe maritima
Crataegus azarolus
Cryptotaenia canadensis
Cydonia oblonga
Cynara scolymus
Cytisus var.
Elaeagnus angustifolia
Elaeagnus multiflora
Elaeagnus umbellata
Ficus carica
Fragaria x ananassa
Ginkgo biloba
Hibiscus sabdariffa
Hyssopus officinalis
Juglans regia
Juniperus communis
Levisticum officinale

Malus 'Bramley's Seedling'
Malus sp.
Medicago sativa
Mellisa officinalis
Mentha sp.
Mimusops elengi
Morus alba
Morus nigra
Morus rubra
Nepeta cataria
Origanum vulgare
Petroselinum crispum var. tuberosum
Phyllostachys bambusoides
Phyllostachys flexuosa
Phillostachys nigra
Philostachys mitis
Pinus cembra
Pinus pinea
Pinus sylvestris
Prunus 'Coe's Golden drop'
Prunus 'Czar'
Prunus sp.
Pyrus var.
Radicchio
Raphanus sativus 'Violet de Gournay'
Rhus typhina
Ribes alpestris
Ribes nigrum
Ribes triste
Ribes uva-crispa
Rosa canina
Rosa damascena
Rosa gallica
Rosa gallica 'Versicolor'
Rosa 'Provence Rose'
Rosa rugusa
Rosmarinus officinalis
Rubus sp.
Salvia officinalis
Sorbus aria
Sorbus aucuparia 'Edulis'
Sorbus latifolia
Spinacia oleracea
Symphytum officinale
Tagetes patula
Taraxacum officinale
Taxus baccata
Thymus sp.
Tragopogon porrifolius
Tropaeolum majus
Urtica urens
Vitis coignetiae
Vitis 'Strawberry Grape'

4 Cottage garden style

The style

We tend to romanticize cottage gardens, thinking of small, whitewashed or mellow stone dwellings nestling beneath thick layers of neat thatch, with swallows nesting beneath the eaves, roses around the door, and a garden overflowing with gloriously coloured flowers, perfume – and of course, sunshine. These enviable dreams do exist, but our ideas mainly come from artists like Helen Allingham, Myles Birkett Foster, Thomas McKay, Kate Greenaway and others of the Victorian and early Edwardian period who captured archetypal cottage gardens in their pictures. As usual, reality is not as rosy and romantic as it is painted to be.

Originally cottage gardens were strictly 'working' gardens, with production of food plants the most important aspect. Flowers were included for purely practical benefits such as medicinal and culinary herbs.

Nectar-rich flowers attracted pollinating insects, ensuring good crops, and were useful for bees busily buzzing to and from the hive in the corner. A few hens scratching around might make dust baths in the beds, but they devoured many harmful pests and also provided eggs and meat. No corner was wasted and everything was packed closely together in rampant profusion. Cottage gardens might look very casual but underlying beds were often formally and practically laid out, although this completely disappeared under the wealth of rampant growth. Necessary and practical paths, made from whatever materials were available, accessed the beds. Neighbours exchanged seeds and cuttings, and unusual plants might find their way into gardens from those employed at the local manor, or as gifts or cuttings, freely given or nipped off in passing.

These carefully tended and productive plots have existed for hundreds of years. They were an eclectic mix

OPPOSITE: *Hens in the cottage garden might make dust baths, but they also devour many garden pests and provide eggs and meat.*

RIGHT: *Grafton Cottage, Staffordshire, an idyllic country cottage buried amidst a profusion of old-fashioned flowers and plants.*

Cottage gardens had carefully tended and productive plots, with the emphasis on self-sufficiency.

of fruit, vegetables, herbs, shrubs, trees, annuals, perennials and ground-cover plants, jostling for space on small patches of land surrounding humble dwellings. The emphasis was always on self-sufficiency and gardens were crammed to capacity with useful plants.

As time passed, flowers became important for their intrinsic beauty rather than purely medicinal or culinary uses. Some gardeners confined vegetables to separate sections, while flower borders were filled with an ever-increasing variety of annuals and perennials, shrubs and roses. Cottage garden style became synonymous with homely, relaxed gardens overflowing with an abundance of colourful plants throughout summer.

Each autumn everything was cut down and ground remained fallow for winter frosts to break up soil and kill off pests. Beds were weeded, plants lifted, divided and replanted and a good dressing of manure or compost applied. The first hints of spring saw tiny, unfurling shoots emerging as warm sunshine and balmy rain encouraged plants back into growth, and the annual cycle began again.

Cottage gardens went through a phase of being charmingly attractive rather than practical but today's gardens once more mix flowers, fruit and vegetables in the traditional manner, creating a new style of modern-day cottage garden.

History

Archaeology reveals man derived food from plants gathered from the countryside as far back as 35,000BC. Eventually it was convenient to have useful plants closer to habitations, and after 15,000BC there is evidence of effective cultivation of plants that provided edible leaves and roots for food and medicinal herbs. Everything served a useful purpose. Around 8000BC, legumes and cereals were cultivated by Neolithic peoples in the Middle East. These reached Greece by 6000BC and continued to spread through Europe, arriving in Britain between 4000 and 2000BC.

Many plants had medicinal uses and these were gathered together in monastic herb and physic gardens, together with food plants. As knowledge increased, treatises on herbs and plants followed. Hippocrates (460–377BC), the 'Father of Modern Medicine', set strict guidelines on the preparation of medicinal herbs. He also wrote a treatise on medicinal plants including comments on coriander, marjoram, mint, saffron and thyme. Many of the 400 remedies he recommended are still in use today. Charlemagne (AD742–814) encouraged organized cultivation of herbs on a large scale, which supplemented smaller physic gardens. His *Capitularo de Villis*, or *Decree Concerning Towns*, detailed plants that should be grown throughout his empire. There were seventy-three herbs including caper spurge, clary, iris, houseleek, lily, mallow, poppy, rose, rosemary, rue, sage and tansy, together with sixteen fruit and nut trees.

Saxons developed some of the first cottage gardens in Britain around their dwellings, with rudely fenced, small plots growing limited numbers of medicinal herbs and food plants. As information and knowledge increased peasants grew greater numbers of herbs and vegetables, always desperately trying to keep starvation at bay.

Monks developed extensive medical knowledge and large areas around monasteries were cultivated to grow herbs and medicinal plants including narcotics such as hemlock, henbane, mandrake and opium poppy for the infirmary and for treating the sick who came to their doors. Food and salad crops ('potage plants') were grown for monastery kitchens, and also to feed passing travellers, lay people and the poor. Orchards supplied fruit, vines and wine, and small gardens were set aside for quiet contemplation and study. The monastic contribution to horticulture was incredibly important and included carefully kept records and plant illustrations in manuscripts. Monastic gardens in Britain eagerly sought new plants for their collections, carried north from medicinal gardens in Europe as monks travelled between various houses. Monasteries probably founded the first nursery gardens within their grounds. Records show a big demand for herbs, fruit and flowers from Westminster Abbey, London, and in 1275 accounts show the Abbey purchased peony roots at 2s a quart, and lily bulbs at 1s a quart.

Medieval gardens are well documented although more has been written about those attached to monasteries and large houses rather than to those

This reconstruction of an Elizabethan garden at Mary Newman's Cottage, Cornwall, contains an eclectic mix of flowers, herbs and fruit typical of the period.

Old cottage gardens filled beds with a mix of flowers and vegetables.

around humble peasant dwellings. Cottage plots were generally limited to small rectangles of land, divided by functional paths. Thorn hedges kept out livestock, a few hens scratched around, and there was often a bee skep, and maybe a pig.

In Elizabethan times most plants were still grown for utilitarian purposes, including medicinal and dye plants, strewing herbs, vegetables and fruit, often in raised beds bordered by low, woven willow hurdles or wood strips, but now flowers began to be grown purely for their decorative value.

New plants had arrived in Britain with the first settlers, and the process continued with succeeding invaders, including the Romans. All were eagerly sought, although these were wild forms rather than later, sophisticated hybrids. Plants from the Americas arrived in Britain during the seventeenth century and by the early nineteenth century there was extensive importation of plants from around the world. Although considered exotic and tender, many adapted well to the British climate.

Saffron Waldon in Essex was renamed after the saffron crocus, *crocus sativus*, which it grew on a vast, commercial scale during the sixteenth and seventeenth centuries, for its culinary, medicinal, disinfectant and colouring properties. Introduced into Europe through the Moorish Empire in Spain, the crocus travelled to Britain through Germany and the Low Countries.

Plant hunters such as Robert Fortune (1812–80), James Veitch (1815–69), Ernest H. Wilson (1876–1930), and numerous others set sail in search of new plants and seeds. Increasing numbers of new and unusual species fuelled the craze for ever more new and different plants for gardens. The return of explorers was eagerly awaited as collectors and gardeners clamoured for the latest discoveries. The aristocracy saw new ideas on their travels and brought these back for their country estates. In turn some of these ideas filtered down into cottage

gardens, including new plants, and soon unusual and striking 'novelty' flowers were growing amongst common species, topiary shapes and decorative trellises.

Early manuscripts and books dealt solely with medicinal plants but with the arrival of printing a spate of books on plants, and eventually gardens, swept through Europe. Master John Gardener's *Feat of Gardening* (*c*.1440) was one such, and John Gerard's *The Herball or Generall Historie of Plants* (1597) contained 1,360 pages listing wide selections of plants available at that time.

Florists' Societies prospered, specializing in collecting, developing and showing particular plants such as auricula primulas, carnations, tulips and ranunculus. These were known as 'florists' flowers'. 'Florists' Clubs' were established in London by 1679, to be superseded by horticultural societies. Ideas found their way from towns into villages and the countryside. Cottagers held their own competitions and shows, with emphasis always heavily on food production rather than flowers. New introductions of plants and seeds were grown alongside traditional favourites. *Curtis's Botanical Magazine* appeared in 1787, and the first lawnmower was developed in 1830. Charles Darwin's scientific expedition on the *Beagle* had far-reaching consequences in the field of evolution, as well as introducing new species. *On the Origin of Species by Means of Natural Selection* caused a sensation when published in 1859.

The late nineteenth century saw historical revivals of romantic cottage-inspired gardens in reaction to highly structured gardens of aristocratic estates with rigidly formal designs and massed planting schemes of greenhouse exotics and bedding plants. Increasingly decorative, 'modern' cottage gardens emerged as lifestyles changed and new plants and hybridized varieties became more easily accessible.

The Arts and Crafts Movement saw revived interest in informal and romantic planting styles and gardens.

Marjorie Fish was the great exponent of modern cottage gardens, using simple flowers to great effect in her garden at East Lambrook Manor, Somerset.

William Morris (1834–96) commissioned architect Philip Webb to design Red House, Kent, in 1859 – the first Arts and Crafts house and garden.

In the early twentieth century cottage garden style passed through a grandiose period, although the jumble of colourful plants which epitomized the style still predominated. Large houses developed cottage garden themes as individual elements in 'garden rooms'. The Industrial Revolution had seen people flocking into towns from the countryside and the tradition of the time-honoured cottage garden declined, but designers such as Jekyll and those who followed, including Lawrence Johnston, Christopher Lloyd, Beth Chatto, and Penelope Hobhouse, kept the genre alive.

Rosemary Verey (1919–2001) designed decorative cottage gardens with vegetables and potagers, including the one at her home, Barnsley House, Gloucestershire. She encouraged the use of vegetables as ornamental features rather than limiting them to a hidden corner of the garden. Marjorie Fish (1892–1969) was the great exponent of 'modern' cottage gardens. She loved simple garden flowers, including many old varieties. She used these to great effect at her home, East Lambrook Manor, Somerset, which she and her husband planted in a

riotous profusion of plants and colour. Her enthusiasm led to striking plant and colour combinations using numerous variegated, purple- and silver-leaved species. The many cultivars named after her garden show what an excellent eye she had for plants.

Claude Monet (1840–1926) created his 'cottage garden' at Giverny, France between 1883 and 1893. Famous for paintings of his garden and flowers including iris and waterlilies, he planted a rampant profusion of colourful plants spilling from a series of long, straight beds in a grand example of cottage garden tradition. The garden was abandoned after Monet's death but has been restored to its former beauty and attracts many thousands of visitors each year.

Recent years have seen a big revival in cottage garden style planting which began in the 1970s with an increasing awareness of organic and wildlife gardening. Gardeners are progressively more interested in producing edible crops as well as having beautiful gardens, and it is now highly fashionable to mix flowers, herbs, fruit and vegetables in attractive, cottage garden style combinations. Many old-fashioned plants, including heritage vegetables, have interesting and diverse mixes of flower colour, which fit well into today's

An attractive and productive potager with flowers, fruit and vegetables at RHS Rosemoor garden, Devon.

Mixed hedges of native species are tumbled with wild roses and honeysuckle in summer.

cottage gardens. Many are far more highly perfumed than modern hybrids, and these plants are increasingly sought-after by gardeners wishing to create truly traditional but modern cottage gardens.

Elements of cottage garden style

BOUNDARIES

Practical, rustic boundaries kept livestock out of gardens. Mixed hedges of native species including hawthorn, holly, hazel and yew, were jumbled with wild roses and honeysuckle in summer. Thorn hedging was popular, offering more protection. Holly and yew could be clipped into whimsical topiary shapes rather than sophisticated designs. Drystone walls depended upon supplies of local stone and plants soon colonized walls. Picket fences created attractive and easily constructed boundaries, and gardens were accessed by simple, rustic gates.

DESIGN

With space at a premium, every corner of the garden was productive, creating intimate domestic plots burgeoning with vegetables, fruit and flowers, with little open space. Plots were purely practical, depending on simple grace and charm, rather than being rigidly structured and carefully manicured. Design was functional with a basic formality to beds, which disappeared under a wealth of vegetation. Gardens were not contrived or pretentious and there was little extravagant hardscaping. There were simple paths and rustic features such as arches, arbours and pergolas, and often a well, stream or duck pond.

MATERIALS

Materials were natural and generally what could be scavenged from the local area. They were traditional, simple, unsophisticated and unpretentious, such as rustic wood, stone, brick, slate, tiles, wooden seats, benches and tables. Woven hazel and willow formed trellises and fencing panels. Hazel branches supported climbing beans, and twiggy hedge trimmings pea plants. Whatever was available was pressed into service.

ORCHARDS

Gertrude Jekyll took orchards away from mundane rows of trees into more natural groupings, underplanted with bulbs and flowers naturalized in grass. Orchards became beautiful and magical places, as well as productive, with a snow of spring blossom and ripening autumn fruit. Old-fashioned varieties are often more flavoursome, and are increasingly grown once more. Modern fruit trees are grown on dwarf rooting stocks making them simpler to maintain and pick, and more suited to smaller gardens.

Cottage gardens are unpretentious and every corner of the garden is productive.

A patterned brick path at Grafton Cottage, Staffordshire, leading between closely-planted borders.

Traditional cottage gardens contained a wealth of smaller, old-fashioned flowers, rather than sophisticated hybrids.

PATHS

Simple, functional paths led where they needed to go, dividing beds for easy access and maintenance. Surfaces consisted of trodden earth, crazy paving, pebbles, cobbles, tiles or bricks, often set into patterns. If not enough of one material was available, a mixture was used.

PLANTS

Plants are important in most gardens but none more so than in cottage gardens where plants were the main, and often the only, feature. These were old-fashioned varieties with smaller, single flowers, rather than large, sophisticated hybrids. Emphasis was on food plants, medicinal and strewing herbs, dye plants, perennials and annuals. Perfume was important. Fragrance started with winter-flowering shrubs; spring bulbs included snowdrops, crocus, narcissi and bluebell, followed by perennials such as lily-of-the-valley, sweet violet, stocks, dianthus, thyme, roses, lilac, lavender and honeysuckle. Annuals filled gaps and sweet peas, mignonette and

tobacco plants were amongst the favourites. Pollen-rich plants attracted insects for pollination and provided nectar for bees, ensuring a good supply of honey.

POTAGER

The earliest kitchen gardens were hedged to keep livestock from eating food plants. Later, walled kitchen gardens were in fashion, growing produce for large estates. Beds were functional for easy crop rotation and maintenance. South-facing walls encouraged early vegetables and stored heat, which benefited fruit trees trained along them. Many date back to Jacobean times when edible plants formed the major part of gardens. Seventeenth-century kitchen gardens were placed close to dwellings for convenience. Later, gardens were built some distance from the house where their utilitarian usage did not impinge on ornamental and pleasure gardens. Cottagers filled small plots with vegetables and herbs. As cheap labour declined, large, highly productive kitchen gardens fell into disuse. Increasing interest in growing fruit and vegetables has seen a renaissance in ornamental kitchen gardens and potagers, with food and flowers growing together in decorative harmony. Coloured vegetables mingle with flowers, herbs and fruit, and beds are edged with low hedges, wooden boards, or wattle panels.

WATER

Cottages often had their own well and it was useful to have water for irrigating plants. Possibly a stream flowed close by which was diverted into the garden, or it could be dammed to create a small pond. Monasteries and country estates had large pools for rearing and supplying fresh fish, but purely ornamental pools in cottage gardens were rare. At best the pond accommodated ducks and geese and was used for water for animals.

A bright and colourful selection of old-fashioned annuals makes a simple but striking display.

Creating the style

Cottage gardens developed from simple, functional, working plots growing produce. An abundance of flowers came later. They are personal and intimate spaces with a touch of nostalgia for times past. Rustic materials are ideal. Design is simple and basic, with unobtrusive hardscaping and unsophisticated paths dividing beds. Natural stone, gravel, pebbles and crazy paving all fit well. Brick paths are particularly attractive especially when set into zig–zag or herringbone patterns, and are soon colonized by soft mosses. Traditional cottage gardens used whatever was available, resulting in attractive combinations of bricks, pebbles, shingle and wood, colours and textures. Paths should be wide enough for easy access, and aromatic plants close to path edges release fragrance when brushed past.

Larger areas can be divided with hedges, fences, trellis or walls to create smaller, intimate areas. Woven willow or hazel hurdles make good dividers, or low hurdles act as edging for beds. Clipped box hedging is traditional as an edging for paths or beds. Holly and yew create simple arches, hedges and topiary. Traditional, native hedging includes hawthorn, blackthorn, hazel and willow. Scarlet *Tropaeolum speciosum*, rioting through darker evergreens such as yew, makes a striking contrast, and established plants seed freely.

Arches, pergolas and arbours, swathed with old cottage garden plants including roses, honeysuckle, jasmine or vines, make beautiful features. Climbing vegetables such as runner beans and gourds also trail arches and fences.

The casual beauty of cottage gardens relies on simple grace, but also has an underlying structure that disappears when plants spill from beds and across paths. Plants self-seed freely adding to the informality, and weeds are hardly noticed with such a preponderance of vegetation. Include lots of old-fashioned flowers such as campanula, daisy, delphinium, foxglove, geranium, hollyhock, honesty, honeysuckle, iris, lavender, lily-of-the-valley, lily, pinks, phlox, rosemary, sweet rocket, tansy, violets and wallflower. 'Heirloom' plants may not be completely authentic but have the appearance of traditional plants, and there are many modern plants that are well suited to contemporary cottage gardens.

A superb potager at Preen Manor, Shropshire, with a carefully trained apple arch, trimmed box and beds filled with herbs, flowers and vegetables.

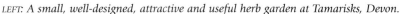

LEFT: *A small, well-designed, attractive and useful herb garden at Tamarisks, Devon.*

MIDDLE: *Eastgrove Cottage Garden, Worcestershire, is packed with a wide assortment of plants, shrubs and trees in various 'compartments' divided by hedges and banks of flowers.*

RIGHT: *In springtime, this mellow stone cottage is smothered with delicate racemes of perfumed, mauve wisteria.*

Include your own particular favourites, and also sections of flowers for cutting, drying, and making pot-pourri. Any gaps that appear as perennials fade can be filled with annuals such as campion, cornflower, cosmos, larkspur, love-in-a-mist, marigold, mignonette, morning glory, nasturtium, poppy, snap dragon, sunflower, sweet peas and ten-week stock.

The soft blue colouring of catmint, *Nepeta*, makes excellent edging, and can be clipped neatly back after flowering. Chamomile creates soft, aromatic lawns (traditional in medieval gardens), and emits a delightful fragrance when lightly crushed. It also spreads between paving, as do thymes, campanula and other creeping plants.

Roses are essential cottage garden flowers, including climbing, rambling and shrub roses. Use old-fashioned varieties such as the very fragrant Gallica, Damask, Provence and Centifolia roses. The Apothecary rose was a great favourite in cottage gardens with its unusual cerise and white striped petals. Foliage of old-fashioned tea roses perfumes the garden, even when not in bloom. Let roses scramble over walls and fences, trail arches and arbours and climb house walls. Older roses bloomed once a year but David Austin's new 'English Roses' give old-fashioned shape, colour and fragrance with repeat flowering and increased disease resistance. Climbing roses also make good hosts for other plants such as clematis and honeysuckle to scramble through.

Plant culinary herbs near the kitchen for easy accessibility. Herbal infusions are beneficial and simply made by dropping a leaf or two into hot water. Chamomile, catmint, lavender, lemon balm and mint are excellent, and make soothing and refreshing drinks.

Plant bulbs in borders, beneath trees and shrubs, and naturalize in grass and orchards. Ornamental grasses add an ethereal element to modern cottage gardens, bringing long-lasting, delicate colour and movement to the border.

Include as many scented plants as possible, and position where perfume can be enjoyed – near the house so the scent wafts through open doors and windows, or close to seating areas. Plants with night perfume, such as night scented stock and tobacco plants, are also a bonus.

Let climbers such as roses, Virginia creeper, clematis, honeysuckle and wisteria ramble over house walls and through fences. Nothing is more romantic than a secluded arbour wreathed in sweetly scented roses, jasmine and clematis. Train a productive vine, climbing beans or gourds over a trellis or pergola. Plants will grow in crevices in walls, which also provide an excellent habitat for many small creatures and insects. Strongly aromatic plants such as French marigold, act organically to deter pests and diseases. Southernwood and garlic deter rodents when planted near peas and beans. Beneficial hoverflies are attracted to yellow flowers such as the poached egg plant. Nasturtiums attract cabbage white butterflies, helping keep caterpillars away from food plants. Companion planting is a wonderful asset in cottage gardens, helping create a natural balance with organic pest and disease control. Mix vegetables with flowering plants along the border, or together in decorative and productive potagers. These dual-purpose gardens, growing food plants together with attractive flowers, make use of companion planting, where plants growing together benefit one another.

Arrange small beds into attractive designs, divided by paths, and edge with box. Shallow woven willow or hazel panels look attractive and also provide windbreaks to protect plants. Herbs such as parsley and chives make pleasing edgings for potagers, and larger herbs such as lavender, rosemary and santolina can be trimmed into hedges after flowering. Alpine strawberry plants make beautiful edging as well as providing delicate white blossoms and delicious fruit over a long period.

Gardens should flow between open space and rampant borders.

A simple water feature, well-suited to a cottage garden, with an old pump spouting water onto a stone trough of pebbles at Grafton Cottage, Staffordshire.

Spires of hollyhocks are one of the favourite and very traditional cottage garden plants.

Variously coloured salad leaves contrast with jewel coloured stems of Swiss chard, and deep purple orach, all intermingled with brightly coloured flowers. Train squash along hedges or up wigwams as well as climbing beans and peas, and perhaps a vine. Some plants require support but close planting means plants help to support one another. Successional sowing extends the time vegetables are at their best. Sow small amounts of seed once a fortnight or when each preceding crop is just established. Beds around 2 metres in width give ease of access.

Every plant in the cottage garden must count, and stand on its merits. Choose good 'all rounders'. Shrubs and trees should provide spring blossom, perfume, attractive foliage, fruit and autumn colour. Trees and shrubs that flower in winter and early spring are assets, providing perfume and pollen when little else is around. Also use plants that flower over a long period. Traditional varieties of fruit often have better flavour and help conserve older varieties. Raspberries enjoy a little shade but need controlling as they rampage across the garden. Grow brambles through hedges and trellis; espaliered and cordon fruit trees along walls. Low cordons make attractive edgings round potager beds, and fruit trees can be trained into a shady tunnel.

Cottage garden style is labour intensive. Perennial plants were cut back in autumn, leaving bare beds in winter. This was the traditional time to give the garden a really good clean up, divide plants, remove weeds, dig borders and apply manure or compost. Modern cottage gardens do not have to be barren canvases during winter.

Leaving seed-heads, stems and leaves on plants rather than cutting them back, creates stunning effects in frost, helps protect plant crowns; in addition, the birds benefit from the additional food, while insects have places to hibernate. Cut down in early spring before re-growth begins, weed and add manure or mulch.

Propagate your own plants from seeds, cuttings and division. Cottage gardeners shared plants and seeds with neighbours and friends and were thrifty, recycling containers for seeds, composting, mulching and harvesting rainwater. Egg boxes, yoghurt pots, empty toilet and kitchen roll tubes all make recycled containers for seeds. Halved plastic milk containers are good for growing plants and seeds, and also make fine plant labels when cut into strips. Nettles and comfrey make excellent fertilizers. Place chopped leaves into a bucket of water and it is ready when it smells extremely unpleasant!

Truly authentic cottage gardens use nothing but old-fashioned plants, but today's gardens include modern varieties and hybrids. Modern gardens also leave more open spaces between heavily planted sections. Gardens should flow between open space and rampant borders, creating an adventurous journey from one area to another. Separate garden 'rooms' can have different themes. Incorporate secret corners and views across the garden. Textures of plants and materials are important, and clipped hedges show off bounteous borders to perfection. Pots and containers should have a rustic appearance, spilling over with colourful plants. Terracotta pots, old sinks and stone troughs are

attractive. Let a few whimsically clipped, topiary trees add a sense of fun to the garden.

Create informal pools and water features. They attract wildlife and amphibians, which help control many garden pests. Ornamental fish soon decimate most water creatures, so wildlife ponds are preferable.

Gardeners are increasingly interested in keeping a few poultry for eggs and meat, even in urban areas. Free range is preferable – damage to plants, and dust baths in borders must be balanced against the harmful insects, and caterpillars hens devour in passing, and the steady supply of manure they deposit onto the soil. Whereas newly emerging shoots can suffer damage, once grown, plants remain relatively unscathed. When confining poultry to runs, try to move them round the garden so fresh grass is available. Hens require a small, weatherproof hut with nesting boxes for roosting and laying. Replace straw each week; used straw makes a valuable addition to compost heaps.

Bees provide honey, but a love of the hobby is

LEFT: *Grafton Cottage, Staffordshire, is a quintessentially English cottage garden overflowing with an abundance of colourful flowers, winding grass paths and arches smothered with old-fashioned roses.*

BELOW: *The robin, a gardener's favourite bird, is never far away, especially when digging is going on, when he cheerfully waits nearby for his quota of worms and grubs.*

paramount, as they require considerable maintenance. There is concern worldwide as bees are suffering from a number of fatal and apparently uncontrollable mites, viruses and diseases, which are decimating hives and completely destroying many colonies. It is vitally important that hives and equipment are kept scrupulously clean in an effort to limit the spread.

Cottage gardens can be bold, colourful and adventurous, or have subtle, restrained, simple colour palettes. Look out for good plant and colour combinations: these often happen quite accidentally, so don't be too concerned if purple verbena grows through bright orange marigolds. It can look stunning.

Accessories should have an unsophisticated feel: rustic tables, chairs and wooden benches, colourful cushions, umbrellas and awnings, terracotta pots, stone sundials and birds baths, simple, stone statues of children or animals.

Increasing awareness and interest in organic methods and cultivation of food and fruit crops, together with concerns for wildlife habitats, has seen a resurgence of cottage garden style over recent years. Cottage gardens will always be quintessentially 'English', a riotous profusion of plants and colour in casual and informal settings. Anyone with a passion for plants will enjoy this relaxed style, as favourites are simply packed into all available space and there is always an excuse to buy just one more plant. Cottage garden style works with both town and country gardens, in large or small spaces. It can be old fashioned or have a modern twist, but overall it creates friendly, informal, family gardens, which are colourful, productive and tranquil. The abundance of multi-coloured flowers, fruit and vegetables, evoke visions of warm, lazy summer days, the scent of new-mown grass, flower perfumes wafting on the breeze, the gentle drone of bees, butterflies collecting nectar, and the smell of freshly baked bread wafting from an open window.

Cottage style

Trees

Traditional native trees and hedges with some ornamentals and an occasional topiary tree or hedge.

Acer palmatum 'Dissectum'
Acer pseudoplatanus 'Brilliantissimum'
Amelanchier lamarckii
Cornus mas
Corylus avellana
Crataegus C. x media 'Paul's Scarlet'
Fagus sylvatica
Laburnum x watereri 'Vossii'
Magnolia x soulangiana
Prunus 'Shirotae'
Malus 'Sturmer Pippin'
Prunus subhirtella 'Autumnalis'
Robinia pseudoacacia 'Frisia'
Salix caprea
Sorbus aria
Sorbus aucuparia
Tilia platyphyllos

Hedges

Again, native species surround and divide cottage gardens, providing shelter and food for birds.

Crataegus monogyna
Fagus sylvatica
Fuchsia 'Riccartonii'
Ilex aquifolium
Ligustrum ovalifolium
Prunus spinosa
Sambucus nigra
Symphoricarpos x doorenbosii 'White Hedge'
Taxus baccata
Viburnum opulus
Viburnum tinus

Shrubs

Shrubs include attractive foliage, flowers, fragrance, autumn colour and fruits.

Buddleja davidii
Camellia japonica
Corylopsis sinensis
Cotoneaster frigidus 'Cornubia'
Deutzia x elegantissima 'Rosealind'
Exochorda x macrantha 'The Bride'
Forsythia x intermedia
Hamamelis mollis
Jasminum nudiflorum
Kolkwitzia amabilis
Lavandula angustifolia
Lavandula stoechas

Cynara cardunculus.

Lavatera olbia 'Rosea'
Mahonia x media 'Charity'
Paeonia delavayi ludlowii
Philadelphus coronarius cv
Potentilla fruticosa
Syringa vulgaris

Climbers

Climbing plants scramble over arches, arbours and trellises and twine into trees.

Clematis montana
Clematis vitalba
Clematis viticella 'Abundance'
Hydrangea anomala ssp petiolaris
Ipomoea 'Heavenly Blue' annual
Jasminum officinale
Lathyrus odoratus annual
Lonicera periclymenum
Lonicera tragophylla
Parthenocissus quinquefolia
Passiflora caerulea
Tropaeolum speciosum

Vitis vinifera 'Purpurea'
Wisteria sinensis

Borders

Old fashioned herbaceous plants stretch back generations and include wild species.

Acanthus spinosus
Achillea fillipendulina 'Gold Plate'
Aconitum napellus
Alcea rosea
Alchemilla mollis
Anemone x hybrida
Aster novi-belgii
Campanula latiloba
Campanula persicifolia
Campanula rotundifolia
Cardamine pratensis
Centaurea montana
Chrysanthemum cvs.
Delphinium 'Butterball'
Delphinium 'Conspicuous'
Delphinium 'Rosemary Brock'
Dianthus 'Annabelle'
Dianthus deltoides
Dianthus 'Excelsior'
Dianthus 'Joe Verdon'
Dianthus 'Mrs Sinkins'
Dicentra formosa
Dicentra spectabilis
Dictamnus albus 'Purpureus'
Filipendula ulmaria
Fragaria vesca
Geranium clarkei 'Kashmir White'
Geranium phaeum
Geranium pratense 'Mrs Kendall Clark'
Geranium sanguineum
Helianthemum cvs.
Kniphofia cvs.
Lamium maculatum 'Roseum'
Lychnis coronaria 'Atrosanguinea'
Lysimachia clethroides
Lysimachia punctata
Mertensia virginica
Nepeta x faassenii
Papaver orientale
Penstemon cvs.
Pentaglottis sempervirens
Phlox paniculata
Physalis alkekengi
Polemonium caeruleum

Polemonium reptans
Polygonatum x hybridum
Primula elatior
Primula sieboldii 'Alba'
Primula veris
Primula vulgaris
Pulmonaria saccharata
Saxifraga 'Aureopunctata'
Silene dioica
Solidago cvs.
Symphytum 'Hidcote Blue'
Viola cornuta
Viola odorata

Low, creeping plants

Ideal for colonising walls, paving and gravel.

Aubrieta cvs.
Campanula poscharskyana
Chamaemelum nobile 'Treneague'
Erigeron karvinskianus
Lysimachia nummularia
Saxifraga moschata
Sempervivum sp
Thymus sp.

Annuals and biennials

Annuals fill gaps and many self-seed prolifically.

Antirrhinum majus
Aquilegia vulgaris
Calendula officinalis
Centaurea cyanus
Chrysanthemum segetum
Clarkia elegans
Consolida cvs.
Cosmos bipinnatus
Dianthus barbatus
Digitalis purpurea
Eschscholzia californica
Helianthus annuus
Hesperis matronalis
Iberis umbellata
Ipomoea cvs.
Limnanthes douglasii
Lunaria annua
Matthiola incana
Matthiola longipetala
Meconopsis cambrica

Philadelphus 'Belle Etoile'.

Myosotis sylvatica
Nicotiana acuminata
Nigella damascena
Oenothera biennis
Papaver rhoeas
Papaver somniferum
Reseda odorata
Tagetes patula
Tropaeolum majus
Viola tricolor

Roses

Shrub roses, climbers, ramblers and the modern 'English' roses that combine old flower shapes, repeat flowering and strong perfume.

Rosa 'Albertine'
Rosa 'Brother Cadfael'
Rosa 'Eglantyne'

Rosa 'Fantin-Latour'
Rosa 'Félicité et Perpétue'
Rosa Gallica 'Complicata'
Rosa Gallica 'Officinalis'
Rosa 'Maiden's Blush'
Rosa gallica 'Versicolor'
Rosa 'New Dawn'
Rosa 'Old Pink Moss'
Rosa 'Paul's Himalayan Musk'
Rosa 'Rose of Picardy'
Rosa 'Roseraie de l'Hay'
Rosa 'Winchester Cathedral'
Rosa 'Zéphirine Drouhin' climber

Bulbs, corms, rhizomes and tubers

A range of different species from the first snowdrops, to peonies, iris and autumn crocus.

Allium moly
Anemone blanda
Anemone coronaria
Colchicum cvs
Convolaria majalis
Crocus sativus
Crocus sp.
Galanthus nivalis
Iris germanica
Iris sibirica
Hyacinthoides hispanica
Hyacinthoides non-scripta
Lilium cvs.
Narcissus pseudonarcissus
Narcissus sp.
Ornithogalum umbellatum
Paeonia lactiflora 'Bowl of Beauty'
Paeonia officinalis 'Rubra plena'

Herbs

Culinary and medicinal herbs are integral to cottage gardens, and many happily grow in gravel and dry gardens where heat releases aromatic oils.

Allium fistulosum
Allium sativum
Allium schoenoprasum
Anethum graveolens
Angelica archangelica
Anthriscus cerefolium
Artemisia dracunculus

Borago officinalis
Chamaemelum nobile
Foeniculum vulgare
Laurus nobilis
Lavandula
Levisticum officinale
Melissa officinalis
Mentha suaveolens 'Variegata'
Mentha spicata
Monarda didyma
Myrrhis odorata
Origanum vulgare
Petroselinum crispum
Rosmarinus officinalis
Salvia officinalis 'Purpurascens'
Thymus herba-barona
Thymus vulgaris

Fruit

Soft and hard fruits are important. Trees are standards, cordons, espaliers or fans, with bulbs and wild flowers naturalized in orchards.

Ficus carica
Fragaria x ananassa
Fragaria vesca
Malus 'Bramley's Seedling'
Malus 'Dartmouth'
Malus 'Discovery'
Malus 'George Cave'
Malus 'Egremont Russet'
Malus 'James Grieve'
Malus 'John Downie'
Malus 'Laxton's Fortune'
Malus 'Ribston Pippin'
Malus 'Sunset'
Malus 'Spartan'
Malus 'Winston'
Mespilus germanica
Prunus avium
Prunus 'Coe's Golden Drop'
Prunus 'Czar'
Prunus 'Denniston's Superb'
Prunus 'Marjorie's Seedling'
Prunus 'Victoria'
Prunus 'Shropshire Damson'
Pyrus 'Beurre Hardy'
Pyrus 'Doyenne du Comice'
Pyrus 'Glow Red William'
Prunus 'Golden Gage'
Ribes nigrum

English rose 'Lady Emma Hamilton'.

Ribes silvestre
Ribes uva-crispa
Rubus fruticosus
Rubus idaeus
Vaccinium cvs.

Vegetables

For cottage gardens and potagers.

Allium cepa
Allium fistulosum
Allium porrum
Allium sativum
Apium graveolens
Asparagus officinalis
Atriplex hortensis
Beta vulgaris var. flavescens
Brassica napus
Brassica oleracea var. botrytis
Brassica oleracea var. capitatus
Brassica oleracea var. gemmifera
Brassica oleracea var. gongylodes
Brassica oleracea var. italica
Brassica rapa

Chenopodium bonus-henricus
Cichorium intybus
Crambe maritime
Cucumis sativus
Cucurbita maxima
Cucurbita pepo
Cynara cardunculus
Cynara scolymus
Daucus carota
Eruca sativa
Helianthus tuberosus
Lactuca sativa
Lotus tetragonolobus
Lycopersicon esculentum
Pastinaca sativa
Phaseolus coccineus
Phaseolus lunatus
Phaseolus vulgaris
Pisum sativum
Raphanus sativus
Rheum rhabarbarum
Rumex acetosa
Solanum tuberosum
Spinacia oleracea
Vicia faba
Zea mays

5 Mediterranean and dry garden style

The style

Thoughts of the Mediterranean conjure up visions of azure seas fringed by bleached, sandy shores, pine trees and rugged mountains. Dazzling white houses and monasteries cling to precipitous hilltops. Shady courtyards, gardens and hillsides are a kaleidoscope of flowers including brilliantly coloured bougainvillea, scarlet poppies, golden crown daisies and purple lavender. The pungent, herby perfume of garrigue fills the air, beneath cloudless skies, endless sunshine and a balmy climate perfect for plants. However, what appears to be an idyllic climate has many drawbacks for growing gardens.

The Mediterranean climate is typified by long, hot, dry summers, scorching sunshine, and little or no rain. There is high light intensity, drought and little water. Winters are cool, with sometimes torrential rainfall, and there can be frost and even snow. Strong winds wreak havoc at various times of year. Mediterranean lands abound with all the raw materials required for garden making, but cultivating gardens has always been fraught with difficulties. Those that were created formed small, green oases in arid landscapes.

In a temperate climate, gardens are at their best from spring to autumn. In Mediterranean climate regions this is reversed, and the main flowering is between autumn and spring. First autumn rains see flowers and greenery spread across gardens and countryside. Tourists first visited Mediterranean countries for the mild winters and sunshine. Later, scorching summer sun beckoned

OPPOSITE: *Roses create a sweetly-perfumed bower above a shady Mediterranean terrace.*

RIGHT: *The arid Mediterranean landscape is a hostile environment for plants, with baking sunshine, little (if any) summer rainfall and high light intensity. Plants have to be tough to survive.*

ABOVE: *Carefully-clipped evergreen shrubs and trees keep this Mediterranean garden green and interesting throughout the year.*

RIGHT: *This Mediterranean garden has an abundance of native species, ideally suited to the harsh conditions. Plants spread and self-seed prolifically.*

bronzed bodies. With the main flowering occurring in spring, tourists found gardens and landscape to be muted tones of scorched earth and bleached rock, with a shimmer of soft silvers, greys and subdued greens throughout summer. But sun seekers wanted flowers in summer, and so gardens were created to be green and flower-full throughout summer months as well as winter.

Originally Mediterranean gardens blended into the landscape, at one with nature and the seasons. Many shrubs were evergreen; many had naturally domed shapes, attractive textures and interesting bark. Summer flowers might be limited but there was still plenty of interest in the baked landscape. Where water was available increasingly sophisticated irrigation techniques enabled development of shady courtyard gardens with palm trees, pools and flowers.

Visitors from northerly climes, used to abundant rainfall that watered lawns and burgeoning borders throughout the year, built new villas, recreating the lush, green, and colourful gardens of their homelands. 'English' gardens became fashionable, with rolling green lawns, vibrant borders, roses and shrubs that demanded water, water, and more water. With little rain, and boiling sunshine, millions upon millions of gallons of water were poured onto gardens to keep them alive and flourishing, year after year after year. Today, with ever increasing concern about climate change, it is apparent such massive use of water cannot continue. It is vitally important we consider the urgent necessity of conserving this precious commodity, wherever we live in the world. Heavily irrigated gardens must find new approaches as water costs escalate and supplies dwindle.

Despite many Mediterranean plants being naturally

dormant in summer, many do still grow and flower with little or no water. Thousands of native species are ideally suited to the harsh conditions, and also adapt well to dry gardens in cooler climates. Summer gardens may have more muted shades, but with careful planning and planting, it is perfectly possible to design colourful gardens with year-round interest, without constant irrigation.

Mediterranean gardens vary from country to country. Rural gardens tend to have small productive enclosures with vegetables, vines, fruit and flowers. Town gardens are more sophisticated with enclosed shady terraces, pools and fountains. Affluent estates have gardens on the grand scale. There is often pierced stone decoration; there are stone walls, coloured mosaic patterns, ceramic tiles, terraces, and gleaming white walls. Today's Mediterranean gardens cover a wide diversity of styles but all have been shaped by history as well as landscape and climate.

History

Mediterranean climate refers to countries bordering the Mediterranean sea, although other areas of the world also have Mediterranean type climates. These areas fall between 30° and 40° latitude in the southern hemisphere, and 30° to 45° latitude in the northern. They include southwestern Australia, the east coast of New Zealand's northern island, Cape Province of South Africa, central and southern California and central Chile. Other areas loosely included in this climate type are Uruguay, Northern Argentina and coastal Chile, also

A new garden on Mallorca using cacti and succulent species that require no additional water.

parts of Britain such as the Scilly Isles, coastal areas of Cornwall and south Devon, and northwest Scotland, aided by the Gulf Stream.

Mediterranean type climates see summer temperatures regularly rising to 30° or even 40°C. Winters average between 5° and 10°C. Some areas have frost and snow. Most rainfall occurs during autumn and spring, little in summer, and varies between light showers and torrential storms lasting for days. Summer drought is inevitable and often prolonged, but drought also occurs during winter. Summer air humidity is low, and can be low in winter. There is scorching sunshine and high light intensity. Many plants have adapted by becoming dormant throughout summer, re-emerging with the first winter rains and cooler temperatures.

Many Mediterranean climate zones are distinguished by coastal plains backed by protecting mountains, creating unique environments. In relatively small areas the climate can be hot and dry at sea level, while suffering frosts at higher altitudes, with temperatures several degrees lower than on the coast. Strong, drying winds are also typical.

At one time distribution and fruiting of the olive, *Olea europaea*, marked the boundaries of Mediterranean climates. Now the evergreen oak, *Quercus ilex*, is used by many as the marker. Mediterranean regions were historically covered by dense woodland, which has been destroyed over centuries. Without this protective canopy, land has eroded, leaving barren rock, or earth lacking in humus and organic matter. Torrential rains wash away

soil and plants. Impoverished soil, drought, high light intensity, limited rainfall, scorching sunshine, violent storms and strong winds mean plants have to be tough to survive. Mediterranean plants evolved sophisticated techniques for storing water and minimizing transpiration. Minute hairs or 'felting' on leaves such as *Salvia* and *Phlomis* reduce evaporation, and inhibit sunlight penetration, and hairs also trap any moisture in the atmosphere. Silver- and grey-leaved plants, such as eucalyptus and lavender, deflect sunlight and heat, keeping leaves cool, limiting water loss. Thick, glossy leaved plants, like camellia and ceanothus, create shade. Small, needle-like leaves similar to heather, broom and rosemary minimize surface area, and have minimal stomata which close in daytime, reducing water loss through transpiration. Succulents and cacti store water in leaves, stems and roots. Bulbs, corms, tubers and rhizomes such as cyclamen, narcissus, crocus, iris, lily and tulip evolved swollen storage units, enabling long periods of dormancy below ground. Most Mediterranean climate regions have always contended with drought and scarce supplies of water, and plants have survived, but as irrigation techniques advanced and maintaining crops became simpler, water was used heavily in gardens as well as fields.

The earliest written plant account is the Egyptian Ebers Papyrus of 1500BC. Records from 3000BC have been found in Mesopotamia (now Iraq). Hippocrates (460–377BC) recorded medicinal plants, and Dioscorides wrote a treatise on plants in the first century AD.

Greek texts were translated into Arabic and Latin, and extensive lists of plants circulated.

Wherever man travelled he took and collected plants and ideas. Mediterranean settlers brought plants to Britain in the Neolithic period. Transportation and movement of herbs and plants between countries was greatly facilitated by such means as the spice trade and incense route, which originated in ancient times. New spices, herbs and plants found their way into Mediterranean regions and from there up through Europe and into Britain.

Egyptian tomb paintings record beautiful gardens and plants. Sophisticated Islamic gardens spread to India and Spain, absorbing Persian ideas on the way. This resulted in the incredible Taj Mahal, India; Spain's great Alhambra Palace, Granada; the gardens of Seville's Royal Palace, the Reales Alcazares; and the oldest enclosed garden in Europe, the Patio de Los Naranjos at the Mosque in Cordoba, dating to AD976. Gardens were oases of peace and calm, shaded by trees, filled with beautiful plants, and the soothing sounds of water and bird song, creating sheltered havens from the relentless heat.

Roman influence can be seen in many areas, including plants and gardens in the various countries they occupied, and Italy created the great fifteenth- and sixteenth-century Renaissance gardens, which had such an impact across Europe. The French too built great gardens on a grand scale as well as having smaller 'working' gardens in rural communities. Until recently, Greece possessed little historical gardening tradition, preferring public parks and open spaces to enclosed, private gardens, but now many new and exciting gardens are being created in Greece.

The first treatise on a Mediterranean plant in Britain was by Henry Daniel, around 1380. He espoused the amazing virtues of rosemary, *Rosmarinus officinalis*, as well as growing 252 herbs in his garden, including a rare novelty, the wallflower. John Gerard's *The Herbal or Generall Historie of Plants* (1597) included Mediterranean introductions. John Parkinson published his *Paradisus Terrestris* in 1629. The first illustrated book on garden flowers, it included ten forms of cyclamen and over a hundred varieties of tulip. In the late eighteenth century, John Sibthorp, an Oxford botanist, wished to identify all plants Dioscorides had included in his treatise, and the magnificent *Flora Graeca* was published between 1806 and 1840.

By the sixteenth century British botanists and herbalists grew large numbers of Mediterranean plants. Species from the Americas arrived during the seventeenth century. Wealthy patrons funded plant-hunting expeditions across the world, supplying plants to private collectors and new nurseries. Joseph Pitton de Tournefort (1656–1708) introduced many Mediterranean plants into Britain. Francis Masson (1741–1805) and William Rollison (1765–1842) brought plants from South Africa and the Mediterranean. Sir Joseph Banks (1743–1820) and Douglas David (1799–1843) scoured North America. William Lobb (1809–64) introduced plants from Chile and California. 'Tender' plants were grown in conservatories until it was found many survived happily outdoors.

As people travelled further so did horticultural skills, ideas and plants. American species grew in Mediterranean gardens. Those from the Mediterranean adapted to Californian and Australian climes. South African plants travelled around the world, and many of these plants came to Britain.

With increasing knowledge, plants were collected in botanical gardens. Pisa, Italy, came first in 1543; the Oxford Physic Garden in 1621. The Society of Apothecaries founded Chelsea Physic Garden in 1673, where fruiting olive and grapefruit trees have grown outside for years. Hanbury Botanical Gardens, Menton, were created in 1867 by Sir Thomas Hanbury. California's Huntington Gardens began in 1903, and Kirstenbosch, Cape Town, in 1913.

Gardens in Mediterranean countries have been adversely affected by the introduction of 'English' style gardens. In the mid 1700s, Charles Louis Montesquieu from France visited England and took detailed descriptions of the gardens he saw back with him to France. Later, Marquis de Giradin created one of the first typically 'English' gardens at Ermonville. Those taking the Grand Tour appreciated the benefits of the Mediterranean climate and scenery but wanted 'English' style gardens. In 1824, Lord Henry Brougham built an 'English' garden on the Côte d'Azure, near Cannes, beginning a fashion that quickly escalated but could not possibly be maintained without massive irrigation. New villas brought more 'English' gardens, with verdant lawns and lushly stocked borders, all requiring vast amounts of irrigation when water is scarce and at a premium. The fashion continues today despite Mediterranean regions having vast numbers of beautiful, native plants ideally suited to prevailing conditions. Conversely, people living in temperate climates have used Mediterranean plants and principles to create Mediterranean style gardens concentrating on plants that require little water or attention once established. At the turn of the century, E.K. Balls introduced numerous plants from Greece into Britain, and in 1909, Sir Frederick Stern included many of these in his coastal garden on an exposed, chalk hillside at Highdown, Sussex, where they grew abundantly.

Lawrence Johnston began designing his magnificent garden of Serre de la Madone, Menton in 1924. Other gardens in the same area include Villa Val Rameh, Les

ABOVE: Santolina chamaecyparissus *clipped into a dome, reminiscent of many Mediterranean species that often have naturally-rounded shapes.*

RIGHT: *The dry garden at RHS Hyde Hall, Essex, was established in 2001 using over 4,000 plants representing around 1,000 drought-tolerant species and cultivars, which have received no additional water since they were first established, apart from the little provided by nature in one of England's driest counties.*

Cedres, and the Fondation Ephrussi de Rothschild. On Ischia Sir William and Lady Walton created La Mortella in 1946, with the help of Russell Page. More recently, in Greece, important new gardens have been and continue to be developed, including Sparoza, headquarters of the Mediterranean Garden Society, near Athens.

The Royal Horticultural Society's gardens in Britain include many drought-tolerant species from Mediterranean climate regions. RHS Hyde Hall, Essex, has a flourishing dry garden that is never watered. Cambridge Botanical Garden has a dry garden, and Beth Chatto's dry and gravel gardens in Essex are renowned worldwide.

Californians and Australians have created wonderful gardens in arid, Mediterranean type climates. California has unlimited water, but as supplies become increasingly expensive and conservation issues move to the fore, such wasteful use of water cannot continue and California must rethink its extravagant water policies. Australia has suffered extended drought, particularly over recent years, and water supplies are worryingly and severely restricted in many areas.

All countries with a Mediterranean type climate have a wealth of beautiful native plants, which, with careful planning and imagination, more than adequately provide year-round colour and interest for arid gardens. These gardens may not be permanently 'green' but as the need to conserve water becomes a top priority worldwide, more and more gardeners are discovering it is possible to create beautiful gardens using drought-tolerant plants, with little or no water. A new style of Mediterranean and dry garden is emerging.

In temperate countries too we are finding increasing numbers of Mediterranean plants available that offer many interesting and exciting alternatives for creating drought-tolerant gardens bearing in mind future predictions of increasing temperatures due to climate change. Many countries, including Britain, have experienced long periods of drought and inadequate rainfall. Reservoir and river levels have fallen dangerously low. In Britain, drought years are interspersed with years where torrential storms create damaging flooding. However, water is a dwindling commodity worldwide and becomes increasingly expensive.

Mediterranean countries are predicted to experience hotter temperatures, more frequent and severe droughts, and increasingly desert-like conditions. Britain is warned to expect drier, hotter summers and milder, wetter winters. Higher rainfall results in flash flooding, and drainage becomes a major issue.

All these factors must be taken into consideration as they affect how our gardens will evolve. With water supplies threatened and water becoming increasingly expensive, gardens that require little or no irrigation will become a necessity rather than a fashion.

Elements of Mediterranean style

CLIPPED GREENERY

Many Mediterranean plants have naturally compact, domed shapes and evergreen leaves. Many shrubs adapt well to clipping into a similar style. Small-leaved plants are ideal for simple topiary. Clipped shapes provide structure, colour, and a subtle harmony to gardens.

COASTAL GARDENS

Coastal gardens bring their own challenges. Sandy, nutrient-deficient soils quickly dry out. Harsh, salt-laden winds and spray, together with strong ultra violet light, wreak havoc with plants. Benefits include little or no frost and milder temperatures, ideal for tender species unable to survive further inland. It is always better to work within the natural boundaries rather than battling against them.

Hedges, woven screens, and fences provide windbreaks and create sheltered areas for seating. Screens of toughened glass offer protection but leave views unimpaired. Sheltered terraces offer wonderful coastal views. Compost and mulches are essential. Many plants have adapted to coastal conditions and establishing microclimates creates further favourable conditions. Tall plants suffer wind damage, but drought-tolerant species, including grasses, sedums and succulents, are ideally suited to coastal conditions. Silver, grey and blue leaves, evergreens, and plants with leathery leaves withstand salt spray. Grow plants in rock crevices and stone walls. Bulbs, spiky leaved plants, and annuals also look natural in coastal situations. Simple and effective gardens are created with drifts of grasses growing in shingle and sand. Link the garden to its surrounding habitat. Use natural materials such as wooden decking and board walks which fit the theme and also provide access across unstable materials such as sand and shingle.

Materials must withstand bleaching by wind and sun, as well as salt corrosion. Accessories should be informal and can include wooden carvings, interestingly shaped driftwood, bleached wood and reclaimed timber, rope, chain, shells and other found objects from the beach.

Driftwood can be fashioned into handrails, furniture and sculptures. Use wooden tables, chairs and benches.

COMPOST

Compost adds humus and valuable nutrients to soil that is often dry and free draining. Compostable materials include: kitchen and garden waste; used potting compost; wood ash; dead leaves; straw; paper tissue; shredded paper and vacuum cleaner contents. Do not compost meat, bread, dairy, perennial weeds or diseased plants. The composting process involves micro-organisms, air and moisture reacting with materials until they are broken down to a friable loam. In hot countries compost heaps may require additional moisture to aid the process.

FIRE

Fire can be a dangerous hazard in hot, arid climates, and is increasingly frequent in temperate climates during periods of drought. Fire is often a necessary part of a plant's lifecycle in promoting re-growth of seeds. It has only become such a major threat since urbanization colonized land in its path. A number of fire-retardant plants help alleviate some problems; these include *Helichrysum petiolatum*; *Atriplex halimus*; *Santolina viridis*; *Cistus ladanifer*; *Crassula argentea* and *Pelargonium graveolens*.

BELOW LEFT: Tamarisks, Devon, is a beautiful garden at the edge of the sea on a windswept coastline, but careful choice of plants and low windbreaks mean it is full of colour throughout summer, despite the adverse weather conditions.

BELOW: The courtyard garden at Tamarisks, Devon, hangs over the sea but the low wall creates a sheltered area for numerous pots of colourful plants.

ABOVE: *Decorative stone paving is common in Mediterranean countries and gardens where inset pebbles create extremely complex, as well as simple designs.*

RIGHT: *An effective and decorative ground covering using two colours of pebbles as a stone mulch.*

GRAVEL GARDENS

Gravel is an excellent medium for drought-tolerant plants that require good drainage. Inexpensive and flexible, gravel and shingle come in various grades and shades, suitable for formal or informal schemes. Stones change colour from wet to dry, adding further interest. Small aggregates are also suitable for paths or infilling between slabs. Other aggregates include small pebbles and marble or glass chippings. Mix smaller grades with larger pebbles for contrast. Loose materials require edging to stop them spreading into surrounding areas.

HARDSCAPING

Natural materials abound, with rock walls, stone slabs, sand, gravel, pebbles, and plain, coloured or glazed tiles. Earth tones and muted colours set drought-tolerant plants off to perfection. Terraces characterize Mediterranean countries and gardens, enabling cultivation of sloping sites. They protect against soil erosion, help retain moisture, establish microclimates, and create strong architectural features with practical and attractive design solutions. Formal or informal paths allow access and delineate areas. Surfaces can include compacted sand or earth, slabs, shingle or gravel – all well suited to 'dry' landscapes. Edge paths with low, clipped hedges or fragrant herbs.

LAWNS

Unless heavily irrigated, lawns dry and burn in hot sun and should preferably be eliminated. Drought-tolerant lawn grasses and lawn substitute plants are available, but it is better to use hardscaping techniques such as paving and gravel.

MATRIX GARDENS

Set into dry earth or gravel, matrix gardens establish attractive, colourful, and easily maintained areas where shrubs, perennials, grasses and bulbs look after themselves and seed around at will.

MULCH

Organic and non-organic mulches, such as chipped bark, shingle, gravel, pebbles, shredded cocoa and almond shells, help conserve moisture in soil. Apply a thick layer to moist earth and limit disturbance, keeping weeds to a minimum. Mulches can also be used to cover polythene sheeting or weed-suppressant membrane.

PARTERRES

Simple or complex designs of low, clipped box, germander, lavender, rosemary, Santolina or herbs, filled with drought-tolerant plants or gravel, make delightful features.

LEFT: *Shaded terraces are essential in hot climates, offering protection and respite from the heat.*

CENTRE: *The pergola with its hidden fountains in the famed Arab Gardens of Alfabia, Mallorca, which could be activated to spray water at unwary visitors.*

RIGHT: *Beth Chatto's renowned dry garden in Essex was established on a compacted old car park. Now a wealth of drought tolerant species create variety, colour and year round interest, receiving no additional water apart from sparse rainfall in one of England's driest counties.*

PLANTS

Drought-tolerant species are tough and require minimal maintenance. Many have good texture and shape. Coloured evergreens supply year-round interest. Grey- and silver-leaved plants abound. Helichrisum, Cistus, Lavandula species and other shrubs, trimmed into low domes after flowering, create interesting visual impact. Shrubs, trees and plant-clothed structures provide shade and restful retreats from summer heat. Drought-tolerant plants vary from tiny ground-hugging species to lofty palms and pines, and many are highly aromatic.

PRAIRIE GARDENS

Many perennials originated in North America and adapt beautifully to prairie style planting, forming large drifts mixed with ornamental grasses. Plants self-seed, require no additional water, and suit full sun and poor soils.

SHADE

Shade is essential in sun-scorched climates, whether from groups of trees, hedges, or plant-covered structures. Shade helps reduce plant transpiration and water evaporation from soil, and benefits plants by providing cooling shadows and additional moisture. Dappled shade is preferable to deep shade.

STONE

The earth tones of natural stone contrast well with evergreens and drought-tolerant plants. Stone balustrades, arches, steps and gateposts, or elaborately carved stone statues and fountains often dominate Mediterranean gardens.

WATER

In hot, dry climates, water provides life-giving freshness and soothing sounds. Pools and canals mirror blue sky; water trickles into stone basins and rills; fountains jet water into the air adding moisture to the atmosphere; low jets arch across pools and canals, and trap the unwary as they spray out unexpectedly along leafy paths.

WATER CONSERVATION

Water conservation is a serious and ongoing issue as costs escalate and supplies dwindle. Irrigation must be severely restricted or cease completely in dry gardens, which should be planted accordingly. Harvest rainwater into suitable containers and re-use household grey water.

Waterwise rules

1. Use drought-tolerant plants, minimizing water consumption and simplifying maintenance.

2. Reorganize plants so water is not wasted on plants that do not need it. Position plants needing no water furthest away, and those requiring water close to the house.

3. Replace labour-intensive annuals and bedding plants with drought-tolerant perennials that survive for years, saving money, time, effort and water.

4. When purchasing new plants choose drought-tolerant species.

5. Plant in autumn so plants establish with winter rain.

6. Use organic methods with emphasis on composting and mulching, conserving moisture.

7. If water is required, limit it to early morning or late evening. Never water in full sun, when it quickly evaporates. Eliminate water run-off.

8. Overwatering encourages shallow rooting making plants weak and susceptible to wind damage.

9. Harvest rainwater into storage containers and recycle household grey water.

10. Use water thoughtfully and efficiently. Make sure every drop counts and none is wasted.

Creating the style

Since the 1970s, interest in Mediterranean style and dry gardens and plants has escalated in cooler climates. Concerns over climate change and water conservation have re-awakened the desire to create ecologically friendly, sustainable gardens using drought-tolerant plants and a waterwise approach, working in harmony with the natural cycle. Before the advent of heavily watered 'English' gardens into Mediterranean countries it was accepted that summer was the dormant period. Mediterranean gardeners now realize they must revert back to traditional principles and favour plants and gardens that require little or no water once established. This requires a new approach, and use of plants and gardening techniques must be rethought and redesigned to take water conservation into account.

Hundreds of Mediterranean plants provide colour and interest throughout the year. Imaginative use of plants and design creates colourful gardens, or serene harmonies of muted tones. Dry gardens are generally informal but can be formal, and easily adapt to any sized area, courtyards, patios, roof terraces or balconies. They should fit harmoniously into their surroundings. Natural materials and drought-tolerant plants provide architectural highlights and year-round interest. In temperate climates, winter is emphasized by bare branches. Plant evergreens rather than deciduous trees, providing colour throughout winter. Evergreens give continuity and harmony and come in varying tones of

Evergreen coniferous trees come in a variety of shapes and colours adding the year-round green element to British gardens which detracts from bare winter branches.

green, grey, blue and silver, while golden tones add a touch of sunshine even on the dreariest days.

Many plants are clipped into simple mounds or topiary. Trim lavender into domed shapes or straight rows after flowering, bringing another dimension to the garden. Strap-like leaves of phormium and cordyline, or spiky leaved yucca, create sharp contrast to rounded forms. Textured and coloured barks add interest. Trees, arbours and pergolas provide essential shade, and a shady corner creates the perfect setting for alfresco dining. The tall Italian cypress, *Cupressus sempervirens* 'Stricta', brings instant Mediterranean atmosphere to any garden, adding good vertical highlights. Clipped hedges of parterres and knot gardens create strong architectural lines and provide year round interest. Infill with sand, gravel, drought-tolerant plants, herbs, or contrastingly coloured plants clipped at a level with hedging, forming a solid plane.

Terraces are traditional Mediterranean features and ideal solutions for sloping sites, linked by paths and steps. They accommodate plants or are paved. Use natural materials for steps, walls, patios and paths. Eliminate lawn and replace with natural materials such as stone slabs, decorative tiles, gravel, or wood. Choose materials that harmonize with their surroundings.

TOP: The recently established dry gravel garden at North Boraston Farm, Devon, with drought-tolerant species.

MIDDLE: Eliminate lawn if possible. This garden at The Wickets, Staffordshire has arrangements of stone slabs and grasses in the gravel garden.

BOTTOM: Agave americana *in the Beth Chatto dry garden, Essex. This plant has proved surprisingly hardy, even in colder areas of Britain.*

If you must have green, try drought-tolerant grasses or lawn-substitute plants such as chamomile and thyme. An increasingly popular alternative is artificial turf which stays pleasingly green throughout the year, whatever the weather – and doesn't require mowing. Purists may blanch at the thought but it provides one solution many Californian gardens have used to advantage, even creating patchwork effects with varying colours.

Drought-tolerant plants have to be tough to deal with harsh Mediterranean conditions. Tougher plants withstand pests and disease better. They adapt well to temperate gardens, but require free-draining soil that does not become waterlogged. Adding sand and gravel improves drainage, and plants grow well in chalk, gravel or sandy soils. Compost aids water retention in light soils, helps drainage on heavier soils, and adds valuable nutrients. Mulches conserve moisture. Group plants depending on their water requirements: those requiring no water should be furthest away, those requiring water close to the house. Maintenance is simplified, and water not wasted on plants that do not require it.

In Mediterranean climates one cannot escape the fact the main flowering period will always be during cooler months of the year, although many drought-tolerant plants flower in summer. Mediterranean gardeners expect to lose some plants during scorching heat. In temperate climates we lose plants to cold winters. Many Mediterranean plants withstand some degrees of frost. *Agave americana* is surprisingly hardy in Britain. In milder areas aeoniums overwinter, or they can be sunk into borders in pots and brought indoors during winter.

All plants require water until established, but planting during autumn means plants benefit from winter rains. Some plants require additional water the following summer but by their second year will be well established and require no other water than nature provides. Plants imported from temperate areas generally flower earlier in Mediterranean gardens, and deciduous trees may remain evergreen. Plants that require full sun in cooler climates may require dappled shade in Mediterranean gardens. Bulbs, corms, rhizomes and tubers are essential for providing brilliant displays as they burst from winter dormancy. They naturalize beautifully as well as fitting into formal schemes or containers.

LEFT: *Beautiful drought-tolerant plants in the dry border at RHS Garden Rosemoor, Devon.*

RIGHT: *No Mediterranean garden would be complete without deliciously fragrant lavender, and when flowering is finished plants can be clipped back to form attractive, low, evergreen hedges.*

Colour is best provided in containers and pots – especially terracotta, which fits well with Mediterranean style. Fill with bright flowers, and keep close to the house for ease of maintenance, or move to strategic points as necessary. Use household grey water or rainwater. Drought-tolerant plants adapt well to containers. Huge terracotta pots of citrus trees make striking features in both Mediterranean and temperate gardens, although require winter protection in cold areas. Concentrate summer colour in the most used areas of the garden such as patio or swimming pool. Gaudy blue pools benefit from differently coloured tiles such as black, dark blue or grey creating shimmering sheets of restful silver. Swimming pools may be a Mediterranean 'must have', but they should be kept small to limit water use. Additional colour can be introduced with paintwork, furniture, bright umbrellas, fabrics and cushions.

Mediterranean and dry gardens provide beautiful, easily maintained, conservation-friendly and water-efficient gardens, but they must integrate into their surroundings and not look out of place. It is also important to capture the true spirit of a culture and style that has evolved through necessity over centuries. Incorporate elements of French, Italian, Spanish or Greek styles, to add authenticity.

Designing Mediterranean and dry gardens, in hot or cool climates, using simple hardscaping and drought-tolerant plants, creates beautiful, easily maintained gardens that require little or no water. They benefit both the gardener and the planet.

Mediterranean style

Trees

Trees add height and shade in hot, dry gardens in a variety of shapes, sizes and colours, evergreen or deciduous.

Acacia dealbata
Acacia longifolia
Arbutus unedo
Catalpa bignonioides
Cercis siliquastrum
Citrus limon
Citrus sinensis

Cornus kousa
Cupressocyparis leylandii
Cupressus macrocarpa
Cupressus sempervirens 'Stricta'
Erica arborea
Eucalyptus dalrympleana
Eucalyptus pauciflora ssp. niphophila
Eucryphia x nymansensis
Juniperus communis
Juniperus communis 'Compressa'
Juniperus communis 'Sentinel'
Magnolia x soulangiana
Pinus contorta
Pinus mugo
Pinus nigra

Pinus pinaster
Prunus armeniaca
Romneya coulteri
Tamarisk ramosissima
Thuja plicata

Hedging and shelter

Good hedging plants show off Mediterranean plants and also create windbreaks and shelter belts, both evergreen and deciduous.

Elaeagnus x ebbingei
Escallonia x langleyensis
Fuchsia magellanica
Griselinia littoralis
Hippophaë rhamnoides
Olearia macrodonta
Populus nigra 'Italica'
Prunus laurocerasus
Rosa rugosa
Tamarix parviflora

Aeonium arboreum 'Schwarzkopf'.

Shrubs

A wide range of evergreen, deciduous and flowering shrubs, add height and interest throughout the year.

Abutilon megapotamicum
Abutilon vitifolium
Brachyglottis 'Sunshine' *(Senecio greyi)*
Brugmansia x insignis
Buddleja davidii
Buxus sempervirens
Buxus microphylla 'Faulkner'
Carpenteria californica
Ceanothus 'Burkwoodii'
Ceanothus impressus
Cistus ladanifer
Cistus laurifolius
Cistus x purpureus
Clianthus puniceus
Cordyline australis
Cytisus battandieri
Cytisus x praecox
Forsythia suspensa
Fremontodendron 'Californian Glory'
Garrya elliptica
Genista aetnensis
Hebe albicans
Hebe ochracea 'James Sterling'

Hebe pinguifolia 'Pagei'
Hebe 'La Séduisante'
Helianthemum cvs.
Hibiscus syriacus
Hoheria lyallii
Hypericum 'Hidcote'
Ilex crenata 'Convexa'
Jasminum x stephanense
Lavandula angustifolia
Lavandula stoechas
Lavatera arborea
Leptospermum scoparium
Melianthus major
Myrtus communis
Phormium colensoi 'Tricolor'
Photinia x fraseri 'Red Robin'
Piptanthus laburnifolius
Pittosporum tenuifolium
Pittosporum tenuifolium 'Gold Star'
Pittosporum tenuifolium 'Tom Thumb'
Punica granatum
Ribes speciosum
Rosmarinus officinalis
Salvia officinalis 'Purpurascens'
Santolina chamaecyparissus

Solanum crispum 'Glasnevin'
Solanum jasminoides 'Album'
Spartium junceum
Teucrium fruticans
Viburnum farreri
Yucca filamentosa
Yucca gloriosa

Palms

Many palms require sheltered positions and some winter protection, particularly in colder areas, but they make attractive trees or container plants, giving the real 'Mediterranean' feel.

Chamaerops humilis
Chamaerops humilis var argentea
Chamaerops humilis 'Vulcano'
Phoenix canariensis
Trachycarpus fortunei

Climbers

Climbers scramble over arches and pergolas to create interest and shaded areas beneath of benefit to other plants.

Actinidia kolomikta
Akebia quinata
Aristolochia durior
Campsis grandiflora
Campsis radicans
Clematis armandii
Clematis jackmanii
Clematis montana
Cobaea scandens
Cururbita pepo
Humulus lupulus
Ipomoea tricolor
Jasminum officinale
Lathyrus latifolius
Lathyrus odoratus
Lonicera x brownii
Lonicera periclymenum
Lonicera sempervirens
Passiflora caerulea
Schisandra rubrifolia
Trachelospermum asiaticum
Trachelospermum jasminoides
Tropaeolum peregrinum
Tropaeolum specisoum

Vitis coignetiae
Vitis vinifera 'Purpurea'
Wisteria floribunda
Wisteria sinensis

Climbing roses

Roses scramble over arbours and pergolas or through trees.

Rosa 'Albéric Barbier'
Rosa banksiae
Rosa 'Cécil Brunner'
Rosa 'Danse du Feu'
Rosa 'Félicité et Perpétue'
Rosa filipes 'Kiftsgate'
Rosa 'Gloire de Dijon'
Rosa 'Madame Alfred Carrière'
Rosa 'Mermaid'
Rosa 'Pink Perpétue'
Rosa 'Wedding Day'
Rosa 'Zéphirine Drouhin'

Borders

There is a vast range of herbaceous perennial and border plants to suit hot, dry conditions.

Acanthus mollis
Acanthus spinosus
Achillea x lewisii
Achillea millefolium
Achillea ptarmica
Ajuga pyramidalis
Ajuga reptans
Alcea rosea
Alchemilla mollis
Anthemis tinctoria
Aquilegia vulgaris
Artemisia ludoviciana latiloba
Asphodeline lutea
Astrantia major
Astrantia maxima
Bergenia cvs
Campanula carpatica
Catananche caerulea
Centaurea hypoleuca
Centranthus ruber
Cirsium rivulare 'Atropurpureum'
Coreopsis tripteris
Crambe cordifolia

Gazania chansonette series.

Cynara cardunculus
Dianthus sp
Digitalis parviflora
Echinacea purpurea
Echinops ritro
Echium pininana
Erigeron glaucus
Erigeron karvinskianus
Eryngium amethystinum
Eryngium giganteum
Eryngium x tripartitum
Euphorbia characias ssp wulfenii
Ferula communis
Foeniculum vulgare 'Purpureum'
Geranium psilostemon
Geranium renardii
Geranium sanguineum
Geranium wallichianum
Gypsophila paniculata
Helenium cvs
Helichrysum bracteatum
Helleborus x hybridus
Hemerocallis liloa-sphodelus
Knautia macedonica
Kniphofia sp
Linaria purpurea
Lychnis coronaria
Monarda 'Croftway Pink'
Nepeta 'Six Hills Giant'
Papaver orientale
Penstemon cvs
Salvia castanea
Salvia nemerosa
Salvia pratensis
Salvia splendens

Salvia x sylvestris
Scabiosa caucasica
Sisyrinchium striatum
Verbascum chaixii
Verbascum thapsus
Viola cornuta

Annuals and biennials

Useful for filling gaps and adding instant colour, while many will self-seed freely into gravel.

Calendula officinalis
Centaurea cyanus
Cerinthe major 'Purpurascens'
Chrysanthemum carinatum
Dimorphotheca aurantiaca
Echium vulgare
Eschscholzia californica
Gaillardia pulchella
Glaucium flavum
Helianthus annuus
Lunaria annua
Nicotiana sylvestris
Nigella damascena
Oenothera biennis
Onopordum giganteum
Papaver rhoeas
Papaver somniferum
Salvia sclarea
Salvia viridis
Tropaeolum majus
Zinnia elegans

Silver leaved plants

Silver leaves predominate in Mediterranean climates, so most require full sun and well-drained soil. Silver foliage reflects light and works well with green, plum, lilac, pink, white and blue colours.

Artemisia ludoviciana 'Valerie Finnis'
Brachyglottis 'Sunshine'
Buddleja 'Lochinch'
Convolvulus cneorum
Elaeagnus x ebbingei
Elaeagnus 'Quicksilver'
Hebe pinguifolia 'Pagei'
Helichrysum italicum serotinum
Helichrysum splendidum
Iberis umbellata

Lavandula angustifolia
Lobularia maritima
Olea europaea
Olearia phlogopappa
Ozothamnus rosmarinifolius 'Silver Jubilee'
Phlomis fruticosa
Potentilla fruticosa 'Vilmoriniana'
Pyrus salicifolia 'Pendula'
Ruta graveolens
Salvia lavandulifolia
Salvia officinalis
Santolina chamaecyparissus
Sorbus aria 'Lutescens'
Stachys byzantina 'Silver Carpet'

Grasses

Slender, vertical, feathery grasses add delicate movement and texture to dry gardens.

Arundo donax
Briza maxima
Festuca glauca
Miscanthus sinensis
Pennisetum villosum
Stipa gigantea
Stipa pulcherrima
Stipa tennuissima

Succulents

Succulents store water in their leaves and are ideal subjects for Mediterranean style gardens. Some may require a little protection during winter.

Aeonium arboreum 'Atropurpureum'
Agave americana
Agave americana var. Medioptica
Agave americana 'Variegata'
Agave filifera
Agave parryi
Echeveria crenulata
Lampranthus spectabilis
Sedum spectabile

Bulbs, corms, rhizomes and tubers

Ideal in hot dry gardens where many disappear below ground during the hot summer months to reappear with the first winter rains.

Ipomoea 'Heavenly blue'.

Agapanthus africanus
Allium christophii
Amaryllis belladonna
Anemone blanda
Anemone coronaria
Canna x generalis
Colchicum speciosum
Crinum x powellii
Crocosmia 'Lucifer'
Crocus sp
Crocus tommasinianus
Cyclamen hederifolium
Fritillaria imperialis
Galanthus nivalis
Gladiolus communis byzantinus
Iris confusa 'Brian Rix'
Iris germanica
Iris unguicularis
Lilium sp
Muscari armeniacum
Muscari commutatum
Narcissus sp
Nerine bowdenii
Ornithogalum umbellatum
Paeonia sp
Scilla siberica
Sternbergia lutea
Tulipa saxatilis
Tulipa sprengeri
Zephyranthes candida

6 Exotic and sub-tropical style

The style

Exotic and sub-tropical gardens look and feel very different from the typical temperate gardens we are used to, and that is the appeal to those who cultivate this style. An abundance of luxuriant plant and leaf forms, and species normally associated with hotter regions of the world, all give the illusion of far more glamorous and exotic climes. This style of gardening is becoming increasingly popular, attracting widening numbers of enthusiasts. Exotic gardens and plants are striking, dramatic and inspirational. They give the impression of being out of the ordinary, transporting one to a completely different part of the world entirely.

Narrow paths meander between an abundance of lush, natural-looking vegetation set into informal landscaping. Large-leaved foliage plants; evergreens and plants with variegated leaves; exotic banana and palms reach up to obscure the sky. Richly coloured purple- and bronze-leaved species contrast with vibrant greens and brilliant splashes of vivid colour. In the background, the sound of gently trickling water amidst dense greenery suggests dripping vegetation and humidity, while half-hidden 'lagoons' are thickly bordered with mosses, ferns and bamboo. The smell of moist earth and damp plants mingles with wafts of delicate flower fragrance.

Exotic, sub-tropical gardens create a massive illusion, a grand deception, luring the onlooker into another and unexpected dimension, in some far distant part of the globe, rather than being in London, Birmingham or Manchester.

OPPOSITE: *The tree house gives a fine view across lush planting in Will Giles' Exotic Garden, Norwich.*

RIGHT: *The exotic garden at Little Indonesia, Birmingham, a sub-tropical jungle in the middle of suburbia.*

History

Tropical areas of the world include much of Africa, southern India, southern Asia, Indonesia, New Guinea, northern Australia, southern Mexico, Central and South America. These zones are found around the equator and fall between the Tropic of Cancer in the northern hemisphere ($-23.4°$ northern latitude), and the Tropic of Capricorn ($23.4°$) in the southern hemisphere. These areas are also referred to as the Tropics and the Torrid Zone. The sun reaches its zenith and shines directly

Plants in Will Giles' Exotic Garden, Norwich, create the illusion of being in an entirely different part of the world.

overhead causing intense heat, while rainfall is reasonably evenly distributed throughout the year. There is an average daily temperature of 18°C. The tropical climate falls into three distinct zones: equatorial, tropical continental and hot desert.

Sub-tropical zones are situated at the edges of the tropical and have a more clement climate with slightly lower temperatures. Summers are hot and generally there are eight months where temperatures average above 10°C. Winters are warm and temperatures rarely fall below 6°C. The sub-tropical climate forms one of the largest climate zones on earth and conditions vary widely, from desert and savannah to humid and monsoon forests. Sub-tropical climates can be found in desert regions of southwest USA, California, much of Florida, the Gulf Coast, northern Sahara, northern India, southwest China, central South America, coastal South Africa, much of Australia, and the hotter Mediterranean regions. The sub-tropical classification also loosely includes areas of Britain such as the Isles of Scilly, Cornwall and south Devon.

Temperate zones fall between the sub-tropics and polar regions. Weather has distinct, seasonal changes of spring, summer, autumn and winter. Northern temperate zones include Great Britain, Europe, northern Asia, North America, and northern Mexico. Southern temperate zones include southern Australia, New Zealand, southern South America and South Africa. The coldest parts of the earth are the Frigid or Polar zones, the Arctic and Antarctic. Days can be either very light or very dark, and the areas are perpetually covered with ice and snow.

Although we think of tropical regions as having an extremely hot and humid climate with an abundance of lush vegetation encouraged by high rainfall, this is not always the case. Some regions contain snow-capped mountains such as Mount Kilimanjaro and the Andes range. Others are desert regions such as the Sahara and the Australian outback.

There are several different classifications of tropical forest, including: equatorial lowland evergreen rainforests; moist deciduous and semi-evergreen seasonal forests; Montane rainforests; and flooded forests. Around half of the world's tropical rainforests are found in South American countries such as Peru and Brazil, but these areas are being rapidly and dangerously destroyed. Rainforests now cover less than 6 per cent of the earth's land surface and many areas have been reduced to mere fragments of their original splendour. These hot, humid regions contain the greatest biodiversity of plant and animal species in the world. They play a highly important role in regulating global climate, store large quantities of carbon, and produce much of Earth's oxygen. The importance of these rainforests to the global ecosystem is inestimable – and yet we continue to destroy them at an increasingly alarming rate.

In deciduous forests decaying vegetation adds nutrients to the soil. In tropical regions innumerable bacteria and micro-organisms quickly break down leaf litter, but because the climate encourages rapid plant growth, nutrients are speedily depleted, as well as being further leached from the soil by abundant rainfall. This leaves ground acidic and infertile.

In Britain, exotic gardens were very fashionable in the latter parts of the nineteenth and early twentieth centuries, especially amongst Victorian gardeners, who first began the trend. The invention of the Wardian case by Nathaniel Bagshaw Ward in 1829, which acted like a mini-greenhouse, meant plants could be more easily and safely transported from their tropical climes, arriving in far better condition. This, together with the repeal of the glass tax in 1845 led to the construction of vast, heated conservatories, or 'Winter gardens', which were filled with collections of the new tropical and sub-tropical plants discovered and brought back by great plant-hunting expeditions. In summer, teams of gardeners moved the often enormous plants from the protection of their conservatories outside into the garden, en masse, where they were artistically arranged in large groups. Before the first frosts everything was carried back indoors again, creating an enormous amount of work as well as leaving a sadly dejected-looking winter garden, distinctly lacking in plants.

Many botanical gardens, worldwide, constructed specialist tropical and sub-tropical glasshouses with carefully controlled temperatures and humidity. Plants romped away, often rapidly climbing into the rafters of quite enormous structures. The exotic palm house at the Royal Botanic Gardens, Kew, was constructed in 1884, and remains the world's most important surviving Victorian glasshouse. It was built to house exotic collections of palms being introduced into Britain in early Victorian times.

More recently, the Eden Project, Cornwall, created two enormous biomes set into an old disused china clay quarry. The rainforest biome houses plants from tropical regions including South America, West Africa, Malaysia and the tropical islands. The Mediterranean biome includes plants from warm, temperate, Mediterranean-type climates of the Mediterranean basin, South Africa

This striking banana flower is about to open on a well-established tree in an exposed coastal garden in Devon.

and California. This type of climate covers only 2 per cent of the earth's land surface, but includes a massive 20 per cent of its plant species.

The National Botanic Garden of Wales opened in May 2000. The great glasshouse is the largest single-span glasshouse in the world, containing plants from California, Australia, the Canary Islands, Chile, South Africa and the Mediterranean basin.

The RHS celebrated its 200th anniversary in 2004 by creating a spectacular new glasshouse at Wisley. Rising to 12 metres high, it represents three climate zones: tropical, moist, and dry temperate; and includes many rare and endangered species. The new pond for tropical waterlilies remains at a constant 28°C.

Such fascinating collections have only fuelled the craze for exotic gardening, which is becoming increasingly popular. With our climate forecast to become milder through global warming and climate change, the trend is set not only to continue but to escalate.

Many gardens in coastal areas of Britain, especially those in close proximity to the Gulf Stream, such as the Scilly Isles, Cornwall, and northwest Scotland, have long grown tender and exotic species outdoors, which perhaps one would not expect to survive the British

Lush planting in the exotic border at Holbrook Gardens, Devon.

Approaching this exotic garden at Little Indonesia, Birmingham, West Midlands, is like entering a jungle stockade surrounded by tender tropical and sub-tropical plants.

climate. Mediterranean plants are also considered exotic in cooler climates, despite the fact many have happily grown in Britain for hundreds of years. These come from countries with a Mediterranean-type climate, including California and South Africa, as well as those bordering the Mediterranean Sea, such as Greece, Turkey, Spain, southern France and Italy.

Converts to exotic gardening are pushing back the boundaries and discovering that tender, tropical and sub-tropical plants can flourish in temperate climates and often need little or no winter protection. Careful choice of plants, planting and management, and establishing protective windbreaks and microclimates within the garden, means many species remain outdoors all year.

In the 1960s, Dave McKenna, who gardens in Birmingham, West Midlands, was captivated by a small banana tree he found for sale. He simply had to buy it, but when he arrived home had no idea what to do with it or where to plant it. Exotic plants such as banana were rare in Britain at the time and little was known or written about their cultivation or hardiness in a temperate climate. Finally the banana tree was planted, bringing further problems, as more plants were needed to complement its striking leaf form and exotic appearance. The passion and search for new plants began, spanning over fifty years, turning a tiny corner of suburbia into a sub-tropical paradise. Approaching Dave's garden, in a traditional Birmingham suburb, gives the impression of entering a jungle stockade. Once through the rustic

brushwood screens, one could easily be in the middle of the Amazon rainforest. Exotic plants cascade over narrow, chipped bark and gravel paths. The original banana tree has been joined by numerous others, which have grown to enormous heights, obscuring the sky with huge, waving fronds. Equally tall *Cordyline* are swathed in large sprays of sweetly scented white blossom. Bamboos, palms, *Gunnera*, *Hedychium*, *Phormium*, and hundreds of other unusual plants fill every available corner of the garden, while strange and unusual climbers trail fences and riot through trees. Originally all the tender plants were lifted each autumn and stored away for protection during the winter months, ready to be replanted outside as soon as late frosts had finished. Over time, the garden eventually established its own microclimates, and plants matured. Now, most tender species happily survive outdoors throughout winter. Banana trees have stayed in the same positions for over twenty years, suffering no detrimental effect.

Another notable sub-tropical garden, Will Giles's Exotic Garden, Norwich, was also established many years ago. This one-acre garden on a south-facing slope incorporates numerous exotics as well as hardy plants with a jungle-like appearance. Many of these have survived the continuing rigours of British weather with minimum protection. Bananas of the *Musa basjoo* and *Ensete* species mingle with other large-leaved plants such as Elephant's Ear, *Colocasia esculenta* 'Mammoth', *Canna*, *Hedychium*, palms, tree ferns, *Phormium* and *Cordyline*. Houseplants such as *Bromeliad*, *Cholorophytum*, *Monstera*,

Will Giles' luxuriant exotic garden, Norfolk, a short distance from Norwich City centre, where plants have survived the rigours of the British winter for many years.

and *Tradescantia* are bedded out for summer. As microclimates established, plants have grown tall, and now offer protection for more tender species, turning the whole area into a lush, tropical jungle. The garden creates a good balance of many different species that can be grown in a sub-tropical style garden. The latest innovation is a Xerophytic or desert garden with flint walls and well drained beds for cacti and succulents. White walls reflect back all available light, which benefits the growth of tender and exotic plants.

These two gardens, in very different areas of the country, show just how successfully exotic and tropical plants grow in Britain, despite its harsh and unforgiving winters. There are many other exotic gardens throughout Britain as well as many in milder coastal regions where banana trees and other tender species happily flourish as standard in the southern parts of the country, as well as northern.

Abbotsbury Sub-tropical Gardens, Dorset, combine both formal and informal gardens in a sheltered, wooded valley on the coast. Originally established in 1765 as a kitchen garden, it has developed into 20 acres crammed with tender species from around the world, many brought to the gardens when first discovered by the great plant hunters. Abbotsbury also has a specialist exotic plant nursery.

At the other end of the country, Inverewe was created by Osgood Mackenzie on a barren, rocky promontory on the northwest coast of Scotland, when he bought the estate in 1862. Despite being so far north, Inverewe

Tender species growing in the Plant World jungle garden, Devon, one of their five Continent gardens.

There are around 1,200 different forms of bamboo, highly evolved forest grasses, ranging from 15cm high up to a massive 40m. With a range of colours and leaf forms, bamboos create a lush tropical atmosphere.

benefits from the warm Atlantic currents of the Gulf Stream. The coldest temperature was recorded at −12°C in 1986, and summers are pleasantly warm rather than very hot. Shelter belts were established to protect tender plants from strong coastal winds and now Inverewe boasts a vast collection of exotic and tender species.

Other gardens include Lamorran House, Cornwall, a lush 4-acre paradise with masses of palms, tumbling down a steeply sloping hillside. Trebah Gardens, Cornwall, has 26 acres filled with sub-tropical plants, tree ferns and palms. Tresco Abbey Gardens are amongst the best-known exotic gardens with collections of *Protea, Acacia,* palms, *Bromeliad, Hedychium* and many other tender species, which happily flourish in the mild climate of the Scilly Isles.

Elements of the exotic style

ACCESSORIES

All accessories must fit the tropical ambience of the garden and common items normally found in any temperate garden should be eliminated. Cane, bamboo or weathered wooden furniture looks good, especially more unusual pieces not commonly found in garden centres. Rustic shelters fit better than brightly coloured awnings. Use brushwood, bamboo or rough wooden fences and screens; canvas awnings can be included, and muted, bleached parasols and cushions with perhaps the odd bright touch of colour.

AGAVE

These are striking plants with sharply pointed, long, thick, strap-like leaves. *Agave americana* was nicknamed the 'century plant' because it was thought to flower only once every hundred years. It has thick, stiff, blue-green, spiny edged leaves; there are also variegated varieties. Some species of *Agave* have attractive thread-like fibres edging the leaves, such as *A. filifera*. Many are surprisingly hardy in Britain, although variegated species require some protection. They also make excellent container plants.

BAMBOO

Bamboo requires a special mention. There are around 1,200 different forms of bamboo, which are rapidly gaining in popularity, especially in sub-tropical gardens where their stately forms and colourings add an authentic feel all year round. Bamboos grow from around 15 centimetres high up to a massive 40 metres in some tropical regions. Leaves come in various widths and lengths, in a range of greens and variegated forms. Attractive canes or 'culms' are brown, green, gold or purple-black. Bamboos grow in pots, act as ground cover, edge pools, and provide screens. They definitely create the impression of more exotic climates, especially when mixed with banana, *Cordyline, Phormium,* palms and tree ferns. There are numerous species; some are invasive, but can be controlled by cutting away surplus with a sharp spade. There are also non-invasive species.

Some bamboos are less hardy but most will stand some degree of frost. Some require cutting to ground level each winter, while others remain happily evergreen, shedding and replacing a percentage of leaves each year. Bamboos enjoy moisture, and sometimes windburn can discolour leaves, but most adapt well to the British climate.

BANANA

Banana plants make stunning and imposing subjects bringing rich overtures of tropical climates. Many happily overwinter with little protection. Several *Musa* species are relatively hardy, even in Britain, especially when sited in sunny, sheltered positions. *Ensete* species

Ensete ventricosum 'Maurelii' has a red trunk and deep red midribs to the stunning leaves, which are suffused red and purple, often so dark as to be almost black.

are less hardy and require protection from frost. Long, lush leaves look very handsome and these tree-like forms create strong architectural features. Bananas regularly flower and occasionally set fruit in Britain. They like deep, humus-rich soil in full sun or partial shade. A little protection stops strong winds shredding leaves. Cut leaves back in winter and protect plants with fleece, sacking or bracken. *Musa basjoo* is probably the best known and hardiest, forming good-sized clumps up to 5.5 metres in height, surviving outside even in colder areas with minimum protection. Frost-damaged plants generally regenerate from the base. *Ensete ventricosum* is considered more attractive than *M. basjoo*, but is not hardy. These plants have stout trunks and large, fleshy leaves, measuring 4 × 0.7 metres, with red mid-ribs, and grow quickly to a statuesque 6 metres. Bananas require copious water and benefit from regular feeding.

BRUGMANSIA *AND* DATURA

These are tall shrubs with sizeable leaves and attractive, often sweetly perfumed, large, trumpet-shaped flowers in shades of white, cream, yellow and orange. They are not frost hardy but can be planted directly into borders in summer. They make excellent container plants, and should be pruned in autumn.

CANNA

The *Canna* is native to tropical and sub-tropical America. They have impressively large leaves and colourful, gladioli-like flowers. Although best lifted and stored in

a frost-free place, in milder areas rhizomes can be left in the ground and mulched during winter. Plant in groups of three or five to create impact.

CLIMBERS

Climbers trail through trees, hang down like vines, or ramble over fences, adding to the rampant, jungle atmosphere. Exotic-looking passion flowers add colour and drama. *Campsis radicans* is increasingly common with bright orange, trumpet-shaped flowers and delicate green foliage, twining to around 10 metres. A wide range of *Clematis* flower at various times of year, starting with the strongly perfumed, evergreen *C. Armandii* in late winter and early spring. *Lonicera japonica aureoreticulata*, a vigorous evergreen growing to 10 metres, has green leaves etched with golden veins. Ornamental gourds, *Curcurbita pepo*, are easily raised from seed. They come in a range of colours, shapes and sizes, and although not hardy, create impact trailing over fences or screens, or climbing arches. Not strictly a climber, the arching branches of *Lespedeza thunbergii*, with racemes of purple, pea-like flowers in late summer, scramble up to 3 metres through shrubs.

Brugmansia x candida grows up to 5m in height with wavy-margined, coarsely-toothed leaves and stunning, strongly perfumed, pendulous, trumpet-shaped flowers.

CORDYLINE

Cordyline australis grows up to 8 metres high in Britain, with long, stiff leaves. After several years, plants carry large panicles of small, highly perfumed flowers. Even when damaged by frost, *Cordyline* generally sprouts again from the roots.

CYCADS

An interesting and attractive group of plants, which have been completely decimated in their natural habitats. They are good architectural plants with long fronds of stiff, green or blue-green leaves. Most require winter protection although some overwinter in protected areas. Cycads do well in pots, making them simple to move for winter. They appreciate full sun and well-drained soil.

GUNNERA

Gunnera manicata is a South American perennial and the largest leaved plant growing in temperate climates. Toothed and lobed foliage is very striking and borne on thick, spiny stems. Tall spikes of green-brown flowers appear in spring. Grow at the water's edge or in moist ground.

HARDSCAPING

Hardscaping must look completely natural and the framework of beds, shelter belts and fences should

Gunnera manicata is a very dramatic, clump forming perennial, growing up to 3m in height, with massive, strongly veined and palmately-lobed leaves, spiny beneath and with spiny stems. In summer unusual and striking spikes, up to 1.8m tall, have a mass of tiny red flowers.

Hedychium *or Ginger Lilies grow up to 2m with large green leaves and spikes of delicate-looking, often highly-perfumed flowers.*

disappear beneath rampant foliage. Wooden boards or cut log edgings to beds are more appropriate than stone or brick. Paths should be wide enough to allow easy access, but narrow enough so plants are pushed aside as one walks through, emphasising the jungle-like qualities of the garden. Chipped bark, sand or fine gravel all make good surfaces for paths. Areas of decking, shrouded by plants, can be used for sitting out.

HEDYCHIUM

Ginger lilies have exotic, fragrant, orchid-like flowers, and grow from 90 to 180 centimetres. Although some survive outside in sheltered positions, most require winter protection. They can be planted in pots sunk into borders during summer and lifted during winter.

HIBISCUS

Cultivated in British gardens since the sixteenth century, *Hibiscus syriacus* is hardy. Exotic looking flowers in shades of red, white, pink or blue are produced over a long period, although individual blooms are short-lived. Species of *Hibiscus* do best in full sun, but tolerate some shade. *Hibiscus sinosyriacus* has a more spreading habit.

MICROCLIMATES

Grouping plants close together enables them to shelter one another, creating microclimates. Once gardens are established, smaller, tender species are protected by larger plants – this is often enough to ensure their survival.

MULCH

Maintenance and weeds are kept to a minimum with a thick layer of chipped bark or gravel mulch. Mulches also help retain moisture in the soil and give plants added protection in winter.

PALMS

No garden can describe itself as exotic without the long, cut leaves of palm trees. The mere outline of palm fronds against the sky immediately conjures up tropical climates and desert islands. Deeply cut leaves make an ideal contrast to broader leaved banana and *Canna*. There are many varieties to choose from, including the Chusan Palm (*Trachycarpus fortunei*), which is slow growing but does well, so buy reasonably sized specimens; and the Chilean Wine palm (*Jubaea chilensis*), which is slow growing but can get huge, with leaves up to 6 metres long. It requires winter protection until established but grows well, especially in south-facing situations. The Canary Island date palm (*Phoenix canariensis*) is ideal for mild, sunny positions: it is not as

Palms, bamboo and Ensete in the exotic border at Brobury House, Herefordshire.

ABOVE: *A 'tropical lagoon' surrounded by lush and tender plants at North Boreston Farm, Devon.*

LEFT: *Tree ferns include over 500 species native to tropical and sub-tropical regions of the Southern Hemisphere.* Dicksonia antarctica *is now easily obtainable from garden centres across the UK.*

hardy as some other palms but withstands a few degrees of frost. The cotton palm, *Washingtonia filifera*, has shiny, fan-shaped leaves with fine, white threads. Most palms are slow growing but require fertile soil, water, and food during summer, and benefit from winter protection.

PHORMIUM

Phormium make superbly striking architectural plants. *Phormium tenax* is the plant most commonly seen, growing up to 3 metres high, with long, upright, evergreen leaves. *P. tenax* 'Purpureum' has good dark purple colouring. *Phormium* require open, sunny situations and well-drained soil. Established plants flower after three to four years bearing tall spikes of small, insignificant flowers followed by attractive, long-lasting seed-heads.

PLANTS

Because plants are the main element in the exotic garden many are described separately here. They comprise the one thing that creates the grand illusion. Countless exotic looking species are fully hardy in temperate climates. Given the right conditions, many sub-tropical plants also overwinter outside. All plants must enhance the tropical theme, so plants with large, lush foliage are important. Variegated-leaved plants, or those with

purple, bronze and silver-grey leaves create contrast. Many palms, *Cordyline*, *Phormium* and *Yucca* are exotic-looking and hardy. Their stiff leaves contrast well with broader leaved plants. Bamboos are a must.

Bedding plants bring brilliant splashes of exotic colour, while houseplants and orchids benefit hugely from being outdoors during summer as well as adding exotic notes to the garden. Many plants normally grown in conservatories can also go outside during summer. Climbers and perfumed plants are included, especially those that add exotic perfumes to night gardens.

TREE FERNS

Dicksonia antarctica has grown in Cornish gardens since the 1880s, when specimens arrived as ballast in ships' cargoes. Denuded trunks are a mass of fibrous roots, which form a root-ball when planted and quickly produce new fronds. Despite the fact that plants generally lose foliage in severe winters, they regenerate in spring. *Dicksonia squarrosa* has a slim, black trunk with dark green, 2m-long fronds, but can be frost tender. Protect plants with straw, hessian or fleece. Tender species grow well outside in summer but need overwintering indoors. Tree ferns grow well in shady, damp areas of the exotic garden.

WATER

Gently dripping or trickling water evokes the sounds of

saturated foliage in sub-tropical jungles, and a pond or 'lagoon' reflects the lush plants surrounding it. A small, rushing waterfall also imparts a jungle feel. Many large-leaved plants require copious amounts of water to survive and water in the garden also helps maintain a good balance of moisture in the atmosphere, further benefiting plants.

WINDBREAKS

Shelter belts arranged round the garden form protected pockets and help plants to establish. These should be of natural materials or living plants, which form protective screens yet allow wind to filter through. Solid fences can deflect wind over the top, causing damage to large-leaved plants.

YUCCA

These are evergreen plants with rosettes of long, pointed leaves, or trunk-like stems. *Yucca gloriosa* grows up to 2.5 metres high and is fully hardy in Britain. *Y. gloriosa* 'Variegata' has green, yellow and pink leaves when young, maturing to green bordered with yellow. It is free flowering, with spikes up to a metre long, smothered with pendant, tulip-shaped reddish-cream blooms.

Creating an exotic style

Plants from sub-tropical and tropical regions of the world, where the climate is hot and steamy, have a truly exotic feel, although we can never recreate the heat and humidity of a tropical jungle in colder countries, unless it is inside large glasshouses. The garden must simply create a grand illusion. Many exotics grow in temperate climates and even more will grow given winter protection. There are also many completely hardy plants with exotic flowers and interesting leaf forms that impart a tropical feel. Gardening in milder areas or on south-facing sites certainly helps, but with careful planning, and by establishing windbreaks and microclimates, it is relatively simple to create the illusion of a garden from another part of the world entirely.

The austerity of winter in temperate climates is emphasized by deciduous plants that lose their leaves, so evergreen species are important in exotic gardens,

At Little Indonesia, Birmingham, the garden creates a grand illusion where windbreaks and microclimates, established over many years, form ideal habitats for many exotic species.

Yuccas have striking, sword-like foliage that contrasts well with larger, broad-leaved plants in the exotic garden, as do the attractive stems of pendant, bell-shaped, fragrant cream flowers, sometimes tinged purple.

especially those with larger leaves. Bedding plants take on a totally different appearance when thickly woven through jungle-like undergrowth. Highlight brilliant splashes of colour and avoid anything that reduces the garden to a mundane level. Look for more unusual elements not normally found in British gardens that would be a common occurrence in exotic jungle regions.

Rich textures, colours and leaf forms in the garden at Little Indonesia, Birmingham.

your way around the garden, as if penetrating deep into the unknown. Beaten earth is soon covered with leaf litter, small plants and other debris in the natural habitat, so chipped bark makes a good substitute in temperate climates. Let plants seed and colonize paths, removing anything too aggressive as necessary. Aim for total ground cover with close planting and mosses to minimize weeds, and use natural bark mulches.

The sound of gently dripping or running water provides background noise evoking the jungle, as well as keeping moisture in the air, benefitting plants. A small 'lagoon', surrounded by lush growth, ferns and mosses, and covered with waterlilies and other aquatic plants fits well, especially with a waterfall trickling in at one end. Avoid any suggestion of ornate or man-made fountains.

Try to screen the area with taller trees and plants to eliminate views of surrounding gardens, which bring the exotic garden down to a humdrum suburban level.

Plants are such an important element in imparting the exotic feel, and plants with massive leaves carry particular appeal. Annual climbers growing through

Use exuberant shapes and styles to create a sense of theatre and fun. Include dramatic architectural foliage, over-the-top plants and colours, interesting plant associations, rich textures and patterns, to produce a primeval wilderness.

Give careful consideration to hardscaping and materials. Make sure they don't fall into the commonplace, immediately reducing the sub-tropical paradise down to that level. Keep things informal and fitting to the picture you are creating. Bamboo fences and furniture look good, as does weathered wood. Use chipped bark and gravel surfaces for paths and mulches, and bamboo, rustic wood or rush panels for fencing and screens. Edge beds with lengths of rustic wood or logs, which create natural-looking barriers as well as providing excellent habitats for insects and small creatures. Avoid paving stones, especially those of regular shape, which immediately bring an element of 'man-made' into the garden. Small areas of wooden decking form seating areas.

In the jungle paths are beaten through the forest by animals, and these should be narrow, natural and meandering, so plants are pushed aside as you make

Bromeliads are long lasting house plants that enjoy a spell outdoors in summer, adding brilliant splashes of colour to the exotic garden.

established, hardy climbers add a touch of the exotic with unusual flowers and colours. The glorious, brilliant blue flowers of *Ipomoea tricolor* 'Heavenly blue', and red-flowered *I. coccinea* look stunning. *I. lobata* is unusual with large clusters of red and yellow tubular flowers. *Maurandya scandens* has small, arrow-shaped leaves and tubular purple flowers, seeds freely and can overwinter in sheltered positions. *Cobaea scandens* grows up to 7 metres, with beautiful cup-shaped purple flowers, and overwinters with protection. Brilliant scarlet flowers of *Tropaeolum speciosum* with small, divided bright green leaves looks stunning rampaging through dark evergreens, and seeds freely in the right conditions.

Many plants have dark red, purple or bronze foliage which fit well in the jungle theme, although it is best not to overdo the darker colours of purple and copper as they can make gardens look gloomy and depressing: rather use as dramatic highlights.

Many houseplants benefit from being outside during summer, but guard against frost. *Bromeliads*, cacti, peace lily, *Clivia*, *Coleus*, rubber plant, *Tradescantia* and many more enjoy the fresh air. Placing orchids outdoors in summer encourages flowering, as well as creating an exotic feel when pots are plunged between plants in borders or wired into trees where many grow in their natural habitats.

Exotic, sub-tropical gardens in temperate climates are a grand deception and a great escape from the ordinariness of the everyday world. Lush planting and bright colours of alluring species in jungle gardens, screened from the outside world, create a very special, magical atmosphere. These are eye-catching, fun gardens, which transport one far away to more exotic and exciting climes. Be prepared to take chances: you will be surprised at what you can grow and how far away from a traditional 'English' garden you can get.

Exotic style

Bamboo

Bamboos can be invasive or tender and difficult. Dwarf varieties make excellent ground cover. Taller, robust species create shelter belts and screens. Stems can be stripped to reveal colourful culms.

Chusquea breviglumis
Chusquea culeou
Fargesia nitida
Fargesia spathacea
Indocalamus tessellatus
Pleioblastus auricomus
Pleioblastus linearis
Phyllostachys aurea
Phyllostachys aureosulcata 'Spectabilis'
Phyllostachys bambusoides
Phyllostachys nigra
Phyllostachys pubescens
Phyllostachys sulphurea 'Robert Young'
Pleioblastus shibuyanus 'Tsuboi'
Pseudosasa japonica
Sasa veitchii
Sasa palmata nebulosa
Semiarundinaria fastuosa

Banana

Superb, striking, lush and tropical with large, ribbed leaves of green or flushed purple. Ensete are less hardy than Musa species, requiring winter protection.

Ensete glaucum
Ensete superbum
Ensete ventricosum
Ensete ventricosum 'Maurelii'
Musa acuminata 'Dwarf Cavendish'
Musa basjoo
Musa 'Rajapuri'
Musa sikkimensis
Musa velutina
Musa 'Yunnan'

Canna

Big, bright, colourful and dramatic leaves and flowers.

Canna 'Alberich'
Canna 'Black Knight'
Canna 'Cleopatra'
Canna 'Durban'
Canna indica 'Purpurea'
Canna iridiflora
Canna 'Louis Cottin'
Canna 'Musifolia Grande'
Canna 'Picasso'
Canna 'President'
Canna 'Stuttgart'
Canna 'Wyoming'

Hibiscus rosa-sinensis.

Cordyline

Long, pointed leaves and scented white flowers.

Cordyline australis 'Torbay Dazzler'
Cordyline australis 'Purple Tower'
Cordyline australis 'Pink Stripe'.
Cordyline banksii
Cordyline indivisa
Cordyline kaspar

Cycad

Date to the Jurassic period, but are a dwindling species and many face extinction.

Cycas circinalis
Cycas panzhihuaensis
Cycas revoluta
Cycas taitungensis
Encephalartos ghellinckii
Encephalartos horridus
Encephalartos lehmannii

Hedychium

Ginger lilies have decorative and exquisitely perfumed flowers.

Hedychium coccineum
Hedychium densiflorum
Hedychium 'Elizabeth'

Hedychium ellipticum
Hedychium flavescens
Hedychium forrestii
Hedychium gardnerianum
Hedychium greenii
Hedychium spicatum
Hedychium thyrsiforme

Palms

Numerous palms are available and many borderline hardy palms can be grown given a little winter protection.

Brahea armata
Brahea edulis
Butia capitata
Chamaedorea microspadix
Chamaedorea radicalis
Chamaerops humilis
Chamaerops humilis var. argentea
Chamaerops humilis 'Vulcano'
Jubaea chilensis
Livistonia australis
Nannorrhops ritchieana
Phoenix canariensis
Phoenix dactylifera
Rhapidophyllum hystrix
Rhapis excelsea
Sabal minor
Sabal palmetto
Serenoa repens
Trachycarpus fortunei
Trachycarpus latisectus
Trachycarpus nanus
Trachycarpus takil
Trachycarpus wagnerianus
Trithrinax acanthocoma
Washingtonia filifera
Washingtonia robusta

Phormium

Phormium cookianum
Phormium cookianum 'Cream Delight'
Phormium cookianum 'Yellow Wave'
Phormium tenax 'Atropurpurem'
Phormium tenax 'Bronze Baby'
Phormium tenax 'Dark Delight'
Phormium tenax 'Maori Chief'
Phormium tenax 'Platt's Black'

Tree ferns

Cyathea australis
Cyathea medullaris
Dicksonia antarctica
Dicksonia fibrosa
Dicksonia squarrosa

Borders

The best of the rest. Trees, shrubs, perennials, succulent, annuals and more with various stages of hardiness.

Acanthus mollis
Adiantum venustum
Aechmea recurvata
Aeonium arboreum
Agapanthus africanus
Agave americana
Agave attenuata
Agave bracteosa
Agave mitis
Agave parryi
Ajuga reptans
Alocasia cucullata
Alocasia gageana
Alocasia macrorrhiza
Aloe arborescens
Aloe aristata
Aloe mutabilis
Aloe striatula
Amaranthus caudatus
Angelica archangelica
Anthurium andraeanum
Arctotis x hybrida
Arisaema fargesii
Arisaema flavum
Artemisia arborescens
Arum creticum
Arum italicum
Arundo donax
Asclepias curassavica
Asplenium scolopendrium
Athyrium filix-femina
Bergenia cordifolia
Beschorneria yuccoides
Beta vulgaris
Billbergia nutans
Blechnum chilense
Brugmansia arborea
Brugmansia x candida

Brunnera macrophylla 'Jack Frost'
Calceolaria integrifolia
Carpobrotus edulis
Choisya ternata
Cleome hassleriana
Colocasia esculenta 'Black Magic'
Colocasia esculenta 'Chicago Harlequin'
Colocasia esculenta 'Mammoth'
Cortaderia selloana
Cotinus coggygria
Crambe cordifolia
Cynara cardunculus
Dasylirion wheeleri
Dracunculus vulgaris
Echium pininana
Echeveria agavoides
Echeveria secunda var. *glauca*
Embothrium coccineum
Euphorbia characias
Euphorbia mellifera
Fasicularia bicolor
Fatsia japonica
Geranium maderense
Geranium palmatum
Griselinia littoralis
Gunnera manicata
Gunnera tinctoria
Hemerocallis altissima
Hemerocallis multiflora
Hesperaloe parviflora
Hibiscus moscheutos
Hibiscus schizopetalus
Hibiscus syriacus
Hosta sieboldiana var. *elegans*
Lampranthus deltoides
Lampranthus roseus
Laurus nobilis
Ligularia hybrids
Ligustrum japonicum 'Rotundifolium'
Liriodendron chinense
Lysichiton americanus
Macleaya micropcarpa
Magnolia grandiflora
Matteuccia orientalis
Melianthus major
Monstera deliciosa
Myrtus communis
Nicotiana glauca
Nicotiana tabacum
Nolina longifolia
Ochagavia carnea
Opuntia imbricata
Opuntia phaeacantha

Bromeliad guzmania.

Opuntia robusta
Osmunda regalis
Paulownia tomentosa
Pennisetum setaceum
Perilla frutescens var nankinensis
Pittosporum tenuifolium
Polystichum proliferum
Prunus laurocerasus
Puya alpestris
Puya berteroniana
Puya chilensis
Rheum palmatum
Ricinus communis
Rodgersia podophylla
Salvia involucrata
Salvia leucantha
Sambucus nigra 'Guincho Purple'
Sedum kamtschaticum
Sedum obtusatum
Sedum spathulifolium
Sempervivum arachnoideum

Sempervivum cvs.
Setaria palmifolia
Schizophragma hydrangeoides
Soleirolia soleirolii
Strelitzia nicolai
Strelitzia reginae
Thunbergia alata
Tillandsia aeranthos
Trifolium repens 'Purpurascens'
Viburnum davidii
Viburnum tinus
Yucca elephantipes
Yucca filamentosa
Yucca filifera
Yucca glauca
Yucca gloriosa
Zantedeschia aethiopica
Zantedeschia elliotiana
Zea mays
Zingiber mioga
Zingiber mioga 'Dancing Crane'

Climbers

Perennial and annual climbers to make a show.

Actinidia kolomikta
Actinidia polygama
Akebia quinata
Akebia trifoliata
Ampelopsis thunbergii
Aristolochia fimbriata
Bignonia capreolata
Campsis grandiflora
Campsis radicans
Clematis armandii
Cobaea scandens
Hedera helix
Humulus lupulus
Hydrangea anomala ssp. *petiolaris*
Hydrangea serratifolia
Ipomoea purpurea
Jasminum officinale
Lapageria rosea
Pandorea jasminoides
Pandorea pandorana
Parthenocissus quinquefolia
Parthenocissus tricuspidata
Passiflora caerulea
Rhodochiton atrosanguineum
Solanum crispum
Thunbergia alata

Eucomis comosa.

Begonia grandis ssp evansiana
Begonia grandis ssp evansiana 'Pink Parasol'
Begonia palmata
Begonia sinensis 'Red Undies'
Cardiocrinum giganteum
Crinum x powellii
Crocosmia x crocosmiiflora
Crocosmia 'Emberglow'
Crocosmia 'Lucifer'
Crocosmia 'Star of the East'
Dahlia coccinea
Dahlia imperialis
Dahlia merckii
Eremurus himalaicus
Eremurus x isabellinus
Eremurus robustus
Eremurus stenophyllus
Eucomis aumtumnalis
Eucomis bicolour
Galtonia candicans
Galtonia princeps
Gladiolus callianthus
Iris confusa
Iris japonica
Nerine bowdenii
Nerine flexuosa
Tigridia pavonia
Tulbaghia simmleri
Tulbaghia violacea

Houseplants

Houseplants enjoy a spell outside during summer.

Amaranthus hypochondriacus
Aspidistra elatior
Begonia carolineifolia
Begonia rex
Chlorophytum comosum
Chlorophytum orchidastrum 'Orange and Green'
Clivia miniata
Cyperus involucratus
Ficus elastica
Lotus berthelotii
Pelargonium tomentosum
Plectranthus madagascariensis
Plumbago auriculata
Russellia equisetiformis
Solenostemon scutellarioides
Solenostemon scutellarioides
Tradescantia fluminensis 'Variegata'
Tradescantia pallida

Trachelospermum asiaticum
Trachelospermum jasminoides
Tropaeolum majus
Tropaeolum peregrinum
Tropaeolum speciosum
Tropaeolum tuberosum
Vitis coignetiae
Vitis vinifera 'Purpurea'

Bulbs, corms, rhizomes and tubers

Mainly hardy.

Alstroemeria aurea
Alstroemeria pelegrina
Alstroemeria psittacina
Amaryllis belladonna

7 Japanese style

The style

Origins of Japanese gardens mainly stem from Shinto, Taoist or Buddhist religions and the first gardens were created around sacred shrines. Both Chinese and Japanese gardens were nature based and highly symbolic, as were the elements in them. Each form of garden had its own particular style including strolling gardens – *Tsukiyama*; tea gardens – *Cha Niwa* or *Roji*; courtyard gardens – *Tsubo Niwa*; and Zen or dry landscape gardens. From the simplest to the most complex, all gardens were based on strict principles stretching back over centuries, which became integral parts of Japanese culture. Every element was significant, sensitively observed and carefully placed to create a balance between masculine and feminine, yin and yang, dominant and subordinate, active and passive. This complementary system meant one element always balanced another.

Meditation was a prime consideration. Gardens and everything in them – including rocks, water, flowers and trees – were all important meditational aids. The careful clipping and training of trees and shrubs over many generations was considered an art in itself, and this, as well as careful raking of patterns into sand and gravel, was used to enhance meditation.

Japanese gardens have extraordinary beauty, peace and serenity, encouraging quiet contemplation and reflection. They may look simple and minimally designed, but they are anything but. Every stone, tree, flower and grain of sand plays its vital role in maintaining the symbolism and harmony of the garden.

History

Chinese gardens

Chinese gardens pre-dated those of Japan and strongly influenced what followed. Both countries had nature-based religions which acted as major factors in garden development. China is a vast country with many

OPPOSITE: *Cherry blossom – quintessentially Japanese.*

RIGHT: *Each Japanese garden has its own particular style, but all should be based on strict principles that stretch back for centuries.*

Gardens have extraordinary beauty, peace and serenity, encouraging quiet contemplation and reflection.

different landscapes and climate zones. It possesses an immense wealth of plants that have benefited gardens worldwide.

The Chinese believed in the 'Immortals' – perfect beings who inhabited the 'The Mystic Isles', or 'Isles of the Blessed', situated somewhere off the coast of China in the Eastern sea. The Chinese sought to emulate these mystic islands in their gardens, which became representative of the landscape, lakes and islands these mystic beings inhabited. Styles were influenced by Confucianism and Taoism, although religious impact was not as great as in later Japanese gardens.

In the Neolithic period the Chinese aligned settlements on a north–south axis with habitations facing south. The earliest landscaped hunting parks date to the Shang dynasty, from around 1766 to 1111 BC. Domestic Chinese gardens developed from these ancient hunting parks and imperial palace gardens. Constant political turmoil led to enclosed gardens. These were required to contain the following seventeen important elements: proximity to house; small; walled; individual sections; asymmetrical; association of space; architecture; rocks; water; trees; plants; sculpture; borrowed scenery; chimes; incense burners; inscriptions; and use of Feng-shui. Covered walkways with small windows directed the eye to specific views and allowed gardens to be enjoyed in inclement weather.

Originally, gardens were only accessible to the privileged few and designed to promote intellectual development and reflection. They were strongly allied to art and poetry. Gardens were informal and, overall, naturalistic. Clever variations of scale created depth and false perspective. Decorative paths were inlaid with designs of coloured pebbles including auspicious birds, animals, and good luck symbols.

Feng shui, the balance between opposing yin and yang forces, dominated Chinese garden design. Chi had both positive and negative effects and the positioning of elements in the landscape was thought to have important repercussions on people living there.

Water was a focal element of classical Chinese gardens, channelled into natural-looking lakes, pools, streams and waterfalls. Still, reflective pools aided meditation. Water was edged with natural-looking rocks and plants, with wood or stone bridges. Yin and yang forces had to be properly balanced: rocks represented yang and water yin. They were also contrasted in many other ways including mountainous areas against flat, rough with smooth, light and shade, and long and short views. Large, carefully chosen, well-shaped rocks were placed singly to represent one mountain, or grouped to symbolize a range of natural looking hills. Rocks were softened by plants or left as unadorned blocks of stone. Some representational mountains were so huge that they were accessed by paths, with small pavilions on the summit.

Architectural elements were important. Chinese buildings were very simple or extremely elaborate, but always functional. They were often built of wood or bamboo with tiled roofs, verandas, and latticework screens.

Despite China's rich plant resources, relatively few plants were used in gardens, and those that were included were selected for their symbolism. The lotus represented purity; plum blossom – strength of will and renewal; bamboo – strong resilience of character; pine – longevity and tenacity; peony – wealth; and chrysanthemum – splendour and courage to make sacrifices.

Sir William Temple's description of the natural,

Chinese landscape garden in 1685 is said to have been the main inspiration behind the British style of landscape garden, developed by Lancelot 'Capability' Brown and Humphry Repton, amongst others.

Japanese gardens

Japanese gardens originated from sacred shrines which were simple, cleared, open areas, edged with rope and dressed with sand. These Shinto shrines resulted in harmonious, minimal gardens of great peace and tranquillity, celebrating nature and encouraging meditation. Later, large, important gardens developed around shrines and temples.

Japanese gardens probably already used stones and water in their design before Chinese styles and Buddhist and Taoist ideas were introduced into Japan from China around the seventh century AD. These ideas and principles heavily influenced Japanese gardens and were adapted to Japan's existing ancient Shinto religion. The Japanese developed the ideas although gardens were generally simpler than their Chinese counterparts. The first recorded Japanese ornamental garden dates to AD613 at the palace of the Empress Suiko.

Open spaces were purified areas protected from harmful spirits. Trees and stones were carefully placed within the boundaries as homes to advantageous spirits. Purifying effects of water were important. Scenery from outside was skilfully drawn into the garden by bending or pruning trees to reveal distant views or objects.

In the eleventh century Tacibana no Toshitsuna, a courtier and poet, wrote the *Sakuteiki* – Essay on Garden-Making. This contained all the information required, including significance of various elements, symbolism, and important restrictions. Much of this information is

TOP LEFT: *The purifying effects of water were highly important in Japanese garden design.*

TOP RIGHT: *Strolling gardens, Tsukiyama, were one of the earliest styles of Japanese garden, encouraging people to walk through and appreciate different viewpoints as here in the Japanese Garden, Cornwall.*

RIGHT: *Japanese gardens developed from sacred shrines, which were open areas edged with rope and dressed with sand.*

Bonsai trees originated in China, but the Japanese perfected techniques for training these miniature trees, many of which are of great age and beauty.

still as relevant today as it was then. A Japanese monk, Gokyogoku Yoshitsune (1169–1206) concentrated on the division between male and female, active and passive, decreeing that each element in the garden contributed towards this strict balance.

The Temple Gardens of Kyoto, Japan, date from the thirteenth and fourteenth centuries. At one time there were over 1,650 Buddhist temples and 400 Shinto shrines in the city, surrounded by beautiful gardens.

As in all gardens, different styles developed, but all were strictly contrived and carefully controlled. 'Strolling gardens' (*Tsukiyama*) were one of the earliest, designed to encourage people to walk through, appreciating different views and components. These might include pools, streams, waterfalls and artificial hills. Screens, fences and gates enclosed but also highlighted areas, and objects were placed to attract or deflect the eye to other viewpoints. Paths encouraged visitors forward, revealing new delights along the way. Gardens often appeared much larger by skilfully drawing views of distant landscape into the scene.

'Strolling gardens' were intended to be experienced from different viewpoints, but 'scenic viewing gardens' were to be appreciated from a single fixed point, from which the whole garden could be seen to advantage. This style was favoured by Samurai warriors, who hosted large, formal gatherings; it was important that guests could view the garden from the house, veranda or other static position. Gardens were generally best viewed from sitting or kneeling positions inside the house.

Early Japanese emperors and nobles fashioned immense gardens, complete with landscaped scenery, vast lakes, streams and bridges. These 'boating gardens' had landscape and planting specifically designed to be viewed from a boat on the water.

Dry landscape gardens first appeared as part of larger schemes in the Heian period, AD794–1185. They later developed into more complex dry gardens of the Muromachi period, AD1336–1573, where rocks and trees represented natural scenery including mountains, rivers and oceans. Tea gardens developed from dry landscape gardens and were first established in the Momoyama period, AD1568–1603.

Although ideas and plants had filtered out of Japan in the past, it wasn't until the early twentieth century that the fashion for Japanese gardens really caught on in the West. Sadly, most Western gardeners failed to appreciate the extreme significance of basic elements and design, and the meticulous balance between yin and yang. Gardens looked very attractive, but were simply Westernized interpretations, making them poor imitations at best. Without the strict observance of balance and principles, the true 'spirit' of the garden was lost. European 'Japanese' gardens featured brightly painted pavilions and bridges instead of leaving them natural; trees and plants grew unrestrainedly, without careful pruning; effects of borrowed scenery were ignored; and colourful flowers detracted from the true harmony of authentic Japanese gardens. Dry landscape gardens ignored principles of design, asymmetry, symbolism, and space.

In 1910, two Japanese gardens were created for an exhibition at White City Stadium, London, but were rightly described as being purely representational. Also included were miniature gardens, *bonkei*. These were arrangements of lakes and islands built in flat trays measuring only 3.7 metres by 2.1 metres, and they attracted great interest. Bonsai trees also caught the imagination. Originally from China, the Japanese perfected techniques for creating carefully trained, miniature trees, many of great age and beauty. As curiosity in Japanese gardens increased, elements and artefacts associated with them were utilized by landscape designers, including the eminent English designer, Harold Peto. Although he never created a specifically 'Japanese garden' he incorporated many elements into his designs. Collections of ornaments, lanterns and other accessories became increasingly available, and plants imported from Japan were stocked by nurseries classifying themselves as 'Japanese specialists'. Interest

The dry landscape garden, Dartington Hall, Devon. Zen or dry landscape gardens, Karesansui, were strongly influenced by Zen Buddhism, incorporating religious and philosophical symbolism.

Irregular groupings of rocks were displayed to advantage against carefully raked patterns of sand or gravel, simulating the movement of water.

continued in the early years of the twentieth century, but sadly, few of these gardens survive. Latterly a new surge of awareness in oriental culture is seeing old gardens restored and new ones created.

Many familiar garden plants originated in China and Japan. Engelbert Kaempfer, physician to the Dutch East India Company, described and drew exquisite watercolours of plants in his *Amoenitates Exoticae*, 1712, which Hans Sloane had translated into English in 1728. Other plant hunters fuelled the desire for exotic plants from the East, including Carl Pehr Thunberg, Philipp Franz von Siebold, S. Wells Williams, James Morrow and Carl Johann Maximowicz. John Gould Veitch (1839–70) regularly travelled to Japan, bringing back collections of plants and trees for his nursery in Kingston upon Thames, Surrey, which looked like a large Japanese garden. Robert Fortune (1813–80) introduced plants from his travels in Japan and China, as did Ernest 'Chinese' Wilson (1876–1930). These remained merely interesting collections of oriental species until the end of the nineteenth century when they were finally included in Japanese style gardens in the West. Josiah Condor's Landscape Gardening in Japan (1893) contained copious details and illustrations of different styles of Japanese gardens.

ZEN GARDENS

Zen or dry landscape gardens, *Karesansui*, first appeared in the Heian period, AD794–1185, and were later strongly influenced by Zen Bhuddism of the Muromachi period (1336–1573), incorporating religious and philosophical symbolism. Gardens should be one with nature and Zen gardens sought the path of enlightenment through meditation. Monks used the careful maintenance of gardens as aids to meditation. These were subtle and simple gardens with natural asymmetry and calm, balanced appearance. It was important they looked completely natural and at one with nature, despite pure artifice being used to achieve this effect. Irregular groupings of rocks were displayed to advantage against backgrounds of sand or gravel. Overlapping flat stones created the effect of streams, with rocks representing islands. Dry materials such as coarse sand and gravel had carefully raked patterns simulating movement of water. Touches of white quartz chippings represented foam. Each pattern had its distinguishing name, and creating the often highly intricate designs, and viewing finished patterns was a ritualistic aid to meditation. Raked patterns of water represented yin, while rocks and land represented yang, keeping a harmonious balance.

Zen gardens were either completely dry – composed of sand, stones and rocks – or they incorporated trees, water, plants and moss. Moss sometimes represented water, while one type of garden used variously coloured mosses spreading like a carpet beneath trees and around boulders.

Zen gardens represent nature in its purest form and should look completely natural and in harmony with their surroundings. Placing of minimal elements within the scene becomes an art form in itself, encouraging contemplation on its simple beauty. Zen gardens are composed of five main elements: stone, gravel, water, space and plants, although not all need be present in one garden. Finished gardens should have simple permanence, muted colours and uncomplicated design, strictly maintaining yin and yang balance. Many Zen gardens have remained unchanged from when they were first created centuries ago, apart from having weathered and gathered suitable mosses and lichens. The Ryoanji garden is one of the most famous. Here, fifteen large stones are set in carefully raked, level quartz sand, and so artfully placed it is impossible to see them all at once, from whichever position the garden is viewed. Zen gardens use a simple palette of plants, in keeping with the harmonious design.

TEA GARDENS – CHA NIWA *OR* ROJI

Tea gardens developed from dry landscape gardens and were introduced in the Momoyama period, 1568–1603. Tea houses were often imposing, but the advent of Zen gardens introduced humble, rustic huts, more in keeping with a ceremony requiring due humility. The tea house stood in a small, enclosed garden and contained little more than a single flower arrangement, *Ikebana*, and calligraphy scroll to aid concentration. A low door meant stooping or crawling humbly through. The ceremony began immediately on entering the garden, leaving behind the turmoil of the outside world. The tea house, *roji*, meaning 'dewy path', was approached by a winding path of stepping stones or pebbles, highlighting pleasant views and encouraging quiet contemplation. Lanterns lit the way and the path was often sprinkled with water as the visitor arrived.

A stone water basin, *chozubachi*, was placed outside the tea house for ritual cleansing of hands and mouth, ensuring purity in action and word. A flat stone protected feet from mud. To the right stood a lantern, and to the left a small stone supported a basin for warm water. A large stone placed behind the composition drew the elements together, creating

Courtyard gardens, Tsubo Niwa, *were often tiny, shaded areas, transformed into exquisite, small-scale gardens.*

balance. Sometimes a few *Acer* leaves placed to one side symbolized the cycle of life. Humbled and purified in mind and spirit, the visitor fully appreciated the meaningful symbolism of taking tea.

COURTYARD GARDEN – TSUBO NIWA

The word 'tsubo' derives from a Japanese measurement equalling 3.3 square metres. Courtyard gardens date back to the fifteenth century when Japanese merchants rose to prominence and houses included access to numerous storage buildings. These tiny yards and passages were enclosed, shady areas with rainwater falling from the roof and poorly irrigated ground. But even these were transformed into exquisite, small-scale gardens. Simplicity was the keynote, with raked gravel and one or two significant stones or plants. With little natural light, plants needed to be shade tolerant. The

ABOVE: *A stone water basin,* Chozubachi, *was placed outside the Tea House for ritual cleansing of hands and mouth, ensuring purity in action and word.*

LEFT: *The Tea House stood in a small, enclosed garden and contained little more than a single flower arrangement,* Ikebana, *and a calligraphic scroll to aid concentration in the important ceremony of taking tea.*

LEFT: *Stone lanterns, Toro, originated in temples, later becoming important features in Japanese gardens.*

RIGHT: *Bamboo is quintessentially a plant of the Orient. Attractive, if sometimes invasive plants they are documented to have over 1,500 uses other than garden plants.*

BELOW: *The bridge at Glendale Japanese Garden, B.C. Bridges come in many shapes and sizes, from highly sophisticated and decorative roofed constructions to simple lengths of slate or stone.*

smaller the area, the simpler the design, often viewed through small openings in screens or walls. Such tiny gardens are easily adapted to balconies or rooftops. Larger courtyard gardens are for walking and viewing from different perspectives.

Elements of Japanese gardens

ACCESSORIES

Stone accessories include granite water features, washing basins and spheres; miniature shrines and temples; carved Buddha and sculptures dedicated to deities and spirits; smooth black pebbles; gleaming white cobbles; and interestingly shaped and marked stones or slate. Stone lanterns, *toro*, originated in temples, later becoming important features in gardens. They require careful placing to validate the objective of lighting paths or water basins. Lamps can also be of wood, metal or bronze. Creating the perfect balance between garden, elements and accessories helped emphasize the beauty, harmony, serenity and completeness of gardens.

BAMBOO

True grasses, bamboos include *Arundinaria, Bambusa, Dendrocalamus, Phyllostachys, Sinobambusa* and *Thamnocalmus* species. They include the fastest growing plants on earth and vary in height from around 15 centimetres, up to an amazing 40 metres. Evergreen or deciduous, they suit sun or shade. Coloured culms are

yellow, green, blue, red, purple or black. Leaves vary from small and needle-like to enormous, long green ribbons, and can be variegated. Bamboo is grown for canes, foliage, screening, ground cover or specimen plants. Attractive, if sometime invasive plants, they also provide fencing, building materials and food. Invasiveness can be controlled by planting bamboo in large containers in the ground. Stems provide tall vertical impact and leaves are often stripped, emphasizing this and revealing attractive culms and views through them.

BRIDGES

Bridges are used in both water and dry gardens, the style of garden dictating the type of bridge. Pieces of flat stone or wood create simple bridges with no handrails. Large, decorative, arched bridges with intricately designed rails and trellis were often roofed. Wooden bridges were left unpainted. 'Guardian stones' were positioned near the corners of bridges.

Mosses are classic plants of Japanese gardens, with carpets of moss creating particularly pleasing effects.

DEER SCARER

Deer-scarers, *shishi odoshi*, are bamboo tubes, see-sawing backwards and forwards as water fills and empties from them. A judiciously placed rock knocks the empty tube, sending sound echoing across gardens to frighten away wild animals. The constant, monotonous click was said to aid concentration.

MOSS

Classic plants of Japanese gardens, mosses prefer moisture and shade, but can be encouraged to grow on stones and rock. Moss carpets spreading throughout the garden create particularly pleasing effects.

PATHS

Paths can be of smooth sand or gravel, or paved with intricate designs using shaped and coloured stones. Stepping stones are also placed through gravel.

PLANTS

Restraint in planting is crucial, with plants included from an aesthetic point of view rather than a desire for a green garden. They should be suited to the garden type, such as mountain species in hilly landscape, and water species near water, so they do not look out of place. Gardens can be lush and green, have minimal planting and muted colours, or have no plants at all, as in some dry landscape gardens. Trees and shrubs are artfully trained or severely pruned to 'replicate' nature, producing effects of tiers and waves. *Satsuki Azalea* was a favourite, particularly in dry gardens, as dense, evergreen leaves could be heavily pruned into rolling waves, mounds and spheres, complementing dry elements and rocks to perfection.

Plant texture and leaf forms are important. Textures create harmony by complementing or contrasting in 'hard–soft' relationships. Plants add depth and perspective to the garden. Placing taller, larger-leaved plants in the foreground with shorter, narrow-leaved plants in the distance makes space appear larger. Use colour sparingly, allowing green and natural tones to predominate. Traditionally, coloured flowers are acceptable near the entrance, but only small touches of colour are preferred inside the main garden. Too many flowers and colours overwhelm the senses, but a few carefully placed blooms attract the eye and aid concentration. Blossom trees, azalea, iris, lily, peony and wisteria are all popular, but not red flowers. Plant symbolism is very important. Pines are auspicious, representing longevity. Bamboo is also considered very lucky, but as many are invasive they can create problems in Zen gardens which should remain unchanging. Evergreens add year-round interest and permanence, while deciduous trees prompt thoughts of life and death.

Other popular plants include bugle (*Ajuga reptans*), Japanese anemone (*Anemone hupehensis*), chrysanthemum, *Dichondra micrantha*, ferns, grasses, daylily (*Hemerocalis fulva*), hosta, iris species, *Lilium auratum*, 'Golden Ray' lily and other lily species, Irish moss (*Soleirolia soleirolii*) and Scottish moss (*Sagina*).

SAND AND GRAVEL

A range of grades and colours may be included, from large to small aggregates, white quartz chippings, or smooth sand. Intricately raked patterns encourage meditation.

SPACE

Too much ornamentation is distracting so careful deployment of space was essential for liberating the mind and allowing other senses such as sound to predominate. Again contrast is important. If one side of the garden has rocks, the opposite side should be balanced with open space. In areas where space is controlled, a carefully trimmed tree emphasizes the point. A judiciously placed screen or ornament leads the eye forward, while an arch enhances what is beyond, even if this is simply open sky. Space can be enclosed or delineated by screens or fences of bamboo, split bamboo, or brushwood – natural materials favoured by the Japanese. Delicate colours and textures are aesthetically pleasing, as well as functional, while natural materials form softer, subtler boundaries than solid walls.

STONES

Japanese treated stones with great reverence, considering them homes to God-like spirits. They were used for paths, stepping stones, bridges, and placed singly or grouped together, representing mountains, islands or coastline and were the yang elements of the garden. Upright stones simulate waterfalls in dry landscape gardens. Well-shaped pieces of jagged rock or smooth boulders add drama. However casual and natural the groupings appear, placing is never random and is carefully planned. Japanese gardens all have significant groupings of rocks and stones. The classical *Sanzon*, or Buddhist 'Trinity Stones', is a three-stone arrangement fundamental to most gardens. One large, upright stone is balanced on each side by two smaller stones symbolizing Buddha with two Budhisattvas. Another arrangement consists of fifteen stones, set either singly or in groups. Careful placing of stones is vital. Uneven numbers of stones should flow naturally together. Spacing should be irregular and care taken so stones do not form straight lines. If the main flow of the garden is outwards, this makes the area look larger. Stones also represent animals and birds such as tortoise and crane, both auspicious symbols of good fortune.

WATER

Water and islands were as important in Japan as in China and water was revered as a symbol of purity and life. Waterfalls became places of pilgrimage, with hours spent gazing into pools and meditating. Water is central to many gardens but the effect must always be of natural pools, streams and cascades, rather than artificial-looking ponds and fountains. This also applies to simulated water treatments in dry gardens. Water preferably flowed from east to southwest, passing under the house, although this was not always possible. Streams symbolized one's passage through life. Rocks created natural-looking torrents, cascades and waterfalls. A one-metre-high stone in a waterfall represented the Buddhist deity, Acala, while two vertical stones at the base were attendants. Carefully placed stones represent islands, or peninsulas projecting into the water, and shorelines were artfully contrived. Reflections add a further dimension to the garden, and water also highlights hidden colours and patina of stones and rocks, not seen when dry. Fountains are too artificial, but bamboo pipes trickle water into pools, and the flow and drip of water creates soothing, musical sounds.

A simple, modern Japanese garden at Bridgwalton, Shropshire, with carefully placed rocks, grey slate forming 'water', and white granite chippings 'foam'.

WISTERIA

Japanese wisteria, *Wisteria floribunda* 'Multijuga', has extraordinarily long, beautiful racemes, while Chinese Wisteria, *Wisteria sinensis*, has smaller racemes of flowers. Wisteria looks spectacular trained along buildings, between rails of bridges, or grown as standards.

Creating the style

Japanese gardens vary from small courtyards to lush vistas. They are suitable for tiny spaces such as high-rise balconies, narrow passages or tiny yards. They form a feature in larger, more eclectic gardens, and suit sunshine or shade. The important basic principles must always be strictly adhered to. Consider the style of garden, whether a strolling garden, one viewed from the house, or Zen garden. Tiny gardens or courtyards, *tsuboniwa*, require carefully selected materials to create simple, elegant designs, ideally viewed from the house. The garden entrance and gate should be in keeping, and created from natural materials such as bamboo or wood. Gates

ABOVE: *Trees and shrubs are carefully pruned and this in itself becomes an act of meditation.*

LEFT: *An attractive but simple archway and gate into the Japanese garden at Bridgwalton, Shropshire. Entrances and gates should be in keeping, enhancing the overall appearance of the garden.*

can be set into simple arches of bamboo uprights and cross bars. Sometimes gateways have a small roof of rushes or bark.

Japanese gardens require regular maintenance to keep them at their best. It is important that harmony is not spoilt by fading flowers, decaying leaves, or leaning bamboo poles and rocks. Nothing must jar on the senses, so order is maintained in mind and spirit, as well as in the garden. Prune trees to develop shape or frame distant views. Japanese gardens are peaceful and serene places of quiet relaxation, contemplation and meditation, away from the turmoil of life. Observe the balance of yin and yang principles – soft moss or plants against hard rock, rough surfaces against smooth, open space against enclosed. Gardens are aesthetically pleasing and careful planning is essential to ensure everything works harmoniously together.

Simple gardens are often the most effective so aim for a strong basic design and list the elements to include. Decide on viewpoints and check whether 'borrowed' scenery can be drawn into the garden. Keep everything uncomplicated, asymmetrical and natural to achieve an uncluttered design. A basic plan helps in positioning elements.

Materials are important. Varying types and colours of stone include blue stone, andesite and granite. Never use synthetic materials. Give time to choosing attractively

weathered, interestingly shaped and coloured stone, allowing one type to predominate. Careful observation determines the best aspect for placing each stone, top or bottom, front or back. Overlarge rocks in small areas look out of place, and large stones may require positioning by a contractor. Place the main stone first. Stones should be firmly set to prevent toppling or leaning later. A layer of gravel in the hole helps, as do small stones and rock wedges below ground to support stones in position. Arrange these as if in a natural landscape. Choose appropriate grades and colours of gravel, taking local landscape into account. Lay gravel to 8 centimetres for a normal landscape garden, spreading onto prepared and firmed ground, or weed suppressant membrane.

Raked patterns require a 20 centimetre depth. Keep patterns simple, as they are difficult to perfect in the early stages. Raking patterns requires concentration and due reverence, treating the process as a meditative exercise which should be calming rather than frustrating.

Bamboo creates stylish fences in many different designs, using vertical, horizontal or diagonal canes.

RIGHT: *The Tea House in an inspirational Japanese garden in Shropshire.*

BELOW: *Japanese tree pruning shapes. Rounded shape; multi-stemmed with pads at various heights; straight stems with cloud forms; s-shaped trunk with cloud forms.*

Raked patterns replicating movement of water also require 20 centimetres of gravel. Special rakes facilitate pattern making. When finished, gently hose dirt from the surface.

Screens and fences are solid or open, decorative or plain, depending on situation, but must be of natural materials. Bamboo fences are stylish, and many designs are possible using vertical, horizontal or diagonal canes. Simple uprights are strengthened by horizontals, *Kenninji-gaki*. More detailed effects have crossed fishnet patterns, *aboshi moyo*, or canes bound together with rope, *tokusa-gaki*. Low bamboo fences, *Kinkakuji-gaki*, make useful path edgings. Fences also incorporate other natural materials such as tree bark or branches.

Water is important whether in ponds, streams, waterfalls or represented through dry, raked patterns. (Water is naturally flat, so it is crucial dry streams and ponds are also level.) Water basins and lamps are available in various shapes, sizes and designs. Choose those in keeping with the specific style of garden being created. Use the best materials available; good-quality materials enhance the garden, remain unchanged and last for years, or even lifetimes.

Moss is beautiful, but successful growth depends on finding the correct type for the location. If the garden already has mossy corners try transplanting into other areas, as the plant is obviously suited to the local conditions. Lift underlying soil when transplanting moss, and water well until established. Numerous moss-substitute plants are available but few give the delicate effect, softness and colour of true moss.

Trees are the main architectural features of any garden. Their eventual height and spread is often restricted in oriental gardens. Trees supply spring blossom and autumn colour. Evergreens symbolize everlasting life, deciduous trees the cycle of life and death. Pines are popular, evergreen, easily trained, and appear nicely 'gnarled' and ancient from a young age. Dwarf pines are versatile and suit a number of situations. Other trees include flowering cherries, with the delicacy of single-flowered varieties preferred to double. Carefully pruned trees are nurtured and manicured over generations. They can be heavily pruned, lightly trimmed, or bent and trained with wires, canes and weights. Aim for shapely,

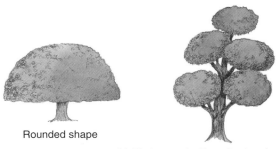

Rounded shape

Multi-stemmed with pads at various heights

Straight stems with cloud forms

S-shaped trunk with cloud forms

harmonious balance and proportion, as well as revealing interesting aspects of smooth or gnarled trunks, peeling or coloured bark, twisted branches, and careful groupings of leaves. Bamboos are quintessentially oriental plants, and wisteria, azalea, peony and chrysanthemum are also synonymous with Japanese gardens.

Japanese gardens require strict adherence to principles otherwise the true essence is lost. They take time to mature, and demand patience and careful maintenance,

all of which are treated as acts of contemplation and reflection. Look to nature for inspiration with landscapes, mountains, waterfalls, rivers, streams, ponds and oceans, her calming greens, natural tones, ancient stones, and soothing play of light and shadow. Japanese gardens have a simple charm and sophisticated skill that appeals to an inner sense of order and harmony. They have great beauty and tranquillity and one cannot fail but be calm and peaceful when contemplating such a scene, especially in today's chaotic world.

Japanese style

Trees and shrubs

The height and spread of trees is often restricted, and trees and shrubs artfully trained or severely pruned to replicate shapes such as clouds or waves. Pines are very auspicious trees, and evergreens add year round interest and permanence, while deciduous trees emphasize the intransience of life.

Abies balsamea 'Andover'
Abies nordmanniana 'Jansen'
Abies nordmanniana 'Golden Spreader'
Acer capillipes
Acer crataegifolium 'Veitchii'
Acer davidii
Acer griseum
Acer japonicum
Acer palmatum 'Asahi Zuru'
Acer palmatum 'Beni Maiko'
Acer palmatum 'Bloodgood'
Acer palmatum 'Crimson Queen'
Acer palmatum 'Dissectum'
Acer palmatum 'Dissectum Atropurpuerum'
Acer palmatum 'Osakazuki'
Acer pseudoplatanus 'Brilliantissimum'
Acer shirasawanum 'Aureum'
Berberis thunbergii
Buxus sempervirens
Camellia japonica
Carpinus betulus
Cedrus atlantica 'Glauca'
Cedrus atlantica 'Pendula'
Chaenomeles japonica
Chaenomeles speciosa 'Geisha Girl'
Chamaecyparis 'Grayswood Pillar'
Chamaecyparis obtusa 'Contorta'
Chamaecyparis obtusa 'Intermedia'
Chamaecyparis obtusa 'Juniperoides'
Chamaecyparis obtusa 'Nana'

Chamaecyparis obtusa 'Nana Aurea'
Chamaecyparis pisifera 'Blue Globe'
Chamaecyparis pisifera compacta 'Variegata'
Chamaecyparis pisifera 'Squarrosa Lombarts'
Chamaecyparis thyoides 'Glauca'
Cornus kousa
Cryptomeria japonica 'Cristata Compacta'
Cryptomeria japonica 'Globosa'
Cryptomeria japonica 'Kohui Yatsubusa'
Cryptomeria japonica 'Sekkan Sugi'
Cunninghamia lanceolata 'Compacta'
Daphne bholua 'Jacqueline Postill'
Daphne x burkwoodii
Daphne mezereum
Daphne mezerum f. alba
Daphne odora
Fatsia japonica
Fothergilla major
Hebe buxifolia
Hydrangea macrophylla
Juniperus chinensis 'Blaauw'
Juniperus chinensis 'Kaisuka'
Juniperus chinensis 'Shimpaku'
Juniperus communis 'Compressa'
Juniperus communis 'Green Carpet'
Juniperus horizontalis
Juniperus procumbens 'Nana'
Juniperus taxifolia 'Lutchensis'
Larix kaempferi 'Pendula'
Larix kaempferi 'Dwarf Blue'
Ligustrum ovalifolium
Magnolia cambellii
Magnolia delavayi
Magnolia x soulangiana
Magnolia stellata
Mahonia fortunei
Mahonia japonica
Mahonia x media
Malus 'Almey'
Malus 'Centurion'
Malus floribunda

ABOVE: *Paeonia suffruticosa.*

RIGHT: *Lilium longiflorum.*

Malus hupehensis
Malus 'Marshall Oyama'
Malus prunifolia
Malus x purpurea
Malus 'Red Jade'
Malus sieboldii
Malus 'Snowdrift'
Malus tschonoskii
Osmanthus x burkwoodii
Osmanthus fragrans
Paeonia delavayi
Paeonia suffruticosa
Pittosporum tenuifolium
Picea abies 'Frohburg'
Picea abies 'Inversa'
Picea abies 'Mariana Nana'
Picea breweriana
Pinus contorta 'Asher'
Pinus densiflora 'Pendula'
Pinus mugo 'Pumilio'
Pinus parviflora 'Negishi'
Pinus sylvestris 'Aurea'
Pinus sylvestris 'Saxatilis'
Pinus thunbergii 'Awaji'
Pinus thunbergii 'Suchiro'
Podocarpus nivalis
Prunus avium 'Plena'
Prunus cerasifera
Prunus 'Fudan-zakura'
Prunus 'Hokusai'

Prunus 'Ichiyo'
Prunus incisa
Prunus incisa 'Kojo-no-mai'
Prunus jamasakura
Prunus 'Kanzan'
Prunus 'Mount Fuji'
Prunus 'Okame'
Prunus padus 'Albertii'
Prunus persica
Prunus serrula
Prunus x subhirtella 'Autumnalis'
Prunus 'Ukon'
Sciadopitys verticillata
Skimmia japonica
Sorbus aria 'Lutescens'
Sorbus aucuparia 'Asplenifolia'
Sorbus cashmeriana
Sorbus 'Ethel's Gold'
Sorbus hupehensis var. obtusa
Spiraea thunbergii
Taxus cuspidata
Thujopsis dolobrata
Tsuga canadensis 'Albospica'
Tsuga canadensis 'Iron Springs'
Ulmus parvifolia
Wisteria floribunda
Wisteria sinensis
Yucca filamentosa
Yucca filifera

Low shrubs

Ideal for ground cover.

Buxus insularis
Buxus microphylla
Cotoneaster cashmiriensis
Cotoneaster congestus
Cotoneaster procumbens 'Streibs Findling'
Cotoneaster 'Skogholm' *syn C. Skogsholmen*
Parahebe x bidwillii 'Kea'
Parahebe hookeriana
Thymus coccineous

Grasses

Grasses add an ethereal quality, while bamboo are auspicious plants.

Arundinaria tecta
Arundo donax
Bambusa multiplex
Bambusa ventricosa
Carex comans
Carex oshimensis 'Buchanii'
Chionochloa conspicua
Cortaderia sp.
Deschampsia flexuosa
Festuca amethystina
Festuca glauca
Miscanthus sp
Nandina domestica
Pennisetum setaceum
Phyllostachys aurea
Phyllostachys bambusoides
Phyllostachys flexuosa
Phyllostachys nigra
Pleioblastus pygmaeus var. distichus
Sasa veitchii
Sinobambusa intermedia
Stipa tennuissima
Thamnocalamus spathiflorus

Ferns

Delicate green fronds compliment hard rock.

Asplenium adiantum-nigrum
Asplenium ruta-muraria
Asplenium scolopendrium
Asplenium trichomanes

Athyyrium filix-femina
Blechnum spicant
Cryptogramma crispa
Dryopteris austriaca
Dryopteris cristata
Dryopteris filix-mas
Dryopteris oreades
Dryopteris pseudomas
Oreopteris limbosperma
Osmunda regalis
Polypodium vulgare
Polystichum aculeatum
Polystichum setiferum

Low growing plants and mosses

Ideal for moss gardens and ground cover.

Acaena microphylla
Ajuga reptans
Amphidium mougeotii
Andreaea rupestris
Atrichum undulatum
Aulacomnium androgynum
Barbula convoluta
Bartramia pomiformis
Brachythecium plumosum
Breutelia chrysocama
Bryum argenteum
Bryum capillare
Ceratodon purpureus
Cratoneuron commutatum
Dichondra micrantha
Dicranella heteromalla
Dicranoweisia cirrata
Dicranoweisia scoparium
Dryptodon patens
Eurynchium praelongum
Hedera helix
Hedwigia ciliata
Homalothecium sericeum
Hylocomium splendens
Hypnum cupressiforme
Leucobryum glaucum
Mnium hornun
Nardia scalaris
Neckera complanata
Philonotis fontana
Plagiomnium undulatum
Plagiothecium undulatum
Pleurozium schreberi
Pohlia nutans

Polytrichum commune
Polytrichum juniperinum
Racomitrium aquaticum
Raoulia australis
Rhizomnium punctatum
Sagina subulata
Saxifrage sp
Scleranthus uniflorus
Soleirolia soleirolii
Sphagnum auriculatum var. auriculatum
Sphagnum auriculatum var. inundatsum
Sphagnum cuspidatum
Tetraphis pellucida
Teucrium pyrenaicum
Thuidium tamariscinum
Thymus sp.
Tortella tortuosa
Tortula muralis
Trichostomum brachydontium
Vinca major
Vinca minor

Iris

Stately species for Japanese gardens.

Iris ensata 'Agripomella'
Iris ensata 'Center of Interest'
Iris ensata 'Chitose-no-Tomo'
Iris ensata 'Kuma Fun-jin'
Iris ensata 'Moonlight Waves'
Iris ensata 'Pink Frost'
Isia ensata 'Wine Ruffles'
Iris ensata 'Rowden Queen'
Iris ensata 'Yako-no-Tama'
Iris kaempferi
Iris laevigata 'Alba'
Iris laevigata 'Atropurpurea'
Iris laevigata 'Flore-Pleno'
Iris laevigata 'Snowdrift'
Iris laevigata 'Variegata'
Iris laevigata x versicolour 'Tamberg Hybrid'
Iris laevigata x versicolour 'Weymouth Midnight'
Iris pseudacorus 'Alba'
Iris pseudacorus var. bastardii 'Flore Pleno'
Iris pseudacorus var. bastardii 'Golden Queen'
Iris pseudacorus 'Variegata'
Iris sibirica 'Blue Moon'
Iris sibirica 'Butter and Sugar'
Iris sibirica 'Chilled Wine'
Iris sibirica 'Snow Queen'
Iris sibirica 'Tropic Night'

Iris tenax.

Iris versicolor 'Algonquin'
Iris versicolor 'China West Lake'
Iris versicolor 'Kemesina'
Iris versicolor 'Rosea'

Miscellaneous plants

Anemone hupehensis
Chrysanthemum cvs
Hemerocallis fulva
Hosta albomarginata
Hosta 'Blue Blush'
Hosta fortunei 'Albopicta'
Hosta 'Frances Williams'
Hosta lancifolia
Hosta montana f aureomarginata
Hosta nigrescens
Hosta ventricosa 'Variegata'
Lilium auratum
Lilium auratum var. platyphyllum
Lilium candidum
Lilium concolor
Lilium davidii
Lilium formosanum var. pricei
Lilium hansonii
Lilium lancifolium
Lilium longiflorum
Lilium regale
Lilium speciosum
Paeonia anomala
Paeonia 'August Dessert'
Paeonia 'Bowl of Beauty'
Paeonia 'Cornelia Shaylor'
Paeonia 'Duchesse de Nemours'
Paeonia 'Krinkled White'
Paeonia officinalis 'Rubra Plena'

8 Islamic style

The style

Islamic gardens developed in hot, dry desert regions to become oases of lush greenery, shade, abundant water and a profusion of perfumed flowers. High walls protect from the intense heat, scorching winds, and prying eyes to create a dream of Paradise. A garden was intended to be a serene refuge from the outside world, a place of tranquillity for peaceful meditation and prayer.

Much inspiration for Islamic gardens was derived from the Qur'an, and gardens were based on elements inherent in Islamic faith and Muslim culture. Geometry and symmetry were absolutely fundamental, expressing harmony and order. Flower beds and pools had precise, geometric shapes. The main theme in many Islamic gardens was the *chahar-bagh*, or four-fold garden.

Water was of paramount importance in designs and traditionally four canals, representing the four rivers of Paradise, emanated at right angles from a central pool or fountain. These in turn linked with other channels running around the perimeter wall, effectively dividing the whole area into four equal sections – the quadripartite garden.

The numbers four and eight have important associations with Paradise, alluding to the four rivers of Paradise, and to the eight-sided form which is a combination of the circle (representing God, perfection and infinity) and the square (representing man, imperfection and finiteness). These numbers are often symbolically repeated in Islamic gardens with four gardens, four pools, four water canals, eight-sided pavilions, eight trees, eight pools, and eight-sided pools or flower beds.

Gardens included many other decorative elements although Islamic culture precluded representational sculptures. There were jewel-like parterres; flowers and trees were composed of gemstones and precious metals; and exquisite glazed tiles on ornamented buildings, walls and paths.

Calligraphy, an important Islamic art form, was inscribed into buildings and was also woven with plants. Detailed garden designs spread into carpets and textiles, with patterns of trees, flowers and pools incorporated into 'garden carpets', which were carried around as a

The delicate columns and fretted stonework in the Court of the Lions at the Alhambra Palace, Spain, inspired by Islamic architecture.

OPPOSITE: *Traditional Islamic gardens were oases of lush greenery, shade and abundant water, surrounded by high walls that protected from the intense heat.*

pleasant reminder to those travelling away from home. Islam produced some of the most beautiful landscape architecture in the world, which had important influences on subsequent European garden design.

History

The Prophet Muhammad lived between AD570 and 632. Born in the Arabian city of Mecca, his mission established both the state and religion of Islam. After his death Islam covered a massive area from the Atlantic Ocean to the Indus River, in what is present-day Pakistan.

Islamic leaders conquered Iran in AD641 and were in Egypt by AD642. By the eighth century, North Africa, Spain, Portugal, India, and Indonesia were all Islamic lands and they were to remain in the Iberian peninsula for the next nine centuries. Baghdad became the intellectual capital of the Empire around AD762, accumulating great wealth and knowledge. Although the Islamic empire began to disintegrate in the tenth century, much of it remained based on Islamic beliefs and law until the early twentieth century.

The main rulers dictated the artistic styles. They were not all Muslims and their art was not all religious. They incorporated ideas from earlier civilizations and despite the different time periods and regions, these retained a fundamental unity.

Islamic gardens drew inspiration from the Qur'an, which mentions gardens 164 times – although the concept of Paradise being a garden originated with the Sumerians and Babylonians, and is inherent in many faiths. The Islamic religion added a new spirituality with

Extensive irrigation systems set into the walls provide the pools and fountains of the Alhambra Palace, Spain, with copious supplies of water.

symbolism in both design and planting. The Qur'an describes Paradise gardens filled with the delights of cool, flowing water, luxuriant plants and welcome shade, as well as descriptions of design, gates, and pavilions. The perfect garden was not created as an outward symbol of show as we tend to do in the West, but as an inner space of peace and beauty to nourish the soul – a place for spiritual reflection, tranquillity and contemplation.

Islamic gardens developed in inhospitable landscapes of dusty plains, arid rocks and stark mountains, scorched by intense heat and sunshine. Valleys, particularly those with springs and streams of water, were highly prized. Later such oases were cleverly engineered and evidence of Islamic hydrological technology can be found throughout the Mediterranean region. The necessity of extensive irrigation systems promulgated the development of numerous devices for collecting, storing, channelling, and moving water. Fountains cooled the hot, dry air as well as adding the refreshing and soothing sounds of water, which overflowed from stone basins and was channelled into pools and canals. Walls excluded the hostile environment without and also provided privacy and seclusion. Trees created welcome shade and the gardens burgeoned with colourful flowers, herbs and fruiting plants. In such a harsh

Fountains form delicate arcs of spray at the Alhambra Palace, Spain, where gardens are filled with the delights of cool, flowing water, plants and shade.

RIGHT: *Water is a highly important feature of the Alhambra Palace gardens, with still, mirror-like pools reflecting blue sky and delicate architecture.*

BELOW: *Painting of an Islamic style garden with central pools, water canals and an abundance of flowers and fruit.*

landscape these green oases truly did represent heaven on earth – The Islamic 'Dream of Paradise'.

The vast Islamic trading network carried ideas out of the Arabian Peninsula to Persia, absorbing additional elements of traditional Persian garden design and crafts. Spreading into Moorish Spain and India these ideas climaxed in Muslim Spain with the legendary courtyard gardens shaded by trees and filled with an abundance of flowers and fruit, reflective pools, cooling fountains and beautiful pavilions. The harmonious proportions of the Alhambra Palace, Granada, begun in 1232, are said to epitomize the unity between internal and natural landscaping and buildings. Contained inside the rough, fortified walls are a variety of exquisitely designed, formal, open 'rooms' or courtyards. The adjoining Generalife, or summer palace (*c.*1319) had a more natural, terraced and open hillside garden. There was less formality in its planning and it contained abundantly more plants and water. Water is a highly important feature of the gardens and the complex system of pools, water channels, and fountains was supplied from a series of reservoirs, gutters and tanks built into the palace walls, dating back to the eleventh century. Still, mirror-like pools and canals reflect the brilliant blue of the sky above, and elegant buildings and gardens surrounding them. Over the centuries the Alhambra, or 'red castle', and its gardens fell into disrepair with little done to safeguard their former magnificence. It wasn't until the nineteenth century that serious preservation work was finally undertaken in an attempt to restore the gardens and buildings to something of their past splendour. Today, the Alhambra and its gardens are renowned throughout the world, although centuries of change and restoration work mean many aspects may differ from their original design.

The courtyard garden of the Mosque at Cordoba, the 'Patio de los Naranjos' ('Courtyard of the Oranges'), was established in AD976 and is the oldest enclosed garden in Europe. Measuring 120 metres by 60 metres, water channels are bordered with orange trees, carefully aligned with the pillars of the buildings, giving the impression of drawing the garden into the building and the building into the garden.

The Qur'an advocated pilgrimages to Mecca (Hajj), and Muslims were inveterate explorers, producing maps and guides of their travels. Ibn-Battuta (1304–69) has been described as the 'Muslim Marco Polo'. He travelled to China, India, Africa, and Russia, holding diplomatic posts with Islamic Sultans, and Mongol and Chinese Emperors. He travelled over 75,000 miles in his lifetime, the most anyone had ever travelled.

In the late fourteenth century most of Eurasia was ruled by the great warlord Timur (1336–1405), known as Tamerlane in the West. He amassed a wealth of artists and skilled craftsmen in legendary cities such as Samarkand in Uzbekistan, creating magnificent gardens inspired by Islamic and Persian designs. Samarkand was irrigated by water from the Hindu Kush Mountains and the city was surrounded by gardens. Majestic tree-lined avenues led to vast walled enclosures filled with trees and flowers. Pools and canals divided gardens into four quarters and defined the main axis. Balconies overlooked fields of flowers, great orchards and tented pavilions of red, blue and gold silk intended for relaxation. Many gardens were immortalized in miniature paintings of the time.

Babur (1483–1531), a direct descendant of Timur through his father, and of Genghis Kahn through his mother, established the Mughul dynasty in India, becoming the first Mughul Emperor. He immersed himself in Persian culture and influences, designing superb gardens including his magnificent quadripartite garden, 'The Garden of Fidelity', *Bagh-i-Vafa*, in Kabul, which was planted in 1508. He left descriptions of his gardens, including the Garden of Fidelity, his first and most important garden. He describes one visit, telling of his delight at seeing the garden when it was in its full

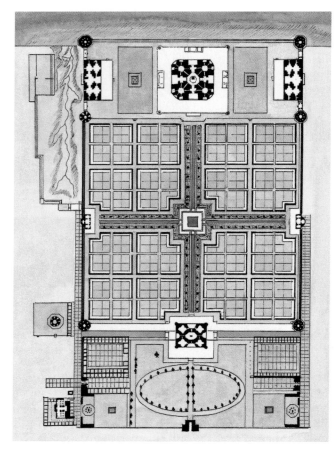

ABOVE: *A plan of the Taj Mahal gardens, clearly showing the quadripartite design, divided by water channels and having a central pool on the cross axis.*

BELOW: *The incredible and beautiful Taj Mahal gardens, Agra, created by Shah Jahan in memory of his beloved wife.*

TOP: *The El Bahia Palace, Morocco, has a complex system of rooms, courtyards, patios and gardens, created between 1894 and 1900 for Ahmed ibn Moussa.*

MIDDLE: *Edwin Lutyens worked on the development of the gardens in Delhi, India. Inspired by Islamic designs, he incorporated many ideals and principles into his European garden designs. He designed a series of canals and pools at Hestercombe Gardens, Somerset.*

BOTTOM: *Distinguished garden designer John Brookes has long been inspired by Islamic gardens and often uses components from them in his designs as here at Ecclesden Manor.*

glory, the grass covered with clover, citrus trees laden with ripe oranges, pomegranates hanging red from the trees, and concluded, 'I was never so much pleased with the Garden of Fidelity as on this occasion.'

Gardens continued to be built by Babur's successors including the Shalimar Gardens of Kashmir, and the remarkable Taj Mahal, Agra (1632–54), built by Emperor Shah Jahan in memory of his beloved wife. This ethereal mausoleum, shimmering above the surrounding lake, epitomizes the pavilions that often served as tombs for the garden owner after their death. Pavilions were usually placed in the middle of rectangular lakes with pools and water channels radiating outwards.

The tradition of creating great Islamic gardens continued right up until the eighteenth and nineteenth centuries. A large and more recent garden was constructed in the Quasba, Marrakech, Morocco, between 1894 and 1900 for Ahmed Ibn Moussa, known as Ba Ahmed. The El Bahia Palace has a complex system of rooms, courtyards, patios and gardens. There are numerous highly decorative features including mosaics, paths, pools and fountains in various materials, colours, shapes and textures. The massive 8-hectare gardens are filled with shady trees, plants perfume the air, and the sight and sound of water is never far away.

Creating Islamic gardens in the West is not a recent concept. Leading twentieth-century architect, Sir Edwin Lutyens worked in India and in 1912 was commissioned to work on redesigning the city of Delhi. One of his greatest works was the magnificent Rashtrapati Bhavan, the Viceroy's residence, classed as the last great garden in the Mughul style. Inspired by designs from Persian carpets, the Carpet Garden covers more than 2 hectares and includes two massive formal pools together with a series of water channels, and fountains, based on Mughul water gardens. On returning to Britain, Lutyens incorporated many Islamic ideas and principles into his garden designs and water features.

School children helped create their own Islamic garden at St Mary the Virgin primary school, Cardiff, in

2003. An Islamic garden opened in the Marzahn Park, Berlin in 2005, called the 'Garden of Four Rivers'. The London Ishmaili Centre has a beautiful roof garden, and a proposed development at Abbey Mills, London plans a new Mosque, school and garden. In Bradford, amongst the many attractions of Lister Park, refurbished and re-opened by Bradford Council in 2002, are the impressive and beautiful Mughul water gardens.

One of the most beautiful modern Islamic gardens in Britain was created by leading garden designer, Emma Clark, based on an idea originally suggested by HRH the Prince of Wales. After the garden was exhibited at Chelsea in 2001, it was moved to his Gloucestershire home, Highgrove. Eminent garden designer John Brookes has also long been inspired by Islamic gardens, often using components from them in his garden designs.

Elements from Islamic gardens can be incorporated into any garden, but although effective, in isolation these features do not make a true Islamic garden as they lack the overall symmetry, symbolism and aura of peace and tranquillity that should emanate from them. With increasing stresses and strains of a frenetic modern world, the peaceful harmony of an Islamic garden becomes increasingly appealing, regardless of one's religion or background. A quiet, enclosed haven, sheltered by walls and shaded by tall trees, pools reflect the sky and provide the sound of gently lapping water or tinkle of fountains, mixed with birdsong. Lush greenery and colourful flowers waft perfume on the breeze. A small 'pavilion' with comfortable seating and cushions promises rest, relaxation and quiet contemplation, looking out upon the beauty, harmony and serenity of the scene. Islamic gardens are an escape from the pressures and tensions of everyday existence, to refresh one's spirit and soul. They are a place to simply 'be'.

Elements of the Islamic garden

ACCESSORIES

All accessories should complement the style of the garden. These could include: Moroccan-inspired furniture and inlaid tables; stone or mosaic pools and fountains; mosaic wall panels; Islamic-style mirrors; small tea light glasses for candles, and a calligraphy panel with an appropriate inscription.

AESTHETICS

The garden should blend with the house and surrounding area so that everything is pleasing to the eye and nothing jars on the senses. Islamic gardens create

Enclosed courtyard with decorative mosaics and central fountain.

beautiful, harmonious, life-sustaining oases. A unique ambience and mystery promote unity between the spiritual, man, and nature. Gardens provide peaceful sanctuaries, refreshing the spirit, and encouraging relaxation, happiness, contemplation and prayer.

COURTYARDS AND WALLS

Courtyards were often open areas in the centre of the house, creating private spaces hidden from public view, forming a divide between the inner and outer worlds. The Qur'an described Paradise as being surrounded by walls with gated entrances enclosing beautiful gardens. Those arriving in Paradise will find 'Gardens of Eternity whose doors will be open to them '. In arid regions the walled garden had purely practical motives, creating private spaces sheltered from the heat, and keeping sand and dust at bay.

DESIGN

There were three specific types of garden. The inner courtyard, *bustan*, was the formal area with pools, water channels, plants and shade trees. The kitchen garden, *rawdah*, provided food and herbs, while the orchard, *jannah*, had citrus and other fruiting trees, vines, and palms, irrigated by canals. These were either treated as separate gardens, or combined into one garden. Geometrically shaped beds were square, rectangular, diamond or star-shaped, placed symmetrically in the garden, and edged with tiles, stone, or low, clipped box hedges. More complex boundaries used a variety of materials and elaborate patterns.

GEOMETRY

Geometry was not simply a method of deploying patterns emphasizing symmetrical design. It carried important connotations in relation to sacred art and symbolism, and was crucial to the design of the garden. Spatial awareness and use of enclosed space was important. Division and sub-division of space add to the beauty, enhance the harmony of the garden and bring peace and tranquillity to those who dwell there. Geometric layouts emphasize the symmetrical appearance of the whole.

LILY

Lilies were favourite flowers in Islamic gardens. They are herbaceous bulbs with a range of flower colours from white, cream, yellow, orange and pink to red and purple, often with attractive marking on petals. Flowers can have open, trumpet-shaped or reflexed petals, and many have exotic perfumes. Lilies flower from early summer to autumn, in sun or shade.

MULTI-USE

Traditional gardens provided for a multitude of diverse elements including shade, relaxation, entertaining, plants, food, recreation and spiritual activities. As well as decorative plants and flowers, gardens contained vegetables, herbs and fruit. Plants provided perfume to assail the senses, particularly at night when the garden was regularly enjoyed and on view.

PATHS

Formal paths had geometrically paved or tiled surfaces,

Paths often had highly intricate, decorative designs incorporating ceramic tiles, bricks, stone, slate or pebbles.

often inlaid with coloured ceramic tiles. Suitable materials are plain earthenware tiles, bricks, paving sets, slate, or pebbles. Glazed tiles are expensive but effective in highlighting certain areas. Narrow, coloured tiles enhance path borders or create geometric designs in paths, paving or walls. Simple designs using plain materials create suitable geometric patterns at little cost.

PAVILIONS

Pavilions were either highly decorative buildings with pierced plasterwork and stone, or fabric tents often of silk. They were filled with beautiful carpets and comfortable cushions providing relaxation and shade, allowing the garden to be viewed to advantage. Ideally pavilions were constructed over running water. The Qur'an states: 'For those who fear their Lord, that lofty mansions one above the other have been built: Beneath them flow rivers.'

PLANTS

Plants are secondary to design in Islamic gardens. Trees were important for shade. Colourful flowers were woven through the garden, including fruit, vegetables and perfumed plants. A wide range of Mediterranean plants grow in cooler climates giving an authentic touch to the Islamic garden. There are also hundreds of plants that achieve the same or very similar effect. The fact that some plants are not authentic does not pose a major problem.

TOP: *This newly designed garden on Mallorca features a very attractive, quadripartite design with central rill.*

BELOW: *Highly decorative pebble mosaics surround the water canal in this Spanish courtyard garden. Water was a fundamental feature of Islamic style gardens, providing soothing sounds and refreshing the dry atmosphere.*

QUADRIPARTITE DESIGN

Classical Islamic gardens were walled squares or rectangles often sub-divided into four equal symmetrical areas, creating the traditional *chahar bagh*, or quadripartite garden. This style was a principle feature of many Islamic gardens. A central pool spilled into four canals, dividing the garden into equal quarters. Alternatively the garden was divided by paths, and usually had a central pool.

ROSE

Roses are the 'Queen of Flowers', much favoured in Islamic gardens as they bloomed over a long period and were also strongly perfumed. Older varieties are more appropriate than floribundas and hybrid tea varieties of recent years, as these look out of place.

SHADE

Shade is highly prized and very necessary in hot countries where relief from the interminable heat of the sun is very important. The Qur'an's promised rewards for the righteous are: 'We shall admit them to shades, cool and ever deepening.' Trees were the main element for creating shade. Avenues were placed in straight lines, or arranged geometrically. *Cupressus* species were popular, as being evergreen they represented eternal life. Fruit trees had added benefits of providing food as well as shade, fulfilling the sought-after multi-faceted use. Date palms were common, as were pomegranate and citrus trees. Vines provided canopies of shade, and pavilions provided respite from the fierce sun.

TULIP

Originally wild plants of central Asia, growing particularly around Tien-Shan and the Pamir Alai mountain range near modern day Islamabad. Tulips were cultivated by the Turks at least as early as AD 1000 and named after the turban, *toliban*. They have a long, rich heritage in Persian gardens. Seventeenth-century tulipmania saw bulbs changing hands for astronomical prices and one poor man actually ate his fortune: having invested heavily in tulip bulbs he came home slightly inebriated one night and ate them all, thinking they were onions! Tulips were popular because of their bright colours and flower shapes from open or deep cups to long, narrow, pointed, upright petals, much favoured in Turkish and Persian gardens.

WATER

Without water there is no life. In hot, arid countries, water is a valuable commodity and irrigation a prime concern. Ingenious engineering enabled water to be carried from the surrounding hills by way of underground canals that fed into a series of channels and pools above ground in gardens. In such hostile environments essential water irrigated plants. Aesthetic qualities of water in the garden as a decorative feature developed from this purely practical beginning. Water was a fundamental feature of Islamic gardens, adding a dynamic element, providing soothing sounds and refreshing the dry atmosphere. Light, reflections, sound, movement, and the cooling, refreshing qualities of water became key elements.

The Qur'an repeatedly mentions water, rain, springs and rivers, and refers over thirty times to 'Gardens beneath which rivers flow'. The Prophet Muhammad also described four rivers in the Qur'an, giving rise to the quadripartite gardens divided by four canals or 'Rivers of Paradise': '… in it are rivers of water incorruptible, rivers of milk of which the taste never changes; rivers of wine, a joy to those who drink, and rivers of honey pure and clear.' Water also enhances and emphasizes architectural elements of Islamic gardens.

Creating the style

A simple, quadripartite garden needs careful measurement dividing the garden into four equal quarters. Four water canals or paths are set at right angles to a central pool and connect to a further path or canal running along the four sides of the boundary. A limited palette of colours, materials, textures and plants creates a calm, unpretentious and harmonious garden, emphasising clear-cut, geometric lines and proportions. Paths can be simply tiled and include a narrow, decorative border.

The four individual squares of the garden are laid to lawn, covered with a layer of aggregate or marble chippings, planted as flower beds, or have inset pools. In traditional gardens flower beds were often sunk below the surrounding paths, creating a carpet-like effect when filled with flowering plants and viewed from above.

Walled areas are ideal for creating an Islamic garden. Walls should be painted white or a natural stone colour. Boundaries can also be of fencing, geometrically designed trellis, or closely clipped, evergreen hedges.

Water is essential, flowing if possible. It symbolizes life and purity. At its simplest, a small, central fountain spills gently into a geometrically shaped pool. Ideally four canals emanate at right angles from the pool. These can be shallow, reflective canals crossed by a small stone slab or bridge giving access to each section of garden. Narrow canals can run down the centre of paths, or paths can be bordered with rills along each side. Water can be still, gently moving or fast flowing, and low, arching fountains further enhance the effect. Often, square pools fill the four divisions of the quadripartite garden, joined by paths. Simple pools are square or rectangular in shape. They can be curved but should still be regular and symmetrical. More complex designs incorporate octagons, six-, eight-, ten- and twelve-pointed stars, or ten- or twelve-sided polygons. Shallow, reflecting pools have still, mirror-like surfaces, or droplets falling from a fountain create gentle ripples across the surface. Long, narrow pools or canals have a central line of low jetting fountains, or fountains edging each side of the water send jets arching across the channel.

Deeper raised basins can be of natural stone or have applied decoration of plain blue or multicoloured ceramic tiles, arranged into geometric designs. Insides of pools and canals can also be tiled, painted blue, or lined with slate, adding an almost 'quicksilver' effect to the

Reflective pools and decorative paving at the Alhambra Palace, Spain.

Moroccan-inspired garden in Paris, designed by Emma Clark.

water. Grandiose fountains are not features of Islamic gardens. Fountains should be small, so small in fact they often do little more than merely create a gentle bubbling in the centre of the pool. There are no naturalistic, representational sculptures. It is the sound and movement of water that is important. Wall fountains have water dripping or tumbling into a basin from a small spout. In turn this can feed canals or pools. Again, these should not be representational and lion masks are definitely out! Moving water in the garden requires pumps and a source of electricity or solar power. Pumps require filters and maintenance.

Complex designs divide gardens into eight equal

sections, or additional multiples. More intricate systems of pools and canals can be incorporated. Varying ground levels include 'sheets' of water falling between one terrace and the next. Fast running rills add more powerful sounds of running water and areas of foaming water are especially effective by moonlight.

Garden pavilions were often highly decorative buildings with pierced plaster and stonework, glazed tiles, latticework, mirrors and mosaics, or they could be simple fabric tents. They faced north to capture as much shade and cooling breezes as possible. A simple pavilion provides a useful and aesthetic element to the Islamic garden, as well as the practicality of shade and a relaxing place to sit in quiet meditation. In a cooler climate, we may prefer to site this facing south to catch sun and provide shelter from cold winds. In smaller areas even a simple canopy would be of benefit.

Iwans are deep, sheltered platforms built into the side of a house or garden wall providing a comfortable resting place to sit on rugs and cushions. Large *iwans* were rooms furnished with couches, tables and a small fountain or pool. Small niches built into walls hold discreet lighting, pottery lamps, or candles, which are particularly effective in gardens at night.

The appearance of free-flowing Islamic script is a joy in itself and calligraphers were revered artists. Adding a small plaque of handwritten lettering recording a phrase or few suitable words in any language makes an interesting feature, although more authentic if in traditional Islamic script. Calligraphic inscription can be incorporated into buildings, walls, ceramics, tiles, or woven with plants. Don't be tempted to cover everything with decorative script or ornamentation. Sacred text should never be walked on, so steps or paths are not ideal places to site inscriptions.

Exquisite glazed tiles are available but designs should be decorative rather than figurative. The wonderful colours and patterns make great adornment for buildings both inside and out. Tiles can also be incorporated into walls, paths, patios, courtyards, raised pools and fountains.

Decorative effects should be kept simple but can include glazed tiles, mosaics, mirrors, shells, metalwork, and calligraphy. The important thing is that nothing should jar on the senses or look out of place. Simpler designs will be far more effective and appealing than more complex creations, especially in smaller gardens.

The main emphasis in Islamic gardens is on basic design and geometric elements, often decorated with mosaics, but plants also had their place. Trees were

Complex series of pools and fountains inspired by Mughul water gardens, at Lister Park, Bradford. Bradford Council restored the gardens, which were re-opened to the public in 2002.

LEFT: *Decorative glazed tiles feature in many Islamic buildings and gardens.*

RIGHT: *Trees wrought from precious metals and jewels often featured in Islamic gardens and this silver tree would make an appropriate addition to a garden.*

essential for creating shade and a border of trees inside the boundary wall adds this all-important element. In traditional gardens, popular shade trees were maple, myrtle, poplar, sycamore, willow, and evergreen *Cupressus* species including the tall, narrow *Cupressus sempervirens* 'Stricta'. Evergreen trees don't lose their leaves and therefore symbolize eternity. Deciduous trees represent life which dies and is reborn again each year. Gardens could incorporate two avenues of trees: an outer line of conifers and an inner, contrasting line of deciduous trees. Fruiting trees were greatly favoured as they provided the multi-faceted use of plants so appreciated, with springtime blossom, summer shade and autumn fruit. Trees were also purely decorative. Olive trees, *Olea europaea*, palms and pomegranate, *Punica granatum*, are suitable trees. Pomegranate trees grow in many areas in Britain but won't fruit, although their red flowers are very decorative. Gardens often incorporated trees crafted from precious metals and jewels. Although this is impossible today, a simply wrought tree of aluminium, steel, or copper could stand in the centre of a pool.

Although the Islamic garden is primarily about order this does not apply to the plants and bold, massed plantings of perennials and annuals are customary within the confines of the geometrically shaped beds. In some respects the style resembles 'cottage garden' type planting with colourful flowers massed together, using the greens and greys of foliage as a foil. It is still important that nothing is too strident to jar on the eye or senses, acting against the Islamic ideal.

Large flowerpots made from natural materials such as earthenware, stone or glazed pottery often adorned gardens and could be moved around to advantage to highlight certain areas or plants, and create points of interest. Pots are massed in groups, arranged into geometrically shaped patterns or used as edging along paths and pools. They are ideal for a wide range of bulbs, plants and small trees.

Citrus trees are attractive and traditional plants but in temperate climates most require winter protection. They make ideal plants for large containers, which can be moved into a frost-free garage, greenhouse or conservatory during the coldest months. The fabulous perfume of waxy, white blossom, appearing at the same time as bright fruit makes the inconvenience of overwintering very worthwhile. Citrus trees will grow outside all year in milder, sheltered areas of Britain.

Dwarf trees are ideal in smaller areas, whether evergreen, deciduous or fruiting, and these again are ideal planted in pots and containers. Vines and other climbing plants are woven through trellis. Waterlilies

Islamic-inspired garden, Hampstead, London, by designer Emma Clark. Tulips have a long and rich heritage in Persian and Islamic gardens.

float upon a pond. Grasses interspersed amongst flowering perennials provide a delicate haze, and their muted colours and soft texture create a good foil against stronger colours and leaf forms. Roses, lilies and tulips must receive special mention as they are fundamental and much loved plants in Islamic gardens.

Above all, it is of paramount importance to achieve the aesthetic quality of the Islamic garden. It should be a place of calm, harmony and order, an escape from the chaos of life. Quieter sounds and simpler designs are often preferable and more appealing to the true ethos of the garden.

The simple and formal design of Islamic gardens radiates peace and tranquillity both in appearance and atmosphere. However small, the Islamic Paradise garden provides an escape from the turmoil of life, to lift our spirits, soothe our souls, and bring an aura of serenity and harmony into our hectic existence. These shady gardens with precise design, gentle, soothing sounds of water, and perfume wafting on the breeze, give a real sense of place. If the garden achieves all of these ideals it is indeed a true Islamic Paradise garden.

Finally, a name. When your garden is finished, in the true tradition of Islamic gardens, it must have a name. 'The Garden of Present Day Tranquillity', perhaps, or the 'Four-fold Garden of Peace'?

Islamic style

Trees

Trees create welcome shade in hot countries, while fruiting trees provide the multi-faceted usage of plants with springtime blossom, summer shade and autumn fruit, much loved in Islamic gardens.

Acer japonicum
Acer palmatum 'Dissectum'
Acer palmatum 'Atropurpureum'
Acer pseudoplatanus
Calocedrus decurrens
Cercis siliquastrum
Chamaecyparis lawsoniana 'Columnaris'
Chamaerops humilis
Crataegus monogyna
Cupressus arizonica 'Columnaris'
Cupressus macrocarpa 'Goldcrest'
Cupressus sempervirens 'Stricta'
x Cuprocyparis leylandii
Eucryphia glutinosa
Ficus carica
Juniperus communis 'Pyramidalis'
Juniperus scopulorum 'Skyrocket'
Liquidambar styraciflua
Magnolia x soulangiana
Malus sp.
Morus nigra
Myrtus communis
Olea europaea
Platanus x hispanica
Platanus orientalis
Populus alba
Prunus armeniaca
Prunus cerasus
Prunus communis
Prunus damascena
Prunus domestica
Prunus dulcis
Punica granatum
Rhamnus cathartica
Salix babylonica
Sorbus aria
Sorbus aucuparia
Tamarix ramosissima
Taxus baccata 'Fastigiata'
Trachycarpus fortunei

Shrubs

Flowering and evergreen shrubs provide year-round interest with foliage, flowers, fruit and perfume.

Arbutus unedo
Artemisia abrotanum
Artemisia absinthium
Buxus sempervirens
Callistemon citrinus
Ceanothus dentatus
Choisya ternata
Cistus sp.
Cytissus x praecox
Daphne mezereum
Daphne odora
Deutzia x elegantissima
Euonymus japonicus
Genista hispanica
Hibiscus syriacus
Laurus nobilis
Lavandula angustifolia
Osmanthus delavayi

Philadelphus 'Virginal'
Phlomis fruticosa
Pittosporum tenuifolium
Pittosporum tobira
Santolina chamaecyparissus
Sarcococca confusa
Sarcoccoa hookeriana
Syringa vulgaris
Teucrium fruticans
Trachelospermum jasminoides
Viburnum sp.

Tender shrubs

These require winter protection but make good container shrubs that can be moved indoors during winter.

Bougainvillea glabra
Citrus limon
Citrus sinensis
Gardenia jasminoides
Hibiscus Rosa-sinensis
Nerium oleander

Borders

Flowering plants
Most perennials suit Islamic gardens, especially the older, less hybridized varieties, with slightly smaller flowers and less flamboyant colours.

Achillea 'Coronation Gold'
Achillea filipendulina 'Gold Plate'
Achillea 'Salmon Beauty'
Alcea rosea
Alchemilla mollis
Anemone x hybrida
Anthemis tinctoria 'E. C. Buxton'
Aquilegia McKana hybrids
Aster amellus
Aster ericoides
Aster novae-angliae
Aster novi-belgii
Astilbe x simplicifolia
Baptisia australis
Bergenia 'Bressingham White'
Bergenia 'Rosi Klose'
Brunnera macrophylla
Campanula carpatica
Campanula lactiflora 'Pritchard's Variety'

Campanula persicifolia
Centaurea moschata
Cheiranthus cheiri
Cirsium rivulare Atropurpureum'
Coreopsis tripteris
Crambe cordifolia
Cynoglossum nervosum
Delphinium x belladonna
Diascia 'Ruby Field'
Diascia rigescens
Dianthus 'Brympton Red'
Dierama pulcherrimum
Digitalis purpurea
Echinacea purpurea
Euphorbia polychroma
Ferula communis 'Gigantea'
Galega 'Lady Wilson'
Gaura lindheimeri
Geranium 'Johnson's Blue'
Geranium psilostemon
Geranium renardii
Geranium sanguineum striatum
Geum x borisii
Gypsophila paniculata 'Bristol Fairy'
Gypsophila 'Rosy Veil'
Helianthus salicifolius
Helleborus niger
Helleborus orientalis
Hemerocallis lilio-asphodelus
Hemerocallis 'Stella de Oro'
Hesperis matronalis
Incarvillea delavayi
Iris sibirica
Knautia macedonica
Kniphofia cvs.
Leucanthemum x superbum
Liatris spicata
Linaria triornithophora
Lychnis coronaria
Macleaya cordata 'Flamingo'
Matthiola incana
Lupinus hybrids
Nepeta grandiflora
Papaver orientale
Papaver somniferum
Penstemon cvs.
Phlox paniculata
Physostegia virginiana 'Summer Snow'
Rudbeckia laciniata
Rudbeckia purpurea
Salvia nemerosa
Salvia uliginosa
Scabiosa caucasica 'Miss Wilmott'

Sidalcea 'Rose Queen'
Sisyrinchium striatum
Thalictrum aquilegifolium
Trifolium pratense
Veratrum nigrum
Veronica austriaca teucrium 'Crater Lake Blue'
Veronica gentianoides
Viola cornuta
Viola odorata
Viola tricolor
Viola x wittrockiana

Perfumed plants

Essential in Islamic gardens, especially night-scented plants that perfume warm summer air, and white flowers, which also look particularly striking in moonlight.

Clematis armandii
Jasminum polyanthum
Lilium candidum
Lonicera caprifolium
Lonicera periclymenum,
Myrtus communis
Nicotiana alata

Herbs

Herbs are included for medicinal and culinary uses.

Allium sativum
Allium schoenoprasum
Aloysia triphylla
Althaea officinalis
Borago officinalis
Chamaemelum nobile
Cichorium intybus
Hyssopus officinalis
Melissa officinalis
Mentha x gentilis
Ocimum basilicum
Origanum vulgare
Petroselinum crispum
Ruta graveolens
Salvia officinalis
Salvia sclarea
Tanacetum vulgare
Teucrium chamaedrys
Thymus vulgaris

Annuals and biennials

Flowering annuals make bright splashes of colour and perfume.

Calendula officinalis
Centaurea cyanus
Centaurea moschata
Dianthus barbatus
Erysimum cheiri
Heliotropium arborescens
Lathyrus odoratus
Lobularia maritima
Matthiola bicornis
Nicotiana cvs.
Nigella damascena
Reseda odorata
Tropaeolum majus

Bulbs, corms, rhizomes and tubers

These can be used in bedding schemes or planted beneath trees and shrubs.

Agapanthus campanulatus
Anemone blanda
Anemone coronaria
Crocosmia 'Lucifer'
Crocus sp.
Cyclamen coum
Cyclamen hederifolium
Hyacinthoides non-scripta
Hyacinthus orientalis
Iris germanica
Iris pallida
Iris unguicularis
Lilium chalcedonicum
Lilium concolor
Lilium longiflorum
Lilium martagon
Lilium monadelphum
Lilium regale
Narcissus sp.
Paeonia lactiflora
Paeonia officinalis
Ranunculus asiaticus
Ranunculus rupestris
Tulipa acuminata
Tulipa biflora
Tulipa clusiana
Tulipa fosteriana
Tulipa greigii

Tulipa linifolia.

Punica granatum flore plena.

Rosa 'Mme Alfred Carrière'.

Tulipa kaufmanniana
Tulipa praecox
Tulipa praestans
Tulipa sprengeri
Tulipa stellata
Tulipa tarda
Tulipa turkestanica

Roses

Roses are a must in Islamic gardens, providing beauty, colour and perfume, although many old varieties have a limited flowering. David Austin's 'English' roses are invaluable, combining traditional, 'old-fashioned' flower shapes, with strong perfume and a long flowering period.

Rosa x alba semi-plena
Rosa 'Albéric Barbier' ramb
Rosa 'Aloha' clg
Rosa 'Belle de Crécy'
Rosa 'Blanche Double de Coubert'
Rosa 'Blush Damask'
Rosa 'Boule de Neige'
Rosa 'Camaieux'
Rosa 'Cecil Brunner'
Rosa centifolia
Rosa 'Constance Spry'
Rosa 'Cottage Rose'
Rosa 'Crocus Rose'
Rosa x damascena

Rosa 'Danse du Feu' clg
Rosa 'Etoile de Hollande' clg.
Rosa 'Evelyn'
Rosa filipes 'Kiftsgate' clm.
Rosa gallica 'Complicata'
Rosa gallica 'Versicolor'
Rosa 'Gentle Hermione'
Rosa 'Gloire de Dijon' clb
Rosa 'La Belle Sultane'
Rosa 'Lawrence Johnston' clb
Rosa 'Maigold' clb
Rosa 'Mermaid' clb
Rosa 'Miss Alice'
Rosa 'Molineux'
Rosa moschata
Rosa moyesii
Rosa x odorata
Rosa 'Reine des Violettes'
Rosa rugosa
Rosa 'Scarborough Fair'
Rosa 'Sharifa Asma'
Rosa 'Souvenir de la Malmaison'
Rosa 'Summer Song'
Rosa 'The Countryman'
Rosa 'The Herbalist'
Rosa 'The Ingenious Mr Fairchild'
Rosa 'The Pilgrim'
Rosa 'The Prince'
Rosa 'Tuscany Superb'
Rosa 'Wedding Day' clb
Rosa 'William Lobb'
Rosa 'Zéphirine Drouhin'

9 Modern style

The style

'Modern' refers to something of the present time. All gardens are 'modern' when first created and gardens worldwide represent their own particular periods. Styles constantly change and evolve, incorporating new ideas, materials, plants and concepts in design. New gardens also draw inspiration from the past and so 'modern' gardens can include historical elements and inspire a wide range of very different and individual styles.

In the 1920s and 1930s, the term 'Modern' was applied to a new style of both interior and exterior design that became fashionable at the time. Many new gardens were still rustic, Arts and Crafts or traditional Italianate styles, but forward-thinking designers began creating very different buildings and gardens along minimalist lines using white painted concrete, sharp angles, straight lines and smooth curves in a cleanly clinical style termed Modernism.

People are often averse to change and anything out of the norm becomes shocking and talked about; this applied to Modernist designs, which were often ridiculed at the time. However, we progress because we are prepared to experiment, try new things, new ideas, new techniques, and new materials in new ways. Today, the shock factor enters many designer portfolios, but in the seventeenth and eighteenth centuries it was just as shocking to ride roughshod over great, formal gardens, turning them into rolling acres of 'natural' landscape as it was to manicure buildings and gardens into minimalist forms in the 1920s and 1930s. On the whole Modernism had limited appeal, and reaction to the stark lines was followed by Post-Modernism and a return to a more exuberant style of design and planting.

Today's designers again rely on unusual hardscaping, geometric shapes, clean lines, modern materials (such as concrete, brushed and galvanized steel, copper, mirrors, glass panels and blocks), innovative styles of paving and water use, with a few carefully chosen 'architectural' plants complementing the style. However, as in the 1920s and 1930s, there are still many people who dislike 'Modern' concepts and prefer traditional styles and plant-orientated gardens, reminiscent of turn-of-the-century country gardens. As we move on in the twenty-first century the fashion is for sustainable and

OPPOSITE: *A modern 'New England' style designed house Devon, 2009, with small gravel garden, architectural plants and box topiary.*

RIGHT: *Anat Golanski's 'Born to be Free' – grey marble. University of Leicester Botanic Garden.*

Strong architectural features, clean lines and bold planting are all hallmarks of today's modern style.

wildlife-friendly gardens. Recycled materials are much in vogue, impacting on garden style by introducing new elements of creativity in the way in which they are used. Recycled materials also have the advantage of looking weathered, immediately giving gardens a feeling of permanence.

Whatever the choice, whether minimalist and clinical, traditional, or a wildlife haven, it is important that the design complements the house and surroundings. Many buildings are now architecturally stronger and less urban than in former years, and gardens should reflect this.

High Cross House, Devon, a superb example of a 1930s International Modernist-style house designed by architect William Lescaze. All aspects of the house, including furniture and furnishings, were designed as an integrated whole, true to Modernist ideals. Renovated by John Winter and Associates for the Dartington Hall Trust, to house the Trust's collection and archives.

History

Britain has a strong history of gardening tradition spanning many centuries, covering different styles and fashions, but it was the twentieth century that heralded a gardening phenomenon that took Britain by storm in the following decades.

Until the early years of the twentieth century it was the aristocracy and affluent individuals who created vast estates and pleasure gardens for enjoyment and sport. Rural cottagers cultivated humble plots of vegetables and herbs to sustain the family. Well-to-do property owners employed a head gardener and team of under-gardeners, but this all largely ended with the First World War, when labour became scarce and increasingly expensive. In the early 1900s great designers such as Jekyll, Lutyens, Page and others had an important impact on garden styles. In general these were still for large houses and wealthy clients rather than suburban dwellings, and designs were still very traditional. But new, avant-garde designers were emerging, including Barry Parker (1867–1947), who planned a garden suburb for 100,000 people near Manchester in 1927.

Oliver Hill (1887–1968) linked Arts and Crafts style with the Modernist movement. He favoured curving lines and formal gardens, used to great effect in his 1930 design for Joldwynds, Surrey. Smooth curves, geometric shapes, white paving and seats, together with pots of columnar evergreens instantly captured the aesthetic of the Modernist garden, although sadly, the house was later demolished.

White concrete was the hallmark of Modernist schemes. High and Over, Buckinghamshire, designed by Amyas Connell in 1934, has a simple, curving drive, truncated triangular beds on the hillside and concrete steps from the terrace leading down to a round, blue pool. Christopher Tunnard (1910–79) was at the forefront of the Modernist movement with innovative,

Front gardens were mainly for show, and here colourful and traditional bedding plants are given a slightly less regimented approach.

functional and minimalist designs. He eliminated anything unnecessary, and disliked an overabundance of plants.

The garden movement was also advancing in America. Thomas Church (1902–78), an American landscape architect, was considered the founding father of Modernist style there, which developed into the 'Californian style'. Having travelled and worked in Europe he favoured classical forms but also incorporated modern concepts, creating over 2,000 gardens.

The big problem was that designers found they were trying to create innovative ideas in smaller and smaller spaces, and added to this was the great conflict between modern and traditional styles. To try to resolve these issues the Royal Horticultural Society held its 1928 international exhibition on garden design, which highlighted the divergence of ideas and confusion facing designers, but appeared to do little overall to resolve the problems. Following this exhibition, the British Association of Garden Architects was established, later renamed as the Institute of Landscape Architects.

Modernism was in vogue roughly between the First World War and the early 1970s as designers looked for new forms of expression. Designs evoked much controversy, especially in local neighbourhoods, but the movement was popular – until challenged by Postmodernism, which advocated a return to traditional materials and forms, roughly from the 1960s on. Geoffrey Jellicoe (1900–96) was one of the first Postmodern designers. He created a 20-foot-square garden on a London housing development, showing that even small gardens could be inspirational. Jellicoe also designed gardens at Sutton Place, Surrey; Ditchley

Park, Oxfordshire; the Water Gardens at Hemel Hempstead; and the Kennedy Memorial at Runnymede.

In the early years of the twentieth century, housing standards, although improving, were still generally poor, with back-to-back terraces and properties fronting directly onto the street. Many had no outside space, and one lavatory, at the end of the terrace, served a number of families. Some houses had small yards, used to store wood and coal, with their own outside lavatory. The advent of modern plumbing meant lavatories moved indoors, creating more space outside – and creativity began to blossom. Little by little, ordinary people began to take more of an interest in gardens. In Britain, the National Garden Scheme began in 1927, with private gardens opening to raise money for charity. An entrance fee of one shilling a head raised £8,000 in the first year when 609 gardens opened. The first 'Yellow Book' was published in 1931. The scheme has now raised in excess of £45 million for charity, with visitors flocking to around 3,600 gardens each year.

Until the advent of the Second World War, agriculture was still considered very much a man's preserve. The introduction of the Women's Land Army during the war years saw women undertaking what were traditionally men's jobs for the first time, opening the floodgates to women in farming and horticulture. With food scarce and the country held to ransom the 'Dig For Victory' campaign had tremendous impact and saw even tiny plots utilized for food.

Britain had been ravaged by two world wars in close proximity, and after the Second World War the big priority was for mass housing to accommodate returning servicemen. Over 150,000 prefabs alone were built, but

Love them or hate them! Exquisitely crafted garden gnomes were introduced into Britain from Germany in 1849. They became popular, and brightly coloured, after the Second World War when their whimsical faces could be seen in gardens across the country. The first commercially mass-produced gnomes appeared in the 1960s.

of necessity, plots were small and tiny spaces around houses were still treated as mainly utilitarian areas. More affluent properties had front and back gardens, but front gardens – like front rooms – were mainly for show. Back gardens, although still largely utilitarian, might now include a small lawn, and a few vegetables and flowers.

The post-war years saw the Chelsea Flower show return, although as more of a social occasion rather than the glitzy shows of today. Despite increasing interest there was still little commercial horticultural enterprise. There were small nurseries scattered across the country, but seed catalogues were simple lists of varieties rather than today's glossy brochures.

The dawn of the 1950s saw a surge in real gardening interest and the smallest gardens exploded with bright and colourful roses, dahlias and bedding plants. Weekends were spent gardening and cutting the lawn. People began taking pride in their gardens, which all tended to follow a standard theme with a small area of neatly mown grass, narrow borders, and minimal selections of flowers and bedding plants in straight rows. Favourites included red salvia, white alyssum, blue lobelia and bright yellow French marigolds. Crazy paving was the height of sophistication, and there might be a sundial, birdbath or wishing well.

In 1951 London's Festival of Britain strove to inspire the populace, promoting traditional crafts and skills and exciting prospects of new commerce and industry. Head designer, James Gardner, and his team, created innovatively styled gardens between complexes of buildings, using unusual plants, including 'architectural' plants. These first 'instant' gardens inspired visitors with new ideas and plants for their own gardens. A rapidly increasing interest in ornamental gardens perhaps included an island bed, a few more unusual flowers, and a goldfish pond with a waterlily. Cutting grass and digging beds was still very much a man's domain, but women began taking an interest in flowers, and they worked in the garden together, while new gadgets and technology saw gardens going more high-tech.

American Flower Power arrived in the 1960s, with hippies and flower children. Flowers were 'in' with vibrantly coloured, flower-embroidered clothing, but that was as far as it went. Gardening was not 'cool' and was still the domain of older people. Bright colours predominated, but with a limited range of plants available gardens still all looked very similar until the 1960s, when some gardens began to get 'trendy' and re-discovered materials such as inexpensive and easy-to-use concrete.

Increased leisure time and cheap air travel saw people holidaying in Benidorm and Barcelona, rather than Bognor and Brighton. Here very different gardens and plants impacted on British gardens as people grew adventurous. 'Terraces' became 'patios' and a taste for outdoor living, experienced abroad, was continued at home. Increasing affluence saw property ownership escalate, together with gardening interest. The first garden centres opened, on a limited scale, stocking items from plants to furniture. Governed by agricultural rules they were able to open on Sundays, making exciting weekend outings. Pots of well-established plants enabled people to have instant gardens, rather than waiting for seeds to grow. However, there was also a down side and vast quantities of chemicals zapped every pest in sight, saving time in the garden, but with little thought of future consequences on environment or health.

In the past, towns had prioritized housing, commercial development, and roads. This all changed when Roy Hay (1910–89), horticultural journalist and broadcaster, introduced 'Britain in Bloom', and towns, villages and gardens competed to win coveted accolades. Flowers covered traffic roundabouts, buildings and bordered suburban roads. Interest in gardening reached new heights and those without gardens rented allotments to grow vegetables, fruit and flowers, introducing a new sense of community and competition.

With increasing free time, gardening became a prime leisure activity through the 1970s. Visitors flocked to National Trust gardens, and private estates open to the public, absorbing inspiring ideas for their own, smaller gardens. Giant topiary hedges appeared incongruously in suburbia, with privet and yew trimmed into extravagant shapes. But the passion for gardening was dramatically gathering force. Garden gnomes, pampas grass, dwarf conifers and heathers were 1970s 'must haves', and you either loved them or hated them. Garden gnomes had originally been introduced into Britain by Sir Charles Isham in 1849, when he displayed twenty exquisitely crafted German gnomes in his garden. This novelty was further encouraged by Walt Disney's 1930s film, 'Snow White and the Seven Dwarfs', and after the Second World War bright colours and pleasing countenances of gnomes adorned gardens across Britain. Germany produced the first mass commercially available gnomes in 1960, developing a whole range of gnome activities including fishing, gardening and sport.

Pre-mixed composts and growing bags arrived. Lightweight and easy to move, they created planting areas on tower block balconies, flat rooftops and in tiny yards, producing arrays of flowers and vegetables. Horticultural shows were on the increase, and enthusiasts vied to produce the largest, prize-winning onions, leeks and cabbages. Size mattered! Gardens became increasingly adventurous and were frequently used as extensions to the house for outdoor living, dining, entertaining and relaxation. Barbecues appeared and aromas of charcoal smoke and singed sausages wreathed suburbia.

In an increasingly affluent society, house ownership continued to escalate throughout the 1980s. Gardens went up-market and glamorous, and fantasy 'theme gardens' were prominent. Gardening was now very big business. Edith Holden's popular book, *The Country Diary of an Edwardian Lady*, recalled the elegance and gardens of a lost Edwardian age. Cottage gardens were suddenly back in style with an abundance of romantic flowers and perfume. Bedding plants took a back seat. As towns grew larger, houses and gardens became smaller, creating privacy issues, resolved by erecting high fences or hedges to keep out prying eyes. Defining boundaries reinforced the long held British tradition of private space, but enclosing gardens meant the sense of community was lost. *Leylandii* became the trees the nation loved to hate as these fast-growing conifers, advocated for screening, grew to enormous heights. This led to 17,000 neighbourhood disputes a year – and even murder – before local councils were given new powers to intervene between combatants.

Hybrid Teas, Floribundas, Dorothy Perkins and Albertines in rose gardens across the country fell from favour as new, exciting varieties of roses became available. Instant, containerized rose gardens could be planted straight out. Well-known rose breeder, David Austin, introduced the new 'English roses' in the 1960s. These incorporated exquisite flowers and perfume with repeat flowering, creating a massive surge of interest in this popular flower.

However, the most important thing in any garden was 'the lawn', which had to be perfect in every way. Weekends were spent fertilizing, spraying, scarifying, weeding and of course mowing neat, straight stripes. This was still usually the man's domain, until the advent of lightweight mowers, which were easy for women to use.

Flower shows were jazzed up. Plants and gardens were still important but one could now buy almost anything at a garden show, however remotely connected to gardening. An RHS Gold Medal at Chelsea became the pinnacle of success. Showpiece gardens were complimented, criticized and copied, but above all created increasing awareness of new styles, fashions and materials.

Along came the 1990s and we wanted everything and wanted it now. Major companies made takeover bids for small garden centres creating vast complexes which sold everything from a packet of seeds, instant gardens in pots, huge mature trees and composts, to saucepans, clothing, books, decorations, toys and pets. Restaurants provided meals, and people flocked by the coachload for a good day out. Profits soared and garden centres turned over £4 billion a year.

Increasing awareness and enthusiasm for gardening had seen 'celebrity' gardeners arrive on the scene as far back as 1931, when Cecil Middleton (1886–1945) was initially heard on the radio in a popular gardening programme averaging 3.5 million listeners. Harry Wheatcroft (1886–1977) attracted attention as much for his flamboyant appearance and moustache as for the roses he cultivated and introduced. He did much to popularize roses in British gardens, and in 1927 his nursery had produced the 'Princess Elizabeth' rose in honour of the royal baby. Percy Thrower (1913–1988) was a very popular figure, and hosted a new and immediately successful television programme, 'Garden Club' in 1956, going on to present the BBC's 'Gardeners' World' from 1969 to 1976. Recorded at his home, The Magnolias in Shropshire, programmes were very much hands on and instructional. The BBC replaced him as presenter when he advertized garden chemicals commercially. Geoff Hamilton (1936–96) took over and promoted organic gardening, with perfect timing as concern escalated over the massive use of chemicals in food and gardens. His passionate and practical approach inspired a new generation of gardeners. 'The nation's favourite gardener', Alan Titchmarsh (b.1949), then hosted 'Gardeners' World', attracting 6 million viewers.

Programmes gained a reputation for being well presented and informative, with everyone feeling they could achieve similar results.

With a public so obviously enthralled with gardening, media intervention such as radio, television, and escalating supplies of gardening books and magazines became great promotional tools in the latter years of the twentieth century. A new breed of designer emerged as garden owners wanted individual creations designed by experts, whether they liked the finished result or not. 'Ground Force' hit television screens in 1997, with Alan Titchmarsh, Charlie Dimmock and Tommy Walsh. This forerunner to a plethora of garden makeover programmes surprised the unwary, often creating controversial gardens that looked better before rather than after. Diarmuid Gavin and Laurence Llewelyn Bowen were notoriously contentious in their programme featuring interiors and gardens, Gavin creating eclectic mixes of contemporary gardens in eye-catching variety. Makeover culture had arrived with a vengeance. Garden magazines became even bigger and glossier. Thousands of gardening books appeared each year and everyone wanted a designer garden, or aspired to be a garden designer.

In the 1990s, gardens were considered the greatest asset for increasing the value and saleability of property after kitchens. Gardens had not only become the nation's favourite pastime: they were also good investments.

Great new gardens developed, such as Postmodern architect Charles Jencks's Garden of Cosmic Speculation at Portrack, in Scotland, where he also created forty major landscape features between 1989 and 2007. This major leap forward in landscape design, with a complex series of differing elements, including a helix sculpture in the DNA garden; Black Hole of lawn and concrete; and a curving, layered path sweeping up and over the Japanese Jumping Bridge – all inspired by the perpetually evolving universe and theory of chaos.

As the Millennium dawned ecological issues and climate change came to the fore. Sustainability became a key word as the world debated what the future might hold. Gardeners started concentrating on growing food again, as concern about diet, food quality, additives and pesticides fuelled awareness. 'Grow your own' saw increased demand for allotments, creating long waiting lists. 'Green' was in. Celebrity gardeners such as Monty Don, a recent presenter of 'Gardeners' World' programme, favoured organic approaches, water conservation, composting and mulching, as well as attracting wildlife into the garden rather than trying to eliminate it. There was emphasis on ornamental decoration, mirrors, recycling, Mediterranean and dry gardens, expensive garden furniture, trendy water

LEFT: *The Universe Cascade, designed by Postmodern architect Charles Jencks at the Garden of Cosmic Speculation, Scotland. Between 1989 and 2007, Jencks created forty major landscape features at the garden and his stunning, innovative and thought-provoking designs are seen worldwide.*

BELOW: *The Daisy Garden designed by Diarmuid Gavin for Chelsea 2008 with trimmed box, Allium and grasses.*

Brick and stone pillars form an attractive, modern and stylish pergola at Brobury House, Herefordshire.

features and planters. Decking was popular, although often criticized – and of course, there were always plants!

Within the short space of little more than fifty years, gardens had gone from being an eccentric hobby, enjoyed by a few, to a highly fashionable pastime which everyone could enjoy. People had finally taken control of their gardens.

Elements of modern garden style

ACCESSORIES

A vast range of well-styled contemporary accessories enhance today's gardens. Look for clean lines; unusual abstract designs and materials; stylish, solid oak and beech furniture carved into smooth, flowing lines; hanging metal chairs; garden sofas rather than traditional benches; trendy mirrors; wirework arches and obelisks; slate and ceramic bird baths; wall art; coloured glass and unusual planters. Keep it simple and do not overdo accessories.

BRICKS

Bricks are moulded from mixtures of fired clay and shale, are cheap to produce and very versatile for buildings, walls, arches, pillars and also paths which can have varying decorative patterns.

Blue planters became popular features in many modern gardens as here at The Wickets, Staffordshire.

CERAMIC TILES

Available in a wide range of shapes and colours, glazed and unglazed tiles are useful for applied decoration, paving, and patios. Ceramic tiles create decorative borders and motifs in plain paths, and craft interesting and inexpensive wall art, but tiles must be able to withstand frost.

CINDER/BREEZE BLOCKS

A twentieth-century product creating lightweight blocks of cinder aggregate. Cast concrete creates higher density, more durable blocks, and aerated concrete lighter-weight blocks. They are useful for large areas of hard landscaping. Blocks generally have unattractive surfaces best hidden from view or treated with decorative finishes of paint, brick or render.

Wooden decking, glass panels and architectural plants in this modern garden created on a sloping site in Worcestershire.

CONCRETE

Although concrete was known in Roman times it has become one of the best modern building materials. A composite made from cement, aggregate and water, it hardens when dry. Durable and long-lasting, concrete was considered unattractive and unsympathetic at one time but recent technology and approaches have made it more aesthetically acceptable. It is ideal for moulding straight lines, smooth curves and abstract shapes, and it can be reinforced with steel bars for added strength and durability, although its production is certainly not eco-friendly.

DECKING

Hardwood decking provides excellent, low maintenance areas for outdoor living, suited to modern gardens. It combines well with water features and plants, is simple to install, and is ideal for uneven or sloping sites, or for those wanting a practical outside space. Deck gardening can be low maintenance with plants confined to containers or small beds, creating interesting interplay between rigidly formal straight lines and edges of decking, and softness of plants. Varying levels may be accessed by steps or ramps.

GLASS

A mixture of sand and silicates, glass is clear and lightweight but brittle. It is increasingly used in gardens in the form of blocks, wall coverings, water features and mirrors, while recycled, crushed glass creates decorative filling for parterres and paths.

HARDSCAPING

With the advent of Modernism many gardens created stylistic impact with prominent hardscaping rather than luxuriant planting. Flat areas of white concrete, concrete walls and steps, geometrically shaped beds, straight paths, and curving lines predominated. More recently, paving slabs, decorative paving and patio treatments, unusual screening (such as steel or copper sheeting and glass blocks), decking, and raised beds edged with railway sleepers were favoured. Sustainability and environmental issues encouraged new approaches to buildings and hardscaping materials, such as recycling and architectural salvage, opening exciting and innovative possibilities.

LIGHTING

Outdoor lighting is increasingly popular and sophisticated, changing a garden's personality at night. Commonplace features take on a completely different appearance when lit from various angles. Clean lines cast strong shadows, and plants create unusual shadow effects. British summers are often cold and wet, and largely enjoyed from the house, so lighting opens up new vistas in the garden when viewed from windows.

Safety with outdoor electricity is important. Lighting must be suited to purpose, specially designed for outdoor use, and fitted professionally, especially when in contact with water. Solar-powered lighting gives softer effects, and many designs have simple spikes to be pushed into the ground. Keep lights and cables unobtrusive, unless lights are specifically made to be seen.

METAL

Decorative ironwork has long been popular for gates, arches, pergolas and other ornamental frameworks. Modern emphasis highlights stainless and brushed steel, aluminium, and metals such as copper, for garden features. Metals are strong and flexible alloys, which last well but eventually corrode.

PLANTS

Plants have always been collected and new varieties

ABOVE: *A simple, modern, steel sculpture in the garden at Hunters End, Worcestershire.*

LEFT: *The David Austin Rose Garden, Staffordshire, where from the 1960s onward David Austin developed the new 'English roses'.*

arrive almost every day. Plant hybridization and propagation techniques have advanced rapidly over the last century and many plants are hardly recognisable from their wild forms. Take the rose for example: hybrid tea roses, popular in the mid twentieth century, saw great advances with increasing colour range and 'perfect' flowers. These were overtaken by many new roses including the 'English' roses pioneered and introduced by David Austin from the late 1960s onwards. These modern crosses look like exquisite old varieties but have repeat flowering, improved shape, wider colour range, increased perfume, and higher disease resistance. As well as creating traditional rose gardens, roses can act as specimen plants, they can be mixed with herbaceous perennials, cover arches, pergolas, trees and houses, and form hedges. Ornamental grasses are much in vogue in the twenty-first century, and a wide range of unusual and exotic plants are fashionable.

PLASTIC

A popular, man-made synthetic or semi-synthetic material increasingly used in gardens for decorative effects, structures, and furniture. It suffered the same

reputation as concrete as being an unsympathetic medium but increasing technology produces more aesthetically pleasing products. Plastic is lightweight, easily moulded into a wide variety of shapes, and simple to maintain.

SCULPTURE

Modern imitations of traditional pieces are more pleasing than in the past, but original pieces are far superior. Antique or abstract forms come in a wide variety of materials, including wood, stone, marble, plastic, resin, and metal. Simple, interestingly shaped pieces of wood or stone make inexpensive, eye-catching features.

SIMULATED STONE

Increasing advances produce new materials more closely resembling natural stone. Synthetic stone products have been used since the eighteenth century, one of the earliest being Coade stone, named after its creator, Emily Coade. Later, inexpensive simulated stone was widely

An attractive and simply created stone feature for the modern garden.

Cool-coloured, green, grey and silver-leaved plants set into textured, flowing lines create a good contrast between light and dark.

made from concrete. Modern cast stones are made from cement, natural sands, crushed stone or gravel, and colouring pigments to achieve natural looking, hardwearing products simulating sandstone, limestone, bluestone, slate, granite and travertine amongst others. These materials are ideal for walls, paving, paths, driveways and ornamental garden features.

STONE

Stone has been used since Neolithic and Bronze Age times for buildings. Durable, adaptable, versatile, and one of the most readily available materials, it fits beautifully into every landscape and cannot be bettered.

WATER

In shallow reflecting pools, narrow canals, rills and runnels, bubbling through and around stones, or cascading down sheets of glass or steel, water can be used in a wide range of unusual features.

WOOD

Originally used as rough, felled timber and later prepared for construction purposes, being a natural material, wood fits well into gardens, especially sustainable, country-style gardens. Easily worked and highly adaptable, it has many different uses, including fences, gates, pergolas, arches, decking, bed edging, buildings and furniture.

Creating the style

Whether the choice is formal or informal, trendy or traditional, truly 'modern' gardens have carefully aligned proportions and simplicity. Colours and textures flow into one another with good interplay of light and shade. Strong blocks of contrasting light and dark plants provide interesting effects. Simple swaths of green, grey, blue and white create cool themes, while terracotta, orange, reds and gold generate warmth.

Striking, architectural plants create impact. Bamboo, grasses, *Phormium*, *Cordyline*, and plants with large and unusually shaped and coloured foliage all have good contrasts with texture and form. Frame entrances and vistas with a dark archway or hedge, emphasizing contrasting lighter areas behind.

Land art forms interesting and unusual features, carved into spiral mounds and mazes, grown over with grass. Glass, steel and copper are popular especially when materials have been recycled. Bold designs, sharp, angular lines, smooth curves, geometrical features, a light and airy, open style, and limited colour palette are all synonymous with modern gardens. Restrained hardscaping in concrete, metal and glass are popular. Glass gives unusual colour and textural effects and recycled glass is environmentally friendly. Advances in simulated stone and concrete mean these are more aesthetically appealing. Try interesting and unusual paving effects, including pebble patterns, various shades and grades of gravel and shingle, plain wood and sleepers rather than rustic, and clean lines of modern metal arches and obelisks.

Sophisticated lighting techniques bring gardens alive at night and are very dramatic especially when highlighting certain plants or features. Different effects are achieved depending on the placing and strength of lights, creating silhouettes and shadows. As well as a safety consideration, lights along path edges and drives provide magical effects, creating dramatic entrances. Highlight a sculpture, column or ornament. Statues and urns set into niches or hedges look particularly attractive when picked out from the surrounding darkness. Tiny strings of lights twine through trees, shrubs or pergolas, but should not be overdone. Lighting in or around water creates good reflections and rippling movement on surroundings. Enhance the effect of a still pool, bubbling water feature or fountain with underwater lighting, or backlighting. Water is included with mirror pools, narrow canals, curtains of water flowing over steel, copper or glass and unusual fountains and bubble effects. Hot tubs, jacuzzis and swimming pools also feature in many gardens.

Specimen trees with ornamental bark create interest all year. Clipped trees are fashionable, contrasting well with modern buildings and design; stylized, abstract forms are preferable to traditional representational forms. Cones, mounds, balls and spirals are all good. Small gardens and courtyards easily adapt to modern style, while larger gardens are divided into 'garden rooms' with different themes.

Today's gardener wants it all. Superb design and stunning plants and features, providing beautiful gardens all year round, including winter, with decorative peeling bark, coloured stems, twisted branches, seed-heads, winter-flowering shrubs and plants. Many winter flowers have a strong fragrance. Camellias begin flowering around Christmas; winter pansies bring bright splashes of colour; hellebores are purple-black, pink, green, yellow and purest white; snowdrop species flower from November; Cyclamen coum naturalize beautifully, giving swathes of pink and white beneath trees; heathers bloom throughout winter; crocuses start flowering early; and enormous varieties of evergreens come in shades of blue, green and yellow.

TOP: A stylish display of architectural plants in gravel at a modern garden, Gladderbrook Farm, Worcestershire.

MIDDLE: Grass maze at The Dower House, Morville Hall, Shropshire. New style land art creates visual impact and is simply designed with patterns of mown grass.

BELOW Modern steel and pebble water feature at Chelsea 2008.`

View across contemporary classic garden with planted rill, copper water feature, Portuguese limestone paving and steps, designed by Charlotte Rowe.

With the twenty-first century, gardens too have come of age. Over the last century they advanced as never before in their history. New materials, developing technology, innovative ideas, and new plants mean gardens are always moving forward. Modern gardens are minimalistic, full of technological advances, or very traditional, drawing inspiration from the past. Avant-garde gardens and designers will frequently become talking points. Modern and futuristic designs may be highly controversial. Some will fail and others stay the course of time. But one thing is sure: today's modern gardens are tomorrow's history.

Modern style

Trees and shrubs

Modern gardens are often small so it is important to include more upright species. Each tree must play its role, so those giving year-round interest, with coloured barks and stems are particularly useful.

Abies koreana
Acer griseum
Acer platanoides 'Columnare'
Aesculus x carnea 'Briottii'
Amelanchier lamarckii
Arbutus x andrachnoides
Berberis darwinii
Betula pendula 'Fastigiata'
Betula utilis jacquemontii var. 'Grayswood Ghost'
Camellia x williamsii 'J. C. Williams'
Carpinus betulus 'Fastigiata'
Cercis siliquastrum
Cornus alba
Cornus alternifolia
Cornus mas
Cornus sericea 'Flaviramea'
Crataegus monogyna 'Stricta'
Cryptomeria japonica 'Elegans'
Erica carnea
Erica cinerea
Erica x darleyensis
Erica vagans
Eucryphia x nymansensis
Genista aetnensis
Ilex x altaclarensis 'Golden King'
Ilex aquifolium 'Green Pillar'
Juniperus communis 'Hibernica'
Liriodendron tulipifera 'Fastigiatum'

Kalmia latifolia
Magnolia x loebneri 'Merril'
Magnolia x soulangiana
Magnolia stellata
Malus coronaria 'Charlottae'
Malus floribunda
Malus 'John Downie'
Photinia x fraseri
Prunus lusitanica 'Myrtifolia'
Prunus lusitanica 'Snow Goose'
Prunus serrula
Prunus 'Shirotae'
Prunus subhirtella 'Autumnalis'
Pyrus calleryana 'Chanticleer'
Quercus castaneifolia 'Green Spire'
Robinia pseudoacacia 'Pyramidalis'
Salix acutifolia 'Blue Streak'
Sarococca confusa
Sorbus aria
Sorbus aucuparia
Stachyurus praecox
Tilia cordata 'Greenspire'
Viburnum x bodnantense 'Charles Lamont'
Viburnum plicatum

Architectural plants

Strong shapes and colours form good focal points in modern gardens with their clean lines and often minimal planting.

Acanthus spinosus
Chamaerops humilis
Chamaerops humilis var argentea
Chamaerops humilis 'Vulcano'
Cordyline australis

Cordyline australis 'Torbay Red'
Cordyline australis 'Torbay Dazzler'
Eremurus x isabellinus 'Cleopatra'
Euphorbia amygdaloides 'Purpurea'
Euphorbia characias
Euphorbia mellifera
Fatsia japonica
Gunnera manicata
Hosta 'Sum and Substance'
Hosta sieboldiana var. elegans
Ilex crenata 'Fastigiata'
Kniphofia sp
Ligustrum japonicum 'Rotundifolium'
Macleaya cordata
Macleaya microcarpa
Phormium tenax
Phormium 'Yellow Wave'
Phormium tenax 'Atropurpureum'
Phormium 'Dark Delight'
Phormium 'Platt's Black'
Rheum palmatum
Taxus baccata 'Fastigiata'
Virburnum davidii

Limnanthes douglasii.

Variegated plants

Attractive and unusual variegated plants create impact and a light, airy feel to modern gardens, although it is important not to overdo them or the range of colours and variations becomes too confusing.

Acer negundo 'Elegans'
Acer platanoides 'Drummondii'
Acuba japonica 'Crotonifolia'
Aralia elata 'Aureovariegata'
Arum italicum
Brunnera macrophylla 'Jack frost'
Buddleja davidii 'Harlequin'
Cornus alba 'Elegantissima'
Cornus alba 'Sibirica Variegata'
Cornus alba 'Gouchaultii'
Cornus alternifolia 'Argentea'
Cornus controversa 'Variegata'
Cornus mas 'Variegata'
Elaeagnus pungens 'Frederici'
Elaeagnus pungens 'Hosuba-fukurin'
Hosta 'June'
Hosta 'Patriot'
Ilex x altaclarensis 'Golden King'
Ilex aquifolium 'Handsworth New Silver'
Ilex aquifolium 'Silver Queen'
Ligustrum ovalifolium 'Aureum'

Osmanthus heterophyllus 'Variegatus'
Osmanthus heterophyllus 'Goshiki'
Pittosporum 'Garnettii'
Pittosporum tennuifolium 'Irene Paterson'

Red and purple foliage

Coloured leaves bring drama to the garden, creating strong contrast amongst other plants. They require good light to maintain their colour.

Acer palmatum 'Bloodgood'
Acer palmatum var. dissectum 'Crimson Queen'
Acer platanoides 'Crimson King'
Bergenia purpurascens
Cotinus coggygria 'Royal Purple'
Cotinus 'Grace'
Hebe 'Mrs Winder'
Hebe 'Pascal'
Heuchera 'Palace Purple'
Heuchera 'Plum Pudding'
Lysimachia ciliata 'Firecracker'
Physocarpus opulifolius 'Diablo'
Pittosporum tennuifolium 'Tom Thumb'
Prunus cerasifera 'Nigra'
Sambucus nigra f. porphryrophylla 'Eva'

Melianthus major.

Gold and yellow foliage

Golden foliage brightens up the darkest gardens on the dullest days, but requires careful positioning so it doesn't become too intrusive.

Catalpa bignonoides 'Aurea'
Choisya ternata 'Sundance'
Cotinus 'Golden Spirit'
Gleditsia triacanthos 'Sunburst'
Ilex aquifolioum 'Flavescens'
Juniperus chinensis 'Aurea'
Lonicera nitida 'Baggesen's Gold'
Philadelphus coronarius 'Aureus'
Robinia pseudoacacia 'Frisia'
Sambucus racemosa 'Sutherland Gold'
Taxus baccata 'Standishii'

Grey, silver and blue foliage

Most plants with this leaf colouring grow in full sun, creating good contrasts with darker-leaved species such as reds and purples and evergreens.

Artemisia arborescens 'Faith Raven'
Artemesia 'Powis Castle'
Ballota pseudodictamnus
Brachyglottis 'Sunshine'
Convolvulus cneorum
Hebe pinguifolia 'Pagei'
Helichrysum italicum ssp serotinum
Helichrysum splendidum
Lavandula lanata
Lavandula sp.
Lotus hirsutus
Melianthus major
Potentilla 'Beesii'
Salix lanata
Salvia officinalis
Salvia lavandulifolia
Santolina chamaecyparissus

Autumn colour

Spectacular autumn foliage is a bonus in any garden.

Acer capillipes
Acer platanoides
Acer rubrum
Aesculus parviflora
Amelanchier lamarckii
Berberis thunbergii
Berberis wilsoniae
Ceratostigma willmottianum
Cercis canadensis
Cornus alba 'Kesselringii'
Cornus controversa
Cotoneaster divaricatus
Crataegus pinnatifida var. major
Crataegus prunifolia
Cotinus sp.
Cotoneaster horizontalis
Cotoneaster splendens
Eucryphia glutinosa
Euonymus alatus
Fraxinus angustifolia 'Raywood'
Ginkgo biloba
Hamamelis vernalis 'Sandra'
Malus coronaria 'Charlotte'
Malus trilobata
Nandina domestica 'Firepower'
Photinia beauverdiana villosa
Populus canadenis 'Aurea'
Populus tremula
Prunus incisa
Prunus sargentii

Prunus verecunda 'Autumn Glory'
Quercus coccinea 'Splendens'
Quercus rubra
Rhododendron luteum
Sorbus alnifolia
Sorbus 'Joseph Rock'
Spiraea betulifolia aemiliana
Vaccinum corymbosum
Vibrunum opulus
Viburnum plicatum

Plants with coloured stems

Cornus alba 'Kesselringii'
Cornus alba officinalis
Cornus alba 'Sibirica'
Cornus stolonifera 'Flaviramea'
Leycesteria formosa
Salix hastate 'Wehrhanii'

Bulbs, corms, rhizomes and tubers

Allium giganteum
Amaryllis bella-donna
Anemone x fulgens
Chionodoxa gigantea
Camassia leichtlinii
Colchicum speciosum
Convollaria majalis 'Fortin's Giant'
Crinum x powelli 'Album'
Crocus chrysanthus
Crocus speciosus
Crocus tommasinianus
Cyclamen coum
Cyclamen hederifolium
Fritillaria meleagris
Galanthus elwesii
Galanthus 'S. Arnott'
Galtonia candicans
Gladiolus callianthus
Gladiolus 'The Bride'
Hermodactylus tuberosus
Ipheion uniflorum
Iris danfordiae
Iris reticulata
Iris unguicularis
Leucojum autumnalis
Narcissus sp.
Nerine bowdenii
Nomocharis pardanthina
Tigridia pavonia

Roymneya coulteri.

Triteleia laxa
Trollius chinensis
Tulipa sp.

Roses

Rosa 'A Shropshire Lad' clg.
Rosa 'Alan Titchmarsh'
Rosa 'Bianco'
Rosa 'Chianti'
Rosa 'Darcey Bussell'
Rosa 'Glamis Castle'
Rosa 'Graham Thomas'
Rosa 'Greenfalls Glory'
Rosa 'Golden Celebration'
Rosa 'Heritage'
Rosa 'James Galway' clg.
Rosa 'Mary Rose'
Rosa 'Perditia'
Rosa 'Queen Mother'
Rosa 'Rose of Picardy'
Rosa 'Sister Elizabeth'
Rosa 'Snow Goose' clg.
Rosa 'Strawberry Hill'
Rosa 'St Swithin' clg.
Rosa 'Wildfire'

10 Water garden style

The style

Water has special, irresistible and magical qualities, from the majesty of immense oceans and huge lakes to winding streams, wildlife pools, formal canals, waterfalls and fountains. Water is invaluable in gardens, providing interest throughout the year. Water can be calming, peaceful, still and reflective; powerful, energizing; or cheerfully rippling, babbling and tinkling. It adds structure, reflections and delicate sounds. During winter frozen water has very different but equally charming qualities. Natural water is a tremendous asset, as however carefully streams, waterfalls and informal ponds are constructed, they rarely look completely natural.

Water provides small features or becomes a major part of garden design. It has functional uses – such as swimming pools – or is purely decorative. Ponds can be any shape or size; they may be fringed with plants or strictly minimalist, they can contain exotic fish or create wildlife havens, or they may be smooth and reflective. Ponds are sunk into the ground or raised above it. Rills trickle beside stone paths, canals are straight and formal, streams chuckle merrily along, while cascades and waterfalls create vibrant sound. Simple fountains bubble low jets over stones, and massive, carved creations spout water high into the air.

In hot countries water delivers moisture to dry plants and atmospheres, provides cooling reflections and soothing sounds. Sheltered courtyards with gentle fountains are green oases in busy towns. Once-productive mills with millstreams and waterwheels are now attractive dwellings. Renaissance villas and grand houses created extravagant lakes, pools and fountains. Modern gardens feature abstract designs of brushed

OPPOSITE: The Serpent Garden, Alnwick Castle, Northumberland, with water sculptures by William Pye.

TOP: Colourful candelabra primula edge the mill pool at Westonbury Mill, Herefordshire.

BOTTOM: Docton Mill, North Devon. Water brings special qualities to a garden and many once-productive mills have been turned into attractive dwellings.

steel, glass and water. However it is used and styled, water always brings special, dynamic and magical qualities to any garden.

History

Without water there is no life and water has always been revered. The Egyptian god, Hapy, brought floods each year, while Proteus ruled the seas. Poseidon was the Greeks' sea god, Neptune the Romans'. The Aztec goddess Chalchiuhtlicue influenced running water, springs, rivers and lakes, and Latis was Britain's water goddess.

In arid countries water was carried through irrigation channels to plants. Later these became decorative features. With advances in irrigation techniques dating back to 3,400BC, Egyptians created formal water gardens with fish and waterfowl. Mesopotamia constructed large reservoirs around 3,000BC, storing water from the flooded rivers Tigris and Euphrates for use during dry seasons. A carved stone water basin discovered in Tello, dated from this period, and a 2,000BC stone goddess holding a water jug, thought to be the earliest ever representational fountain, was found in Mari.

In ancient Greece springs were decorated with sculptures. An early fountain from between 560 and 510BC in Athens has water flowing from lions' mouths, and records from the first century AD describe fountains and mechanical devices for moving water. In the sixteenth century, reviving this technology led to massive and complicated water devices in Italian Renaissance gardens, a technology that spread throughout Europe.

Ancient Rome had eleven aqueducts carrying thousands of litres of water each day from surrounding hills. Emperors and aristocrats had private supplies, while surplus water was piped into bathhouses and public fountains around the city so everyone had access. Aqueducts declined in the sixth century but some were revived during the Middle Ages and more during the Renaissance.

Water was significant in nature-based Chinese and Japanese gardens. Records show Chinese gardens and parks featured water gardens from around 1,000BC, including 'rock islands' linked by paths and bridges. Ideas filtered into Japan with major garden developments between the eighth and twelfth centuries. Dry Zen gardens incorporated representational water with fine sand or gravel, raked into patterns of waves and swirling currents, and rocks representing islands.

Renowned for their beauty, Persian gardens channelled water into canals and pools through long, underground conduits, *qanats*. Islam celebrated the four rivers of Paradise with canals dividing gardens into equal quadrants, the *chahar bagh*, with a central fountain or pool. *Chadar*, gently sloping chutes of water, usually around a garden's perimeter, were carefully angled to

LEFT: The Neptune statue at Brobury House, Herefordshire.

RIGHT: The Mari fountain goddess is thought to be the earliest representational fountain ever discovered, dating back to 2000BC.

Nymphaeum were originally natural grottos with springs dedicated to water nymphs, but later became vast rotundas adorned with paintings and sculpture providing sanctuaries, reservoirs and assembly rooms.

reflect sunlight. In the mid seventh century Islamic ideas were carried into Persia, absorbing Persian garden traditions, moving west into Spain in the mid eighth century, and later east to create great Mughul gardens in India.

Thirteenth- and early fourteenth-century Moorish gardens of the Alhambra and Generalife, Granada, Spain, incorporated exquisite water features, including pools, canals and fountains, channelling water through complex systems of ducts in the castle walls. Important gardens developed in India between 1508 and 1707, with intricate sunken flower beds and ponds, raised paths, fountains and bathing pools. In 1632 Emperor Shah Jahan created the majestic Taj Mahal in memory of his wife, incorporating the traditional four-fold water garden.

The Italian Renaissance surpassed everything with spectacular pools, fountains and water features that were the wonder of their age. The *nymphaeum*, originally a natural grotto with a spring dedicated to water nymphs, later became vast rotundas adorned with paintings and sculpture, providing sanctuaries, reservoirs and assembly rooms. Renaissance gardens had spectacular formal pools, canals, water rills, water staircases, and massive marble fountains. Extremely sophisticated Italian hydraulic skills were in demand throughout Europe.

Joseph Paxton's spectacular gravity-fed Emperor Fountain at Chatsworth, Derbyshire, spouting water 200ft into the air.

Medieval gardens incorporated water for the practicalities of providing ponds for fresh fish and irrigation, but as ideas filtered into the country from Europe, flowers and water increasingly played important roles in British gardens.

Formal canals were features of geometrically styled seventeenth-century gardens. Queen Elizabeth I had a fountain installed at Hampton Court Palace around 1590, and water features became increasingly complex. Chatsworth, Derbyshire, has some of the finest examples in Britain, including the only original cascade still in existence from 1696. The Long Water at Hampton Court dates from 1666 and there is a superb example at Melbourne Hall, Derbyshire from 1704.

In France, François I commissioned Italian artists to renovate his castle and gardens in the 1520s, flooding moats with water and creating artificial lakes, beginning a new era of water garden design. The first ornamental canal was created in France in the late sixteenth century but it was André le Nôtre who developed great canals and water gardens at Vaux-le-Vicomte in the mid 1650s, and the magnificent Versailles in the 1660s. Versailles has 1,400 fountains with water supplied from a vast pumping station on the banks of the River Seine. Charles II commissioned le Nôtre to design a canal in St James's Park, London, but André Mollet was sent

instead. This canal, constructed in the 1660s, was converted into a formal lake early in the eighteenth century.

Medicinal cold baths and plunge pools were prominent in Roman times, often constructed near springs that provided a constant cold water temperature. William Kent included a cold bath at Rousham in 1738 and although cold baths were constructed during the Victorian era, their popularity waned.

The first fountains were simple pipes spouting water into stone basins. Later, water was angled upwards. As technology advanced, the nineteenth century saw new, important water features and fountains. Joseph Paxton's 1843 Emperor Fountain, Chatsworth, Derbyshire, jetted water 88 metres into the air, the highest in the world at the time. William Nesfield's Perseus and Andromeda fountain (1860s), Witley Court, Worcestershire, had 120 jets and a central plume sending water 100 metres high. '*Giochi d'acqua*', trick fountains, popular in Renaissance gardens, suddenly sprayed water at unsuspecting passers by. They also included automata fountains sounding like birds or church organs. The Arab garden of Alfabia, Mallorca, had hidden fountains in the stone pergola spraying out unexpectedly. The fashion continues today with a recently constructed water maze at Hever Castle, Kent, which sprays unsuspecting visitors.

Early estates in Britain were generally unsophisticated hunting parks, but Italian, French and Dutch ideas soon began dominating English gardens. Westbury Court, Gloucestershire, remains little changed from the seventeenth century. The 4.5-acre garden has two topiary-bordered canals, parterres and walled flower gardens. A Dutch style summerhouse faces up the Long Canal. Early plans do not show the T-canal, which was probably added around 1715. The statue of Neptune is said to have been discovered in the River Severn three hundred years ago. During the seventeenth and eighteenth centuries, larger, more formal stretches of water developed and lakes became popular features of the eighteenth-century landscape school. Stourhead, Wiltshire, has temples and garden buildings at intervals around the massive lake. Lord Cobham's estate, Stowe, Buckinghamshire, was very influential in the history of landscape design. William Kent worked on the gardens, creating eight lakes (including a vast 11-acre lake), favouring informal, serpentine stretches of water. Over thirty temples were constructed and the ha-ha introduced. Lancelot 'Capability' Brown began his career in the kitchen gardens, becoming head gardener, and developing Stowe further. Water became important features of Brown's work, blending great sheets of water into the landscape, including Blenheim Palace and Wootton, Oxfordshire.

Early in the eighteenth century Lord Bathurst created the first 'natural' winding stream but was criticized and told he should have spent more money and created a proper formal canal. Longstock Park Water Gardens, Hampshire, has been voted the finest water garden in the world by the Water Lily Society. As part of the John

The magnificent modern cascade at Alnwick Castle, Northumberland, the largest of its type in the country.

A series of pools and fountains form the spectacular new Mughul Water Gardens, Lister Park, Bradford.

Lewis Partnership Leckford Estate, the superb garden was created by John Spedan Lewis and Terry Jones, a botanist, in 1946, redeveloping the original 1870s lake. There are more than eighty different waterlilies, marginal, bog and aquatic plants creating unique and diverse wildlife habitats.

The twentieth century saw ornamental ponds in suburban gardens rising in popularity, together with 'wishing wells' and small fountains. Now, wildlife ponds are fashionable, replacing many habitats lost in the wild. With increasingly innovative technology and new materials water gardens continue to evolve. There are endless features to choose from to suit everyone's taste and pocket, and fulfil the demand for water in today's gardens. Tiny pools and fountains suit small patios. Water runs down sheets of stainless steel, copper and glass to spectacular effect. Natural swimming ponds are becoming fashionable. Abstract forms abound, and water gardens are taking on a spectacular new lease of life.

Outstanding water gardens continue to be created across Britain, including those at Alnwick Castle, Northumberland, which has the largest modern cascade of its type in the country, and water sculptures by William Pye in the Serpent Garden. Bradford Council carried out extensive restorations at Lister Park in the Manningham area of Bradford, re-opening it to the public in 2002, including amongst its many new attractions magnificent Mughul water gardens. The Diana, Princess of Wales Memorial Fountain opened in Hyde Park, London in 2004 – a long, wide, curving stream bed of Cornish granite blocks, creating interesting interplay and flow of water. Water gardens will always endure and continue to develop with new technology, throughout the coming generations.

Elements of water gardens

BOG GARDENS

Bog gardens complement pools and are an ideal situation for many attractive, moisture-loving plants, which create additional wildlife habitats.

BRIDGES

Bridges span water, rock gardens, ravines, ditches or bog gardens. They should be strong, safe constructions, fitting the design of the garden. Bridges are made from wood, stone or metal, and ready-made designs are available. Planks of wood, railway sleepers, and blocks of stone or slate form simple bridges. Styles may be rustic, traditional, Japanese or contemporary. Note that pressure-treated timber in close proximity to water can leach toxic chemical into the water.

CONSTRUCTION

Ponds and water features are created from varied materials including puddle clay, concrete, liners and pre-formed fibreglass shapes. Clay is superb for natural ponds. Concrete can be shaped, is initially expensive, but lasts a lifetime. It requires a sealant and can also be tiled. Butyl liners are cheaper and are simple to lay on prepared ground, but are easily damaged. Pre-formed pools come in many shapes and sizes including formal, informal, streams and waterfalls. They must fit smoothly onto prepared, contoured ground, be completely level,

An attractive arrangement of half barrels for plants and water at The Wickets, Staffordshire.

Water canal and fountain designed by landscape architect Lance Hattat.

and carefully backfilled to avoid cracking. Liners must be well disguised, even when water levels drop. A covering of grass turves eliminates this problem and creates planting areas, while edges of liners are buried, paved or grassed over.

CONTAINER WATER GARDENS

Tiny water features fit the smallest gardens. Containers can be terracotta, wood or fibreglass, and could include simple washing up bowls, kitchen sinks and old baths. Fill with plants and fish or simply include stones and pebbles, or a small fountain.

DRY WATER GARDENS

Japanese-style dry gardens have arrangements of stones, shingle and sand to represent water; these adapt well to any garden. Fine aggregates form streams winding through rocks crossed by wooden bridges or slabs of stone or slate. Scatterings of white chippings suggest foam. Wave patterns are raked into the aggregate and rocks represent islands.

FISH

Goldfish probably originated from China, where records of ornamental fish date from AD960–1279. They were in Japan by AD1500, arriving in Britain around the early seventeenth century. They include *Carassius auratus* – the common goldfish; Koi, the epitome of the fish world; gold and blue Orfe, *Leuciscus idus*; Shubunkin, *Carassius auratus*; green or gold Tench, *Tinca tinca*, and Veiltails. Establishing the correct ratio of fish to pond is important. Having too many fish disturbs the oxygen balance, causing distress, disease or death. The best ratio is 155cm of water surface area for every 2.5cm length of fish. Warmer water holds less oxygen but air pumps increase levels. Clear ponds of debris and leaves regularly. The 1981 Wildlife and Countryside Act and the 1984 Diseases of Fish Act, make it illegal to dispose of fish in areas of natural water.

FOUNTAINS

Fountains are popular features. Early fountains relied on a single jet of water. Later, massive, elaborately carved constructions spouted water from numerous apertures.

Pumps are used to circulate water; ensure that fountains have enough space so water falls back into the basin and is not wasted.

GROTTOES

Ancient Greeks enclosed sacred springs in grottoes, and grottoes became decorative features in water gardens throughout Europe.

HARDSCAPING

Pools generally require excavation and disposal of soil, which can be used to landscape surrounding areas. Hardscaping around water gardens should fit the overall garden design and not look out of place. Rock gardens fit well. Copy how nature creates natural-looking streams and waterfalls. Paving around pools should be smooth and stable. Raised pools require substantial walls.

ISLANDS

Large expanses of natural water often have islands; man-made islands should be of solid construction, not easily undermined by water. Islands can include shelters for waterfowl but make sure they are easily accessible – small ramps may be necessary.

JETTIES

Simple, strong and secure jetties are useful on larger stretches of water, lakes and rivers, for access and launching of boats.

LAKES

Lakes are large inland bodies of fresh or salt water, or scenic ponds. They are spring-, stream- or river-fed, often with stone beaches. Man-made lakes are ideally made of puddled clay, while extreme care must be taken with synthetic liners.

LIGHTING

Lighting enhances water features at night. Get electricity installed by experts because of the dangerous mix of water and power. Solar lighting is easily installed and modern lights have energy-storing batteries as well as solar cells. Some have fluorescent bulbs, which

The beautiful lake in the Beth Chatto Gardens, Essex, creates a tranquil and relaxing setting.

maximize light. Floating lights are also available. Solar-powered fountains and pumps generally operate only in daylight, although some have back-up batteries. Lighting creates atmosphere, whether dim and mysterious or bright and open, and underwater lighting is especially effective.

MAINTENANCE

Establishing good balances of plants and pond life aids maintenance. Silt should be cleared and silt traps emptied regularly. Vacuums are available for cleaning debris from ponds. Fallen leaves need regular removal especially in autumn. Plants require thinning, and spreading species should be kept in check. Blanket weed needs to be removed. Maintain pumps and other equipment. Newly established ponds generally turn green and then clear; green water is not harmful to aquatic life, but affects the aesthetic appearance. When aquatic plants are unable to use all the nutrients in the water, microscopic algae multiply, turning water green. Chemical controls are available, and ultraviolet lights minimize problems, but the best solution is to use plants (such as waterlilies) that absorb nutrients and shade the water surface, cutting down excess light. An annual spring clean also helps by removing decaying debris.

Clean, uncluttered lines of the formal pool at Kiftsgate Court, Gloucestershire.

PLANTS

Many plants grow in or around water. Oxygenating aquatics help maintain balance in ponds, keeping water clear. Marginals grow along the edges but require control, especially vigorous species. Many perennials suit damp conditions, including *Caltha*, *Lythrum*, *Iris*, *Lobelia*, *Meconopsis*, *Primula*, *Rodgersia*, *Trollius*, and other attractive species. *Iris spuria* grows naturally in waterlogged soil that dries out in summer, a difficult habitat for many plants. Selections of cultivars make attractive displays, especially in full sun.

POOLS – FORMAL

Formal pools create ornamental features in formal gardens. They are rectangular, square, octagonal or round, and built from concrete, pre-formed fibreglass, or liners. Line reflective pools with black or dark-coloured tiles, paint or liners, and clean regularly to enhance reflective qualities. Minimal planting around formal pools enhances strong outlines. Paved surrounds should be stable. Filters help to keep the water clear.

POOLS – INFORMAL

Informal pools have natural, curving shapes blending

Beautifully-planted, informal pool at Stockton Bury Gardens, Herefordshire.

into the landscape. Ponds may have established over generations but new ponds are constructed of puddle clay, concrete, pre-formed shapes or liners. Natural pools suit semi-shaded positions. Too much sun encourages algae, and too many trees create problems with falling leaves affecting water quality. Pools reliant on rainfall flood after excessive rain, or dry up in drought. A piped water supply enables pools to be topped up, while overflow pipes drain surplus away. Excavate, lay liner and cover with grass turf that has not been chemically treated. Plant directly into the turf. The depth of water dictates which plants will grow, and exuberant planting falls naturally over pond edges.

POOLS – RAISED

Raised pools make attractive features especially in courtyard settings. Strongly constructed from brick, stone, concrete or wood, wall tops provide comfortable seating to watch fish or reflections.

POOLS – WILDLIFE

Wildlife ponds are useful in replacing habitats lost in the wild. Even tiny containers attract surprising numbers of amphibians and insects into gardens, helpful in devouring many garden pests, while lush vegetation protects against predators. Pools with backward sloping steps from centre to edge allow various depths of water for different plants, and aid creatures that fall inadvertently into the water. Occasional ramps placed round ponds at intervals, or sections of wire netting flat against banks also act as footholds. Newts, toads and frogs require water for breeding but spend much time on land. Wildlife ponds provide breeding grounds for amphibians and insects; marginal plants supply nectar for bees and butterflies; muddy edges provide nesting material for birds; and creatures drink the water. True wildlife ponds use only native plant species.

ROCKS

Rocks in water features must look completely natural. Nature includes a mixture of large and small stones, so look for good combinations. Local stone looks better in local landscapes.

ROCK GARDENS

Rocks combine well with water but they should achieve a good balance and rock gardens should look natural,

Water is a great attraction, but can be extremely dangerous, particularly for children. This metal cover is not only extremely strong; it is an extremely attractive feature in its own right.

with appropriate planting. Limestone pavements filled with alpines look particularly attractive around pools or streams, and plants happily naturalize and spread.

SAFETY

Although highly desirable, water is extremely dangerous and due consideration must be given to the potential hazards, particularly with children who can drown in a few centimetres. Pool covers are not generally aesthetically appealing but are useful particularly until children are older. Wooden frames with strong, wire mesh, or metal grills fit smaller ponds and canals. Larger areas might require suitable walls or fencing and a locking gate.

Herons devour fish and various methods help protect from such predators. Trip wires edging pools, about 30 centimetres high, stop herons wading into the water. Alternatively, replica herons sometimes help.

It is against the law to change natural water sources, even on your own land, so if you have a stream check before making any alterations to its pattern or flow.

SCULPTURE

Great Renaissance fountains were spectacular affairs incorporating huge figures, mythical scenes, animals, sea creatures, water nymphs and of course, Neptune. An attractive sculpture or urn near water creates good reflections.

STEPPING STONES

These are good for crossing shallow water or moist ground. Watch sharp edges with synthetic liners. Stepping stones should be stable and have flat surfaces.

STREAMS

Man-made streams often look unnatural. Water should look as if it has worn into the ground over long periods of time so construct streams in hollows rather than on raised ground, and include areas of shallow and deeper water. Streams have gentle curves, widening as they enter pools. Pre-formed shapes are available, and liners, concrete or puddle clay are all suitable materials. Line with turf or flat stones and construct pebble or shingle shorelines and planting areas. Pumps circulate water.

SWIMMING POOLS

Bathing pools were recorded in 3000BC, but Roman pools and bath houses turned swimming into a fun activity. Swimming pools in cold countries are generally better undercover. They are expensive to install and require costly maintenance. Harsh blue colouring looks unnatural and more subtly coloured grey, dark blue or black tiles provide softer effects ranging from sheets of silver to inky black. Conservatory-type pool houses enable year-round use and add an exotic dimension when filled with tender plants that thrive in warm, moist atmospheres. Pools can be formal, informal or abstract but must integrate into garden design. Check planning permissions or restrictions. Pools require good margins for access, furniture, and possible safety fencing, especially with children. Smaller plunge pools, jacuzzis and hot tubs fit on patios, roof terraces or large balconies.

SWIMMING POOLS – NATURAL

The pleasure of swimming in rivers or lakes is completely different to chemically treated pools, and natural swimming pools are increasingly popular, fitting well into garden landscapes. They are environmentally friendly, low maintenance, and use no harmful chemicals. Shapes can be formal or informal and are divided into two areas comprising a naturally planted, shallow surround, and deeper swimming area. Plants help purify water, which is pumped and filtered through sand and reed beds. Plants and micro-organisms help maintain natural balances, sustaining a range of pond life, aquatic and marginal species. Fish are not included because they have a detrimental effect on plants and water quality. Plants include iris, bulrushes and waterlilies, grouped in 'regenerative' areas of shingle or sand, absorbing nutrients from the water. Roots aid purification, absorbing pollutants and bacteria. Pools can be gently heated but this affects choices of plants and aquatic life. Pools change and mature but require little maintenance, apart from occasional topping up in dry weather.

WALL FOUNTAINS

Carved stone animal heads created gutter outlets for water, later becoming decorative wall mounted features trickling water into stone or lead basins, wreathed with plants. They are ideal in small gardens, on patios or balconies.

WATERFALLS

Waterfalls should look natural adding drama to streams, cascading between pools or tumbling down rock faces. Water also slides down smooth, vertical surfaces of slate, glass or metal, circulated by a pump.

WELLS

Brick-lined wells originated around 2500BC. Few of us are lucky enough to have old wells but they make attractive features. Wells can be extremely deep so safety is important. Metal grills or toughened glass may be used as covers. Water was originally drawn in buckets and later by pumps but most original pumps have disappeared or have resurfaced as garden ornaments.

WINTER

Freezing water expands, affecting construction of ponds and triggering cracks and leaks. Decaying matter beneath ice affects water quality, increasing potentially dangerous carbon dioxide levels. Snow cuts out light, detrimental to plants and fish. Floating rubber balls can be used to prevent ice forming, and a kettle of hot water makes a hole in the ice. Pond heaters also help. Never break ice with a hammer, as shock waves kill fish.

Creating water gardens

Natural water in gardens is a blessing few of us are lucky enough to possess so we create artificial features for their beauty, sound, movement, and wildlife habitats. Water in gardens, however minimal, attracts insects and amphibians, but creating a true wildlife pond is a great asset when so many natural habitats are being lost. Traditional pools and fountains come in all shapes and sizes but there are many abstract and modern designs to fit the most avant-garde gardens. Waterfalls, rills, canals and reflective pools all create interest. Sheets of water flowing down glass or metal screens are striking, particularly in tiny gardens. Whatever the choice, features must integrate into the overall garden design. You cannot simply go out, dig a hole, pop in a liner and fill with water. Careful planning is important, eliminating later pitfalls.

Style and positioning of water features is important. Water falls to the lowest level so building a stream on raised ground immediately looks out of place. Curving

ABOVE: A picturesque stream with waterfalls at Brobury House, Herefordshire.

RIGHT: This narrow rill and stone trough create a simple and very attractive water feature at Stockton Bury Gardens, Herefordshire.

However minimal, water always creates an attractive feature in the garden and is a magnet for wildlife.

Tiny ponds are best as simple ovals as trying to create curves in small areas looks unnatural. Larger spaces provide more opportunity to create natural looking ponds. Minimum dimensions are at least 75 centimetres deep and 3 metres in diameter. Avoid trees to minimize problems from roots and falling leaves. Dig natural ponds with sloping sides or steps and construct ledges around the outer edge, about 30 centimetres below the waterline, and around 25 centimetres wide, for marginal plants. Many liners come with a guaranteed lifespan, so choose the best you can. Don't skimp on size as surplus material can be used for bog gardens, but it is difficult joining liners if you run short, creating weak areas and possible leaks. Approximate measurements should be the width of the pond plus twice its maximum depth plus an additional 40 centimetres of overlap, and the length of the pond plus twice its depth and an additional 40 centimetres. Remove sharp stones, tree roots, or anything likely to pierce liners. Line the hole with old carpet, a thick layer of cardboard or newspaper. Liners handle better when warm so leave in sunshine for half an hour. Carefully lay the liner, smoothing out creases and pushing into hollows. A layer of turf, grass side down, is the perfect medium for covering liners, moulding up the sides and creating good planting areas. Fill with water and allow a few days to acclimatize. Take care not to damage liners when planting. Buy plants from reliable sources so they are not contaminated with blanket weed. Put oxygenating plants into the water and plant marginals. Fancy fish have a detrimental effect in wildlife pools. Most pools need to settle and often go green until a natural balance establishes. Small pebble or shingle beaches also look attractive.

Measure formal pools carefully before excavating. Turf to the edge of the pool, or pave the perimeter to provide boundaries between lawn and water. Carefully conceal liners.

Raised pools must be carefully constructed to support the internal weight of water. Wall tops provide seating and spaces for compost and plants. Walls require solid foundations. Use bricks, stone or concrete blocks, lined with concrete or pool liner, concealed beneath the top layers of stone. Paint sealant inside concrete pools to stop harmful toxins leaching into the water.

Fountains, streams, rills and waterfalls add sparkling movement and sound. Low jets bubble through stones. Larger fountains can be abstract or have carved decoration, spraying water into the air. Streams weave down a hillside, waterfalls cascade over rocks or down sheets of steel or glass.

Waterlilies are popular plants for pools and containers, preferring still water to moving. Small pygmy lilies suit tiny containers and pools. Deeper water accommodates vigorous species allowing leaves to spread. Rampant lilies eventually require thinning. Plant

lines of informal pools fit well in naturally landscaped gardens where lush planting encourages wildlife. Formal designs look better in formal gardens, especially when space is limited. Keep reflective ponds and canals free of plants to emphasize mirror reflections. Raised ponds are useful where ground cannot be excavated, fitting well into small spaces and on patios.

Any artificial movement of water, including fountains, cascades, or waterfalls, requires correct installation and materials. Solar or electrically powered pumps move water around; filters remove sludge and debris, which is useful if ponds are stocked with fish. Extreme care must be exercized with electricity in conjunction with water and is best left to experts. Most ponds require excavation with disposal of soil an important consideration. It can be transported from the site or landscaped into the design.

Large ponds and lakes require strong planting with trees such as alder, dogwood and willow. Reeds, rushes, iris and waterlilies are excellent additions. Oxygenating plants help maintain water quality. Once correct balances are achieved, natural ponds largely look after themselves needing only the occasional removal of leaves and thinning of plants.

ABOVE: Well-established and beautifully planted man-made pond at The Wickets, Staffordshire.

RIGHT: Burrow Farm Gardens, Devon. Water adds special magic to any garden and creates focus and drama.

them in humus-rich compost in special baskets, topped with gravel, and lower gently into deeper water over time as plants grow. Oxygenating plants keep water in good condition, but become invasive and need controlling.

Bog areas around pools utilize pond water supply. Bogs can also be created from saucer-shaped hollows covered with liner or overlapping sheets of polythene. Water seeps away through joins in the liner. Cover with turves and plant, or top dress with gravel or shingle, blending into natural surroundings. A small-bore pipe maintains moisture in dry weather as many bog plants die if they get too dry. Planked walkways or stepping stones cross boggy ground. Many interesting and beautiful species grow in moist conditions, adding further interest to gardens. Safety considerations include non-slip surfaces on bridges, jetties and walkways; handrails on bridges; pool covers; and security fencing.

Water adds special magic to gardens, creating focus and drama. It has soothing, relaxing and therapeutic qualities, prime considerations in today's hectic climate.

Water garden style

Trees and shrubs

Reflections in water are an important feature of water gardens and the beautiful shapes and shades of trees and shrubs throughout the year create reflected images around larger stretches of water. Many trees and shrubs have good winter colour with bark or stems.

Alnus glutinosa 'Aurea'
Alnua glutinosa 'Imperialis'
Alnus incana 'Lacinata'
Amelanchier lamarckii
Betula nigra
Betula pendula
Betula pubescens
Cornus alba 'Aurea'
Cornus alba 'Sibirica'
Cornus florida
Cornus kousa var chinensis
Cornus stolonifera 'Flaviramea'
Crataegus laevigata
Eucryphia lucida
Eucryphia x nymansensis 'Nymansay'
Gaultheria shallon
Hippophaë rhamnoides
Illicium anisatum
Kalmia latifolia
Lindera benzoin
Magnolia virginiana
Mespilus germanica
Metasequoia glyptostroboides
Nyssa sylvatica
Photinia villosa
Picea sitchensis
Prunus spinosa
Pyrus betulifolia
Quercus palustris
Salix alba sericea

Salix babylonica
Salix babylonica var 'Pekinensis Tortuosa'
Salix caprea 'Kilmarnock'
Salix hastate 'Wehrhanii'
Salix irrorata
Sorbus aria
Sorbus aucuparia
Spiraea x vanhouttei
Spiraea veitchii
Taxodium ascendens
Viburnum opulus

Grasses

Ornamental grasses are increasing in popularity and although many don't like to be waterlogged, many appreciate moister soils.

Arundo donax
Briza maxima
Carex echinata
Carex elata 'Aurea'
Carex flacca
Carex hachijoensis 'Evergold'
Carex pendula
Cortaderia selloana
Deschampsia caespitosa
Festuca glauca
Glyceria maxima var. variegata
Hakonechloa macra 'Alboaurea'
Holcus mollis 'Albovariegatus'
Milium effusum 'Aureum'
Miscanthus sacchariflorus
Miscanthus sinensis 'Zebrinus'
Molinia caerulea 'Variegata'
Panicum virgatum
Phyllostachys cvs.
Pseudosasa japonica
Sinarundinaria nitida
Stipa arundinacea

Stipa gigantea
Thamnocalamus var.
Yushania anceps

Plants for heavy shade

Acuba japonica
Buxus sempervirens
Camellia japonica
Camellia x williamsii
Cornus canadensis
Daphne laureola
Euonymus fortunei
Fatsia japonica
Hypericum androsaemum
Ilex x altaclarensis
Ilex aquifolium
Juniperus x media 'Pfitzeriana'
Lonicera nitida
Mahonia aquifolium
Osmanthus decorus
Podocarpus alpinus
Podocarpus nivalis
Prunus laurocerasus
Rhododendron ponticum
Ribes alpinum
Rubus odoratus
Sarcocca sp.
Skimmia sp.
Taxus cvs.
Vaccinium vitis-idaea
Viburnum davidii
Vinca major
Vinca minor

Bog gardens and marginals

The following plants enjoy boggy conditions. Some appreciate a few inches of water, while others grow well in damp borders.

Acorus calamus 'Variegatus'
Acorus gramineus 'Variegatus'
Ajuga reptans
Alchemilla mollis
Aponogeton distachyos
Arum italicum 'Marmoratum'
Aruncus dioicus
Asclepias incarnata
Astilbe x arendesii 'Amethyst'
Astilbe x arendsii 'Fanal'

Gunnera manicata.

Astilbe 'Bressingham Beauty'
Astilbe chinensis taguetii 'Superba'
Astilbe japonica 'Deutschland'
Astilbe x simplicifolia 'Bronze Elegans'
Astilboides tubularis
Athyrium filix-femina
Butomus umbellatus
Calla palustris
Caltha palustris
Cardamine pratensis
Cardamine pratensis 'Flore Pleno'
Chaerophyllum hirsutum 'Roseum'
Cimicifuga simplex
Colocasia esculenta 'Black Magic'
Cotula coronopifolia
Cyperus papyrus
Darmera peltata
Eichhornia crassipes
Eriophorum angustifolium
Eupatorium purpureum
Filipendula purpurea
Gentiana pneumonanthe
Geum coccineum 'Coppertone'
Geum rivale

Primula pulverulenta.

Glyceria maxima variegata
Gunnera manicata
Gunnera tinctoria
Hemerocallis 'Black Magic'
Hemerocallis citrina
Hemerocallis 'Crimson Icon'
Hemerocallis 'Dubloon'
Hemerocallis dumortierii
Hemerocallis 'Hyperion'
Hemerocallis 'Lark Song'
Hemerocallis lilio-asphodelus
Hemerocallis 'Morocco Red'
Hemerocallis 'Pink Damask'
Hosta crispula
Hosta decorata
Hosta fortunei var albopicta
Hosta fortunei var aureomarginata
Hosta siebodiana
Hosta undulata var. albomarginata
Houttuynia cordata 'Chameleon'
Houttuynia cordata 'Flore Pleno'
Hypericum elodes
Inula magnifica
Iris ensata 'Barr Purple east'
Iris ensata 'Flying Tiger'
Iris ensata var. spontanea
Iris fulva
Iris laevigata 'Variegata'
Iris laevigata 'Alba'
Iris laevigata 'Atropurpurea'

Iris laevigata 'Elegante'
Iris laevigata 'Snowdrift'
Iris pseudacorous
Iris pseudacorus 'Bastardii'
Iris pseudacorus 'Variegata'
Iris sibirica 'Caesar'
Iris sibirica 'Cambridge'
Iris sibirica 'Ruffles Velvet'
Iris sibirica 'Butter and Sugar'
Iris sibirica 'Wisley White'
Iris sibirica 'Dreaming Yellow'
Iris spuria
Iris versicolor 'Kermesina'
Juncus effusus 'Spiralis'
Ligularia dentata 'Desdemona'
Ligularia 'The Rocket'
Lobelia cardinalis
Lobelia fulgens
Lobelia 'Queen Victoria'
Lysichiton americanus
Lysichiton camtschatcensis
Lythrum salicaria 'Feuerkerze'
Matteuccia struthiopteris
Mentha aquatica
Menyanthes trifoliata
Mimulus guttatus
Mimulus sp.
Myosotis scorpioides 'Mermaid'
Onoclea sensibilis
Orontium aquaticum
Osmunda regalis
Peltandra undulate
Persicaria affinis
Persicaria amplexicaulis
Persicaria bistorta 'Superba'
Persicaria vaccinifolia
Persicaria virginiana 'Painter's palette'
Petasites japonicas giganteus
Pontederia cordata
Primula x bulleesiana
Primula burmanica
Primula florindae
Primula japonica
Primula pulverulenta
Primula rosea
Primula vialii
Ranunculus lingua 'Grandiflorus'
Rheum alexandrae
Rheum palmatum 'Atrosanguineum'
Rodgersia aesculifolia
Rodgersia pinnata 'Superba'
Rumex sanguineus
Sagittaria sagittifolia

Schoenoplectus lacustris
Tabernaemontani 'Zebrinus'
Tabernaemontani 'Albescens'
Thalictrum aquilegiifolium
Thelypteris palustris
Trollius x cultorum 'Canary Bird'
Trollius x cultorum 'Helios'
Trollius europaeus
Typha minima
Zantedeschia aethiopica

Aquatics

Decorative plants which float on the water or act as oxygenators in the water.

Aponogeton distachyos
Azolla filiculoides
Callitriche hermaphroditica
Callitriche palustris
Ceratophyllum demersum
Eichhornia crassipes
Elodea canadensis
Hippuris vulgaris
Hottonia palustris
Hydrocharis morsus-ranae
Myriophyllum aquaticum
Myriophyllum spicatum
Nymphoides peltata
Orontium aquaticum
Persicaria amphibia
Polygonum amphibium
Pontederia cordata
Potamogeton crispus
Ranunculus aquatilis
Sparganium erectum
Stratiotes aloides
Trapa natans

Waterlilies

These beautiful flowers that sit on the water come in a wide range of colours, with attractive, rounded leaves. They vary from small pygmy lilies up to large, rampant species, while some are not hardy and only suited to ornamental, indoor pools.

Nelumbo lutea
Nuphar lutea
Nymphaea alba
Nymphaea 'Blue beauty'

Nymphaea 'Attraction'.

Nymphaea 'Burgundy Princess'
Nymphaea caerulea
Nymphaea 'Emily Grant Hutchings'
Nymphaea 'Gladstonia'
Nymphaea 'Gonnere'
Nymphaea 'Joey Tomocik'
Nymphaea lotus
Nymphaea x marliacea 'Carnea'
Nymphaea moorei
Nymphaea odorata 'Alba'
Nymphaea 'Perry's Baby Red'
Nymphaea pygmaea 'Alba'

Ferns

Asplenium scolopendrium
Athyrium filix-femina
Azolla filiculoides
Dryopteris carthusiana
Dryopteris cristata
Dryopteris filix-mas
Dryopteris pseudomas
Gymnocarpium dryopteris
Hymenophyllum wilsonii
Onoclea sensibilis
Ophioglossum vulgatum
Oreopteris limbosperma
Osmunda regalis
Phegopteris connectilisglobulifera
Polypody interjectum
Thelypteris thelypteroides

11 Small garden style

The style

Small gardens are symbiotic with modern day living where time and space are at a premium. They are a challenge but also highly rewarding, with many positive advantages. Even tiny areas can be eye-catching, stylish and attractive by maximizing space and creating atmosphere. Good design and planning are essential, and keeping things simple often achieves the maximum effect.

Inner city and urban gardens are generally smaller than their country counterparts as space is much more limited. Inevitable demands for housing cause increasing urbanization; the cost of land escalates and houses have ever smaller gardens. Town gardens are often closed in by buildings, walls, hedges and trees, all of which affect the design in assessing light and shade. Shape of plots is dictated by local developments and small gardens tend to be rectangular, square, long and narrow or triangular. Many flats and apartments have no garden at all, but may have a balcony, tiny courtyard or roof terrace, and it is surprising what can be achieved in such small areas. Tiny gardens can be very low maintenance simply because of their size, they require less effort, and costs are inevitably lower than larger gardens. Styles vary widely between severely minimalistic with simple floor treatments and limited plants, to a plantaholic's paradise, or exotic areas crammed with plants.

With limited space, the first priority is to assess how the garden will be used. Children, pets, entertaining, relaxation and utility areas must be taken into consideration. Some facets need emphasizing and others concealing. Inevitably sacrifices are made, sadly meaning favourite plants or ornaments may have to be eliminated.

Small gardens make clever use of any views, creating an illusion of extra space. Skilful use of perspective and

OPPOSITE: *This small garden is packed with colour and interest. Careful planting makes it look far larger.*

RIGHT: *View looking down onto a small town garden designed by Charlotte Rowe, with patio, raised beds,* Dicksonia antarctica *and a place to sit with tables and chairs.*

ABOVE: *Newly planted front garden with box edging and cottage garden plants creates an attractive welcome for visitors.*

LEFT: *This tiny London courtyard garden is packed with plants, and vertical interest is emphasized by plants continuing upwards on the balconies.*

blurring boundaries also suggests gardens are larger. Emphasize width in long, narrow gardens, rather than length, while wide, shallow gardens can appear to have more depth. Strong lines and varying levels also create illusions of space. Increasingly popular green roofs and living walls make use of every available surface. Pale-coloured materials reflect available light, while repeating a shape, colour or specific material aids continuity. Planning small gardens is about creating deceptions and illusions. Perspective and false perspective play important roles. The deployment of mirrors and *trompe l'œil* create further illusions.

Plants in small spaces should be the best available, as they are seen close to. A simple palette of green looks relaxed and cool; bright colours glow; tall plants draw the eye upwards; columnar or fastigiate trees add height with little width and create less shade.

Front gardens are usually smaller than back and are generally used for 'show'. They form the traditional 'welcome' to your home, so develop the space to create stylish impact even though it may only be a few pots at the door. Small gardens can be packed full of stunning style. They can be lush and mysterious, bright and open, clean and simple, or intimate and romantic. They have inevitably involved careful planning but they should look natural and effortless when finished.

History

Agriculture in Britain developed from the Roman invasion where fields, and villa courtyards and gardens were enclosed spaces. During Medieval times, land was divided into strips farmed by peasants, for the Manor, Church and (on a limited scale) for themselves. Space around dwellings could support a pig, poultry, and grow vegetables and herbs, known as 'pot herbs'. Town gardens were small and used for vegetables, or a pig – often let out to forage in the streets as space was so limited. Slowly land strips were amalgamated and eventually enclosed into large estates. As trade increased and merchants rose to prominence Medieval and Tudor gardens became more decorative and included bowers and knot gardens. Although gardens were larger they were often divided into smaller, intimate areas.

Britain had always been rooted in agriculture, despite increasingly impressive gardens being created around important houses over the centuries. In the late eighteenth and early nineteenth centuries, one of the most important events in history dramatically changed everything. In little over a hundred years the Industrial Revolution created enormous manufacturing towns. Introduction of agricultural machinery meant less work in the country and times were hard, but suddenly employment was available in textile mills, mines and smelting works, and people flocked to towns. Hargreaves' Spinning Jenny (1764), Arkwright's water frame (1771), and Watt's steam engine (developed between 1763 and 1775) had a major effect on the socioeconomic and cultural conditions in Britain, which spread around the world. Factories required vast labour forces, towns rapidly expanded, and there was a dramatically increased need for cheap housing. Workers were ruthlessly exploited and often had to pay extortionate rents for appalling accommodation. Almost immediately these developments became severely overcrowded slums. Rows of back-to-back terraced houses were crammed into the smallest possible area. Often one earth closet was shared by many dwellings, and emptied at night by the 'soil man'. In very deprived areas, evil-smelling effluent was piled near the houses, seeping into the ground, resulting in contaminated water and deadly diseases such as cholera. Better properties boasted tiny, cramped yards for storing wood and coal, and might also house a lavatory. These tiny yards were purely utilitarian areas and people had little time for anything but work to stave off starvation and the workhouse.

Factory conditions were horrendous and men, women and children slaved mercilessly until Parliament passed a series of Factory Acts, beginning in 1802, attempting to limit working hours to ten hours a day. Writers such as Charles Dickens recorded the appalling conditions experienced at the time. There was little education, as it was believed that ignorant workers would not rebel or question their rights. Over the years machinery became increasingly sophisticated, resulting in less manpower being required, therefore creating mass unemployment. Cheap, imported products meant many mills closed. Buildings were abandoned or demolished and those left were eventually used for other purposes.

Two World Wars encouraged the general populace to look at what space they had and utilize it for growing food. The twentieth century was well advanced before gardening became the all-consuming pastime of today. The Second World War encouraged the 'Dig For Victory' campaign and tiny spaces were used for growing vegetables. Returning servicemen, desperate for accommodation, were housed in massive new developments. With space at a premium, properties were small, with minimal outside space, but soon these tiny areas began to blossom with flowers as well as vegetables, and people began taking pride in what they could achieve with small plots.

The continued expansion of towns and cities saw increasing development and the growth of tiny gardens, which followed a similar theme of lawn, small flower border, and vegetables. Larger houses inevitably had bigger gardens, looked after by gardeners, although apart from a few notable designers, there was little direction.

The Royal Horticultural Society's 1928 International Exhibition of Garden Design vividly illustrated the confusion as designers tried to cram new as well as traditional elements into ever smaller gardens. This led to a distinct lack of cohesion and garden design needed a complete re-think. Top designers of the time, including Edwin Lutyens, Percy Crane, Clough Williams Ellis and Reginald Blomfield, were represented in the exhibition's 'Garden Planning for Town and Country' section. Barry Parker (1867–1947) engineered many large schemes but was particularly interested in designing smaller houses and gardens for working people, such as his 1927 garden suburb at Wythenshawe, Manchester, for 100,000 people.

Gardens had too many elements packed into every available corner. The *Studio* magazine illustrated a 1936 design for a small garden, claustrophobically crammed with a miscellany of conflicting features, and a tiny Japanese-style garden which contained water, bridges, willows and a thatched tool shed. Most gardeners continued with traditional roses, border, rockery and lawn, fitting everything they liked into a small space.

White concrete, grey slate, gravel and topiary trees in a minimalistic new garden.

Gardens became jumbles of vegetation and odd items such as sundials, wishing wells, garden sheds and tiny, crazy-paved terraces.

In Hyères in France, a young Persian designer, Gabriel Guevrekian, created a small triangular garden surrounded by white walls; this proved a revelation and was much admired and copied. Christopher Tunnard (1910–79), a forward-thinking designer in the 1930s, stripped things down to minimal basic forms and clean lines. He introduced 'architectural' plants and interesting textures, shapes and colours, which fitted beautifully into small courtyard gardens. Plants such as *Hebe*, ivy, *Fatsia japonica*, bamboo, *Hosta*, *Euphorbia*, *Phormium*, and white-flowered plants were used, complementing the areas of white concrete appearing in designs at the time. Landscape architect, Richard Sudell, promoted carefully designed small gardens and his 1940s book, *The Town Garden*, contained numerous designs.

In the post-war period, garden architects of necessity turned to designing smaller gardens. Two important influences were the large, sweeping, Modernist styles of Brazilian designer, Roberto Burle Marx (1909–94) and American designer, Thomas Church (1902–78), who developed garden rooms using simple forms and flowing lines. In the early 1950s Geoffrey Jellicoe (1900–96) designed a small London garden measuring only 20 feet square, demonstrating that even tiny spaces benefitted from the designer treatment. A rapidly expanding post-war population and immigration all meant housing was once again at a premium. Larger cities began building high-rise tower blocks, accommodating large numbers of people on small ground areas. 'The Lawn' in Harlow, Middlesex, was the first, in 1951. Slums were cleared and people re-housed in modern tower units. This created its own problems and developments gained reputations for being deprived areas of low-cost housing. In recent years, many high-rise buildings have been refurbished and sought out by city professionals, and small balconies have been transformed into green and colourful oases.

John Brookes (b.1933) has a reputation as one of the most innovative garden designers of the twentieth century at a period when gardens were moving quickly forwards, benefitting from new ideas and materials. His development of Denmans Garden in West Sussex includes many ideas that adapt well to smaller spaces. His numerous books, including *The Small Garden*, are inspirational for any gardener.

The urgent demand for housing continues and gardens get correspondingly smaller. Inner cities re-develop brown field sites, and new houses and flats are wedged into tiny corners. Small gardens and courtyards are the norm on new developments, leading to many designers and publications concentrating specifically on this area. The twentieth century saw gardening escalate into a popular hobby, but increasingly hectic schedules mean many people actively seek tiny gardens. In the end, it is not the size of the garden that is important; it is what you do with it to create your own beautiful, harmonious and relaxing outside space.

Elements of small gardens

ACCESSORIES

Keep accessories simple and do not overcrowd. Bright colours or a tall object placed at the furthest point of the garden bring it closer, while lighter colours and smaller objects lengthen perspective. Add groups of stones or shells, quirky driftwood, old stone flagons or an urn, mosaics, a niche for a light or ornament, and wood or metal chimes. An old zinc watering can fits well and being useful does not look out of place on show. Accessories must integrate into the garden rather than looking as if they have been accidentally dropped and are simply waiting to be cleared up.

Attractive and very small courtyard garden in Shropshire, massed with container plants to create an oasis of green in the centre of town.

A peephole cut through the hedge adds a further dimension to a small garden, drawing in views from outside.

It is surprising what can be achieved when there is not space for a garden at all. Two stone troughs are massed with colourful plants and climbers right at the edge of the road.

BALCONIES

Tiny balconies create beautiful gardens. Plants grow luxuriantly in containers or grow bags, and can cling to – or trail down – walls. Tier plant stands and fix pots and window boxes securely to railings and walls, using every available space. Projecting beams and overhead structures are useful for hanging baskets and plant supports. Make sure balconies will safely take the weight of containers, and guard against falling pots and debris. Suitable flooring enhances the effect: quarry or ceramic tiles are attractive and as balconies often receive protection from above it is possible to use materials not suited to the open garden. Decking makes a suitable foil for plants. Adjustable awnings protect from bright sunlight.

BORROWED VIEWS

Attractive features from outside, drawn into the garden, immediately make space look larger. Frame views with a window in a wall or with a shape cut through a hedge.

CONTAINERS

Containers give year-round interest in small spaces and can be moved around to create focal points. They can be formal, informal or quirky, and can include terracotta pots, glazed or metal containers, chimney pots, clay drainage pipes, old boots, toilet pans, stone troughs, sinks, hanging baskets, bathtubs, wooden boxes, refuse bins, wheelbarrows, window boxes, halved tyres or stacks of tyres wired together and painted white. Some containers last longer than others, but most can be treated with suitable preservative to maximizes their useful life. Pots grouped outside doors create an attractive welcome, as do standard bay trees, topiary box, and perfumed plants. Basement steps are enhanced with a single pot on each step. Use good plants and, unless containers are for single specimens, plant luxuriantly to create impact. Plants can be limited to evergreens, single colours, pale pastels, or a riot of brilliant colours. Evergreens are attractive all year and are eco-friendly, as they do not need to be constantly renewed. Most plants grow well in appropriately sized containers. Be creative and mix flowers, vegetables, fruit and herbs.

TOP: The door to nowhere, but it opens up the clever possibility that it leads through into another garden. Hunters End, Worcestershire.

BELOW: Retaining walls and small terraces maximize space on a sloping site, while raised beds add interest and create planting areas. Brobury House, Herefordshire.

Containers require drainage holes, broken crock across the base, good compost, and a mulch of pebbles, shingle, bark or cocoa shell, which conserves moisture and protects from slugs and snails. Raising pots slightly also limits habitats for pests. Control pests in the early stages rather than letting severe infestations develop. Water plants copiously in summer and feed to keep at their best and maximize flowering. Water-retaining crystals help conserve moisture, swelling to a hundred times their original size. If pots dry out, a few drops of washing up liquid in water helps compost to become absorbent again. Safely secure window boxes, especially above first storey level. Two or three liners, planted with seasonal plants, can be exchanged at the appropriate time rather than removing the whole box. Miniature gardens grow in stone troughs or sinks and these also make excellent containers for Alpine gardens, which require special conditions.

COUP D'ŒIL

As in *trompe l'œil*, this deceives the eye into thinking it is something it is not. Such objects, carefully placed, create focal points. They can be bold but simple, such as a painted, wooden cut out shape of a column, figure, bust or urn.

HARDSCAPING

Concentrate on simple, basic structure and hardscaping. Continuity and spaciousness are enhanced by one flooring medium across the whole area, taken to the outer boundary, with small pockets for planting. Alternatively pave completely and group planted containers. In long, narrow spaces emphasize width by using strong horizontal lines from side to side; a meandering rather than straight path; divide the area up with sections of varied materials such as paviors, slabs, gravel, cobbles, brick, decking, lawn or water. In very small areas eliminate lawn, replacing with easily maintained all-weather paving.

Retaining walls and small terraces on sloping sites maximize level areas for planting. Raised beds add

interest and increase planting areas. They are simply constructed from railway sleepers, concrete blocks, bricks or stone (kits are also available). Site a feature arch implying the garden continues behind it, increasing the sense of space.

HERBS AND EDIBLE PLANTS

Many edible plants can be grown in the smallest of spaces. Herbs, vegetables and fruit mix in with flowers or grow in containers, including tomatoes, salad crops, beans, potatoes, courgettes, herbs, strawberries and blueberries. Fruit trees grow well in containers and cordon- or fan-trained trees grow against walls. Create a small, formal herb garden, or include herbs in borders, window boxes or pots near the door. Many vegetables have the added advantage of attractive flowers.

LIGHTING

Lighting is often used purely for security, but subtle lighting is very effective in small areas, helping create an illusion of space. Illuminate the whole garden or simply highlight particular features such as a special plant or ornament. Candles set into niches, or lanterns look particularly attractive, as does underwater lighting in a small pool. Lighting gives plants an ethereal quality at night, adding another perspective to the garden. Tiny basement areas come alive with minimal planting and good lighting. Small lights threaded through trees or shrubs are also attractive if not overdone.

MIRRORS

Mirrors reflect light as well as areas of the garden so make sure they reflect attractive views. Mirrors can be set into walls, trellis or hedging, framed like a picture, or be surrounded by plants. They must be waterproof to withstand outdoor conditions and kept clean, especially when viewed close up in small areas.

PERFUME

Perfumes intensify delightfully in restricted areas. Place perfumed plants near windows so that their fragrance wafts indoors.

This small courtyard garden is massed with colourful plants to give year-round interest.

PERSPECTIVE

Artfully designed, false perspective makes space appear larger, or even smaller. Long, narrow gardens seem broader divided into separate areas, creating intimate rooms. Avoid straight lines from end to end which emphasize length. A simple path zig-zagging across the space imparts an illusion of width. Create false impressions of distance by aligning receding trellis to an imaginary point. Narrowing a path, border, lawn or decking as it recedes makes it look longer. Objects or geometrical shapes that decrease in size as they move away emphasize receding perspective.

PLANTS

Good quality, carefully maintained plants are important, as they will be seen close to. Plants become focal features rather than merging en masse into large borders. They must suit the situation such as hot and dry, dry or damp shade. Tender and exotic plants grow well in sheltered, warm gardens. Choose plants for year-round interest and colour such as evergreens, or trees and shrubs with spring blossom, attractive foliage, good autumn colour, autumn fruits, and attractive bark. Always take final dimensions of trees into account.

Massed planting encloses, while small groups of plants open up an area. One or two strong, architectural plants in a minimalist space create impact. Too many groups of tiny plants look disjointed. Achieve cohesion by using groups of the same plant. Climbers on walls and fences make use of all available space; creeping species meander through paving; plants trail down steps, tumble from borders, or hang from balconies. Annuals and bedding plants fill short-term gaps. Tall plants in the foreground with smaller plants behind create distance. Pale-coloured flowers at the end of a border extend its length, while bright flowers appear closer.

ROOF GARDENS

Here the major priorities are a flat area and safety. Weight is the limiting factor, but a simple survey soon shows if the roof is suitable. Stunning roof gardens offer exciting, secret spaces high above the world. Guard against falling pots, debris, and seeping water. Treating the whole floor area with the same material makes the space look larger. Avoid heavy paving and stone, but many lightweight and attractive alternatives include ceramic tiles, wooden decking and glass fibre. Plastic deteriorates with sunlight, but new products are longer lasting and more aesthetically pleasing.

Build raised beds with railway sleepers. Grow bags are lightweight, easily transported and suitable for wide ranges of vegetables, plants and flowers. Put houseplants outdoors during summer, imparting an exotic feel. Foliage plants enjoy shade, while cacti and succulents prefer hot sunshine. Take surrounding conditions into account and see if you can incorporate an attractive view. Water must be carried for plants so try to provide a tap or rainwater tank on the roof. Install adequate drainage or waterproof membrane and ensure leakage does not cause problems with neighbours. Roof gardens must withstand wind. Windbreaks that allow wind to pass through minimize effects of turbulence, including galvanized or plastic mesh, trellis, hedging, split bamboo or wattle hurdles.

Space can be found for a small figure or sculpture in the tiniest garden.

SCREENING

Screens create an illusion the garden continues behind them; they also shield unsightly views including utility areas, provide privacy from neighbours, and support plants. Dividing small spaces into partially screened areas for different uses – such as terrace, play area or vegetables – creates interest and illusions of space. Low walls, hedges, trellis, arches, metal, clipped evergreens, bamboo, or glass blocks create a range of contrasts.

Evergreens and permanent screening are good throughout winter as well as summer. Bamboos make attractive, living screens but can be invasive especially in small spaces. Larger grasses and *Cortaderia* species make delicate, elegantly moving screens. Enclosed gardens offer shelter but might also suffer turbulence as wind bounces off walls and buildings; carefully placed screening helps to alleviate these problems.

SCULPTURE

A single, well-placed sculpture enhances even the smallest space. Abstract designs in steel, wood or stone; traditional or modern figures; a section of broken column in a border; a stone mask; or glazed relief on a wall. Plain backgrounds or evergreen hedges make good foils for sculpture.

SEATING

Even tiny gardens can provide somewhere to sit out: small, simple tables and chairs; seating built into a wall alcove, or along the edges of raised beds.

TROMPE L'ŒIL

These are attractive features especially useful in small areas where painted murals create any number of illusions. A painted alcove including an urn and flowers; painted or false door suggesting the garden continues on behind; a half-open door with glimpses of landscape, buildings, flower borders or courtyard, inviting exploration – all these deceive the viewer into thinking space is larger.

WATER

Try to include water even in the smallest of areas. A tiny pool sunk into a border; a wall-mounted mask dripping into a stone basin; a waterfall cascading into a trough; water sliding down a wall-mounted, steel sheet; a half-

Water adds interest even in the smallest garden and creates a habitat for wildlife.

barrel or even a small bowl can hold aquatic plants, attracting wildlife.

Creating style in small spaces

Careful design and attention to detail is the key to small garden style, which often requires as much planning as larger gardens where one gets away with more. Beware too many distracting features, which lead to confusion in the mind as well as the garden. Subdividing small areas often increases the sense of space rather than reducing it as one would expect. Whether formal or informal, schemes should look harmonious and flow together, giving a feeling of unity. Vistas are important, even in small areas, and remember to use vertical space as well as horizontal.

The garden should be easy to access and the most obvious choice is to create an open, central space with narrow borders around the perimeter. Interestingly, this only makes things look smaller. Design a garden that cannot all be seen with one view, despite it being small. Lead the eye from side to side rather than straight to the end. Let a path seem to disappear round a corner, leading to further delights. Decking achieves strong horizontal lines across the garden, making a narrow space appear wider. Alternatively, run decking lines from front to back in wide shallow gardens, creating depth.

Formal gardens adapt well to square or rectangular plots. Setting beds, paths and other features at an angle in a square garden makes the area more interesting. Use straight lines, geometric shapes and symmetry, creating a sense of order. One side of the design can mirror the other. Keep flooring simple with weathered bricks, stone slabs, cobbles, terracotta tiles, slate or shingle. Completely paved areas have plants in containers, or a couple of carefully positioned architectural plants. Tiny

Dividing up a small space can make it seem far larger as in this formal courtyard garden at the South Pavilion, Morville Hall, Shropshire.

parterres of low clipped box (infilled with gravel, coloured or recycled glass chippings, or plants) look great in formal schemes. Replace box hedging with paths creating flat designs. Small pots of topiary fit well. Include a wall niche, arch, column, classical urn, sculpture, pond or narrow canal.

Informal gardens suit irregularly shaped plots, are less rigid, more asymmetrical and use curving lines. Planting is softer, similar to cottage garden style. Light, airy plants including grasses fit well. Meander a path between informal borders. Use weathered bricks in herringbone or basket weave patterns for paving and paths, stepping stones set between plants, and rustic features. Thyme, chamomile and Corsican mint creep between paving stones, creating pleasing perfume when lightly crushed underfoot. Include an informal pool, small fountain or water bubbling over stones.

Exotic and sub-tropical gardens adapt well to small spaces where surrounding walls and buildings help create microclimates. Large-leaved plants and evergreens, palms and *Agaves* form a backbone while tender species such as *Ensete*, planted in tubs, can be moved to a frost-free area for winter.

Small, enclosed courtyards, creating havens of peace from the outside world are common in Spain, where they are tiny, green oases of shady seating, palms, citrus trees and gentle sounds of water from pool or fountain. Japanese gardens also suit small areas or narrow passageways. They are minimalist and uncluttered, simple to maintain, look attractive, and create an aura of peace and harmony. A simple area of raked gravel and carefully placed stones dominates the design.

Plantaholics want as many plants as possible, but it is important to prevent gardens looking cramped and impractical, so careful planning is vital. Too many distracting features are confusing. Lots of small plants give a cluttered, disjointed appearance, so choose fewer larger plants. Each item must make its own valuable contribution. Small gardens can also be productive gardens with fruit, vegetables and herbs. Fastigiated trees add height with little width in confined spaces. Feathery plants add an ethereal, open touch. Small areas of lawn are impractical and require storage facilities for mowers. Grass dries out in summer and is wet in winter. Lawn substitute plants provide green covering with less maintenance, or create interesting designs and textures with paving, adding your own particular style. Gravel is relatively inexpensive and creates an attractive, easily maintained surface which drought-tolerant plants love. Many seed freely and can be simply removed if growing in the wrong place.

If the garden is hot, dry and in full sun, a Mediterranean theme fits well. Many Mediterranean plants are evergreen, often having attractive silver leaves. Herbs appreciate sunny, well-drained soils and many are aromatic. Naturalize smaller plants such as thyme in

RIGHT: *Tender and exotic plants adapt well to small spaces where surrounding walls and buildings create microclimates.*

BELOW: *Small areas of lawn are impractical and grass has been replaced with gravel in this tiny garden, which has many different and interesting elements including decking, an arbour, pots, and space for chairs and table.*

LEFT: *White walls and pale coloured gravel increase the illusion of space in this very tiny garden in Devon, which overflows with colourful plants. The* Argyranthemums *flower almost year round in the mild climate.*

BELOW: *Different treatments of two almost identical gardens. Both have elegant curving paths to the door, but one concentrates on bricks, gravel and a few architectural plants for interest, and the other has low, clipped box hedges and a border of* Sisyrinchium *and* Euphorbia *that look good year round.*

A small, low-maintenance garden in London designed by Charlotte Rowe, with raised concrete beds, box balls in paving, wooden pergola, table and chairs.

gravel, between paving, or along the tops of low walls. Lavender and *Santolina* create attractive edgings for borders and paths when clipped after flowering. Painted white walls reflect available light and soft blue is also good for Mediterranean themes. The warm glow of terracotta tiles and bricks fits well, as do container plants. Choose suitable accessories such as white painted furniture, with brightly coloured cushions and parasols. It is important to emphasize light in small spaces. Include pale-coloured paintwork and plants; polished steel; glass and mirrors; light paving and chippings; small pools or water canals. Mirrors reflect useful light, especially in shade, while steel sheeting gives softer reflections.

Urban gardens are often dwarfed by large buildings or surrounding trees, creating dense shade. Many plants tolerate dry or damp shade. Foliage plants create a harmonious and relaxing atmosphere, and all green schemes can be relieved with a few white or pale blue highlights. Golden-coloured plants introduce sunlight even in the dullest areas. Concentrate on leaf forms, textures, woodland plants, ivies that clothe walls or creep beneath trees and shrubs, ferns, and mosses. Privacy is necessary especially where gardens are overlooked. Walls, fences and screens help. Also try lightweight awnings or thin wires across the garden above head height, supporting light-leaved climbers. Grow climbing roses along thick rope strung above walls.

Raised beds offer better drainage and the soil in these warms up quickly, useful for tender plants. They also enable plants to be admired close up. Hedges are difficult in small gardens, taking up valuable space and light as well as leaching nutrients from the soil. Small clipped box hedges look stylish and a small knot or parterre makes a formal feature in small courtyard gardens. Fences take up little width and also support plants. White or pastel-coloured picket fencing is always attractive. Small courtyards are often surrounded by walls, which can be painted, have a mosaic, or *trompe l'œil* design. Plants grow in crevices or along the tops of walls. Trellis extends the height of existing walls or acts as screening when clothed with plants, although it requires strong supports.

Front gardens are generally smaller and often overlooked in favour of back gardens. However, they set the scene for what follows, so should create attractive approaches. Paths curve or meander towards the front door (though people take short cuts if paths wind too much). Car parking is often necessary and should fit into the overall design. Gates emphasize the style of garden, with wooden gates suiting cottage styles, and wrought metal more appropriate for formal designs. Keep schemes simple, stylish and welcoming.

However small the garden or courtyard it is important to include seating, either with appropriate garden furniture, a bench set into the top of a low wall, a hanging chair or hammock. Good quality furniture looks better in small areas as it is seen close up. Try to include a small compost bin to recycle leaves, weeds and vegetable waste into your own nutritionally rich compost to go back onto the garden.

No matter how severely space is limited, it is still possible to create tiny gardens packed full of style and interest making them beautiful, welcoming and comfortable places with their very own special atmosphere.

Small garden style

Trees and shrubs

Add vertical interest without creating too much shade in small spaces.

Arbutus x andrachnoides
Betula pendula 'Fastigiata'
Camelia japonica 'Adolphe Audusson'
Camelia x williamsii 'J. C. Williams'
Carpinus betulus 'Fastigiata'
Cercis canadensis 'Forest Pansy'
Chamaecyparis lawsoniana 'Albospica'
Chamaecyparis lawsoniana 'Columnaris'
Clereodendrum trichotomum fargesii
Cornus kousa
Corylus maxima 'Purpurea'
Cotinus coggygria 'Notcutt's variety'
Crataegus monogyma 'Stricta'
Cupressus glabra 'Pyramidalis'
Decaisnea fargesii
Elaeagnus pungens 'Maculata'
Euonymus europaeus 'Atropurpurea'
Ilex aquifolium 'Green Pillar'
Juniperus chinensis 'Pyramidalis'
Juniperus communis 'Hibernica'
Liriodendron tulipifera 'Fastigiatum'
Olearia x macrodonta
Pinus sylvestris 'Fastigiata'
Sambucus racemosa 'Plumosa Aurea'

Sorbus vilmorinii
Photinia x fraseri 'Red Robin'
Philadelphus coronarius 'Aureus'
Pittosporum tenuifolium 'Irene Paterson'
Prunus serrula
Pyracantha rogersiana
Pyrus calleryana 'Chanticleer'

Slim trees

Trees of narrow, upright habit take up minimal space without creating too much shade.

Cupressus sempervirens 'Stricta'
Juniperus communis 'Hibernica'
Prunus sargentii 'Rancho'
Prunus 'Spire'
Pyrus calleryana
Taxus baccata 'Standishii'
Taxus baccata 'Fastigiata Aureomarginata'

Small shrubs

Aucuba japonica 'Nana Rotundifolia'
Artemisia 'Powis Castle'
Berberis thunbergii 'Rose Glow'
Buxus sempervirens 'Suffruticosa'
Choisya ternata 'Sundance'
Convolvulus cneorum

Camellia japonica.

Cornus alba 'Elegantissima'
Coronilla valentina 'Citrina'
Daphne cneorum 'Eximia'
Daphne mezereum
Daphne odora
Deutzia x elegantissima 'Rosealind'
Erica carnea 'Eileen Porter'
Erica x darleyensis 'Arthur Johnson'
Erica x darleyensis 'Ghost Hills'
Gaultheria mucronata 'Mulberry Wine'
Genista pilosa 'Lemon Spreader'
Halimium ocymoides 'Susan'
Hebe x andersonii 'Variegata'
Helianthemum 'The Bride'
Helianthemum 'Wisley Pink'
Hydrangea paniculata 'Kyushu'
Hypericum 'Hidcote'
Lavandula angustifolia
Lavandula stoechas
Lotus hirsutus
Mahonia x wagneri 'Moseri'
Myrtus communis tarentina
Nandina domestica 'Firepower'
Paeonia suffruticosa
Pittosporum tenuifolium 'Tom Thumb'
Prunus glandulosa 'Alba Plena'
Prunus incisa 'Kojo-no-mai'
Ribes sanguineum 'Brocklebankii'
Rhododendron yakushimanum
Rosmarinus officinalis Prostratus group
Rosmarinus officinalis 'Sissinghurst Blue'
Salvia officinalis 'Purpurascens'
Skimmia japonica reevesiana
Spiraea japonica 'Goldflame'
Spiraea japonica 'Little Princess'
Thuja occidentalis 'Rheingold'
Thuja orientalis 'Aurea Nana'
Ulmus parviflora 'Frosty'
Vaccinium corymbosum
Viburnum davidii
Weigela florida 'Foliis Purpureis'
Yucca gloriosa
Yucca filamentosa

Wall shrubs

Shrubs that can be trained close to walls or fences are invaluable in small gardens as are those that can be trimmed into low hedges and screens.

Buxus sempervirens
Buxus sempervirens 'Suffruticosa'

Alstroemeria hybrid.

Carpinus betulus
Chaenomeles x superb 'Crimson and gold'
Cotoneaster horizontalis
Euonymus fortunei 'Emerald Gaiety'
Euonymus fortunei 'Emerald and Gold'

Climbers

These climbers stay close to their supports, taking up less space.

Akebia quinata
Clematis alpina
Clematis 'Hagley Hybrid'
Clematis cirrhosa var balearica
Hedera helix 'Oro di Bogliasco'
Jasminum nudiflorum
Jasminum polyanthum
Jasminum officinale
Trachelospermum jasminoides

Larger climbers

Clematis 'Beauty of Worcester'
Clematis 'Duchess of Edinburgh'

Clematis 'Ernest Marckham'
Clematis 'henryi'
Clematis 'Lady Londesborough'
Cobaea scandens
Hedera helix
Ipomoea tricolor
Jasminum officinale
Lapageria rosea
Lathyrus latifolius
Lonicera x brownii
Lonicera sempervirens
Passiflora caerulea
Trachelospermum jasminoides
Tropaeolum speciosum
Vitis vinifera 'Purpurea'

Roses

Climbers, ramblers and low growing species.

Rosa 'Alhoa'
Rosa 'Altissimo'
Rosa 'Bantry Bay'
Rosa 'Baroness Rothschild'
Rosa 'Boule de Neige'
Rosa 'Buff Beauty'
Rosa 'Cécile Brunner'
Rosa 'Danse du Feu'
Rosa 'Dapple Dawn'
Rosa 'Felicite et Perpetue'
Rosa 'Gloire de Midi'
Rosa 'Golden Showers'
Rosa 'Maigold'
Rosa 'Marie Pavie'
Rosa 'Marlena'
Rosa 'Miss Edith Cavell'
Rosa 'Mrs Doreen Pike'
Rosa 'Old Blush China'
Rosa 'Portland Rose'
Rosa 'Queen of Denmark'
Rosa 'Wild Edric'
Rosa 'Wildfire'
Rosa 'Zephirine Drouhin'

Borders

Acanthus mollis
Achillea 'Moonshine'
Ajuga pyramidalis
Alchemilla mollis
Anemone x hybrida

Anthemis punctata cupaniana
Aquilegia McKana hybrids
Armeria maritime
Aster novae-angliae
Aster novi-belgii
Bergenia 'Baby Doll'
Bergenia 'Bressingham White'
Campanula carpatica
Campanula lactiflora 'Prichard's Variety'
Centaurea hypoleuca 'John Coutts'
Crocosmia x crocosmiflora
Delphinium x belladonna
Echinacea purpurea
Euphorbia characias wulfenii
Euphorbia griffithii 'Fireglow'
Geranium 'Johnson's Blue'
Geranium sanguineum striatum
Gypsophilla paniculata
Helleborus orientalis
Hemerocalis lilioasphodelus
Hosta fortunei
Iris germanica cvs.
Iris sibirica cvs.
Leucanthemum x superb 'Beaute Nivelloise'
Phlox paniculata
Pulmonaria rubra 'Redstart'
Rudbeckia fulgida sullivantii 'Goldsturm'
Salvia nemerosa 'Ostfriesland'
Scabiosa caucasica
Sidalcea 'Rose Queen'
Sisyrinchium striatum
Stokesia laevis
Thalictrum aquilegifolium
Viola cornuta

Container gardening

Bulbs, corms, rhizomes and tubers

These give colour and interest from spring to autumn.

Agapanthus africanus
Agapanthus campanulatus
Begonia x tuberhybrida
Crocus sp.
Cyclamen coum
Cyclamen hederifolium
Gladiolus callianthus
Hyacinthus orientalis
Iris danfordiae
Iris reticulata

Lilium auratum platyphyllum
Lilium 'African Queen'
Lilium 'Cote d'Azur'
Lilium 'Elvin's Son'
Lilium 'Enchantment'
Lilium regale
Muscari comosum
Narcissus 'February Gold'
Narcissus 'Minnow'
Narcissus 'Tete-a-Tete'
Tigridia pavonia
Tulipa 'Johann Strauss'
Tulipa 'Apricot Beauty'
Tulipa marjoletii
Tulipa 'Peach Blossom'
Tulipa praestans
Tulipa 'Red Emperor'
Tulipa 'Shirley'

Plants

Include trailing plants, climbers, half-hardy, and foliage plants.

Ageratum houstonianum 'Blue Danube'
Antirrhinum Monarch series
Argyranthemum 'Jamaica Primrose'
Begonia x carrierei
Bidens ferulifolia
Brachycome iberidifolia
Brassica oleracea
Clematis 'Madame Julia Correvon'
Coleus scandens
Convolvulus sabatius
Corydalis flexuosa 'Pere David'
Diascia rigescens
Eccremocarpus scaber
Felicia amelloides 'Santa Anita'
Fuchsia cvs.
Gazania 'Daybreak'
Helichrysum petiolare
Heliotropium 'Princess Marina'
Hosta fortunei 'Auromarginata'
Hydrangea quercifolia 'Snow Queen'
Impatiens New Guinea Hybrids
Ipomoea purpurea
Lathyrus odoratus
Lobelia erinus
Lotus berthelotii
Nicotiana Domino Series
Osteospermum 'Whirligig'
Oxalis enneaphylla

Penstemon 'Burgundy'.

Pelargonium cvs.
Petunia cvs
Plectranthus madagascariensis
Rhodochiton atrosanguineus
Salvia splendens
Scaevola aemula
Senecio cineraria 'Silver Dust'
Tagetes erecta
Tagetes patula
Thunbergia alata
Tradescantia fluminensis 'Quicksilver'
Trifolium repens 'Purpurascens'
Tropaeolum majus
Tropaeolum canariensis
Verbena 'Silver Anne'
Viola 'Padparadja'
Perennial foliage plants
Glechoma hederacea
Hakonechloa macra
Hedera helix
Huechera micrantha diversifolia 'Palace Purple'
Heuchera 'Snow Storm'
Hosta sieboldiana elegans
Houttuynia cordata 'Chamelion'
Lysimachia nummularia 'Aurea'
Phormium 'Bronze baby'
Tolmiea menziesii 'Taff's Gold'

12 Gardens of the future style

Future style

Gardens always have and always will continue along established styles, with avant-garde designers creating often controversial visions contemporary to their times. The essential element in the twenty-first century will not simply be style and design of gardens, but the whole concept, from soil to sustainability. Gardens of the future must be whole, organic combinations: creating satisfying places in which to work or relax; providing beauty and food; helping sustain wildlife; enhancing local environments; and creating working partnerships with nature, rather than attempting to control nature as in the past. We continually damage the environment, but there are many ways we can help alleviate the problems within our gardens by recreating habitats man seems so intent on destroying. Gardening in tune with nature benefits us as well as future generations who follow.

Gardeners are increasingly interested in 'eco-design', organic cultivation, keeping bees or poultry, and encouraging wildlife into gardens. Plants, sustainability and water conservation issues are all influenced by the enormous challenges of climate change. Scientists predict that by 2050 the world will not be able to produce enough food to feed a rapidly increasing population. Coupled with the effects of climate change, soaring energy and transport costs, food exports will dwindle as countries once more become reliant on their own produce. Food will become increasingly expensive, there will be less choice and diets must change to reflect this. Traditional, mainstay vegetables will come back into fashion again as gardeners strive to produce their own crops.

Gardens of the future will not simply regurgitate past trends, or create quirky, new designs – although these will all feature. Gardens of the future will be a whole new way of life, a new concept, and the sooner we embrace this, the better for our gardens, the planet and for us.

OPPOSITE: *An interesting carved sign at Hestercombe Gardens, Somerset.*

RIGHT: *Gardens of the future will still be beautiful places in which to work and relax, but they must also become sustainable and create working partnerships with nature.*

Gardeners are increasingly interested in creating largely self-sustainable gardens, and keeping bees or a few poultry. This little hen house fits beautifully into a small, suburban garden and the trellis screen is used to support climbing roses and beans.

History in the making

History provides ideas and knowledge from the past including Medieval gardens, the Renaissance, influences of Islam, China and Japan, English landscape style and Modernism. Past styles have influenced their times and what has followed, one reacting against another and stimulating change. Once rare and exciting discoveries by plant hunters are now common plants in our gardens. Sadly, over-collecting depleted many wild species, some to total extinction. We have robbed and raped the planet's assets for our benefit and are suffering because of it. Plants help maintain the extremely delicate balance of our world. For years we have destroyed vast tracts of earth's green mantle, denuding forests, creating desertification. Climate is affected and carbon dioxide levels rise, exacerbating the 'greenhouse effect'. Sunlight enters the atmosphere through a mixture of gases. The Earth's surface absorbs sunlight, reflecting it back into the atmosphere. Some of this energy escapes into space but much remains trapped by greenhouse gases, causing the world to heat up. This process is natural and essential and without it Earth would be too cold to sustain life, but imbalance in this natural cycle, for whatever reason, has created problems.

Climate change is a major concern. In the last forty years we have experienced recordbreaking weather patterns. In Britain, spring comes two to six days earlier each decade. Summers are currently longer by two days per decade, pushing autumn back. The growing season has extended by one month since 1900. Winters are milder and wetter with less frost and snow, and average temperatures are rising. In the last sixteen years Britain recorded ten of the hottest years ever. Kent experienced a record 38.5°C in August 2003. By the end of this century temperatures are predicted to rise between 1°C and 4°C, with damaging heat waves of up to 40°C, increasingly severe droughts, and highly unpredictable weather patterns. We are entering unknown territory. 'Milder' winters could become severe winters. The winter of 2008–09 was the coldest in Britain for twenty years and the summers of 2007 and 2008 were unusually wet, following previous droughts. Flash flooding is widespread and devastating with unseasonably severe storms and torrential rainfall. Urban development results in increased impermeable surfaces, intensifying water run-off and flooding which becomes progressively severe and widespread. We could experience up to 50 per cent more rain on a winter's day by 2080, resulting in an increase of more than 80 per cent water run-off in urban areas. Drainage therefore becomes a major consideration. Polar ice caps are melting at unprecedented speed, raising sea levels. Eventually low-lying land will be lost. Mediterranean countries are predicted to experience hotter temperatures, more frequent and severe drought, and increasingly desert-like conditions.

Numerous native species are in crisis from overuse of harmful chemicals and loss of habitats. Many insects and butterflies face extinction, so provide nectar plants and habitats and encourage them into the garden.

Climate zones are predicted to shift, and the effects of climate change will be felt worldwide. Rising temperatures will see more people dying from heat, higher instances of skin cancer and tropical diseases, increased wild fires, water rationing, withered crops, diseased trees, and animals and plants thrown into turmoil, unable to evolve fast enough to cope. Mediterranean butterflies and insects are already colonizing southern Britain and moving northwards. New pests and diseases are appearing and surviving through damper, milder winters. The way in which we live will alter, and also the way we garden. Water is a dwindling commodity and becomes increasingly expensive.

Governments worldwide cannot agree on climate change strategies, and this creates unprecedented problems for the future. The British Government is committed to reducing greenhouse emissions by 60 per cent by 2050. Massive deforestation has had a major impact on climate change, and we must create more green spaces to help counteract persistent pillage of rainforests. University of Manchester research shows that increasing green space in towns by as little as 10 per cent would reduce surface temperatures by up to 4°C (equalling the predicted average rise in temperature through climate change by the 2080s).

Another major concern is that overuse of harmful chemicals will have detrimental effects on land, food, animals, and result in a serious reduction of biodiversity. It is imperative we farm and garden sustainably. Once the delicate balance of nature is upset it is difficult to restore. Annihilating one species of bug inevitably increases another. In Britain for instance, cabbage fields treated with insecticide to control root fly saw more damage than untreated fields, since cabbage root fly eggs, larvae and pupae were controlled by over thirty species of beetle the insecticides killed as well. Pesticides are not selective, targeting good and bad. Numerous native species are in crisis from use of pesticides, and loss of natural habitats such as woodland, hedgerows and meadows. Many native insects and butterflies face extinction.

Predictions are dire, but nature is clever and has ways of righting wrongs. The planet has survived past devastations: species have become extinct and new ones evolved. One effect of climate change in China has seen increasingly regular typhoons draw large quantities of plankton up from the sea bed. In turn this beneficially absorbs sizeable amounts of carbon dioxide. We cannot risk complacency, however. History and science have shown what can and might happen. In our own small way gardeners can change things for the better, having a positive and long-lasting effect on what the future holds.

Elements for gardens of the future

BEES

Bee populations are mysteriously disappearing across the globe and at the time of writing, despite extensive research top scientists have no idea why. Viral and mite attacks also decimate hives. The loss of such important pollinators will have disastrous consequences. In the southern Sichuan area of China pesticides completely wiped out bees in the 1980s, and villagers have to hand-pollinate commercial fruit crops on a massive scale.

BIRDS

Many bird species have seriously declined since the 1970s as food sources and habitats disappear. Birds devour numerous garden pests, so encourage birds by providing nutritious foods, feeding stations, and nesting boxes. Keep them clean to avoid spreading disease, and place them round the garden where infestations such as greenfly occur. Leave berries and seed-heads through winter. Establish hedges rather than fences, which offer nesting sites, food and shelter. It is illegal to damage bird nests, so be careful when trimming hedges or trees.

CHILDREN

Children are gardeners of the future, and gardening provides fresh air, exercise, contact with nature, as well as

Children are our gardeners of the future, so encourage them to help and enjoy gardening from an early age.

encouraging healthy eating – and patience. With current obesity levels, outdoor activities and exercise are important, so let children join in and enjoy gardening. Encourage them from an early age to look, touch, feel and smell plants, pointing out dangerous species. Visit parks and gardens so they absorb style and scale. Look at country lanes. Let children take photographs, draw and write in journals, and make nature tables. Children are impatient, so raise fast-maturing plants.

The Royal Horticultural Society's 'Campaign for School Gardening' encourages school gardens, offering children free access to RHS gardens. In collaboration with the RHS, the BBC launched 'Gardening with Children', providing informative and fun projects. The Government's 'Building Schools for the Future'

programme offers opportunities for young people in horticulture, introducing basic skills and helping with environmental issues.

Start school gardening clubs. Many schools have established gardens, encouraging children to grow, prepare and eat the produce, selling surplus towards school funds. Investigate council grants and approach garden centres for sponsorship, plants and tools. Press publicity often generates help and donations. Gardens benefit understanding of curriculum areas such as geography, history, science and cookery. If land is limited consider raised beds or container gardens.

Create child-friendly areas in gardens and encourage children to have their own plots. Choose areas with good soil as success is important. Create dens with robust, tactile plants such as bamboo and grasses that children can run through and brush against. Family gardens must be tough and planting should take into account damage caused by games. Avoid poisonous plants, thorns and sharp points near play areas. Include space for ball games, paddling pool, and play equipment. Sand pits convert into pools or raised beds later. Create fun areas with chessboards on patios, low-level mazes of clipped grass or herbs, grass spirals and land art. Make gardens exciting and inviting places that will keep children enthusiastic.

COMPOST

Include space for compost and recycle vegetable peelings, fallen leaves, weeds, and garden trimmings, creating nutritious, crumbly loam for the garden.

Although the idea of green roofs dates back many thousands of years, they are becoming increasingly popular in the twenty-first century, supplying a whole range of benefits including improving energy efficiency of buildings, and providing sustainable habitats for wildlife. Rolls Royce Motor Cars have installed an impressive sedum roof, the largest green roof in the UK and one of the largest in Europe at 32,000m², on their headquarters in Goodwood, West Sussex.

GREEN ROOFS

These date back thousands of years. Countries such as Tanzania used them to protect buildings from heat. In Scandinavia, Scotland and Iceland, turf roofs insulated against cold. Germany has installed over 30 million square metres of green roofs since 2000. They were briefly fashionable in Britain in the 1930s and 1960s, but recently there is increased interest and demand in both commercial and private sectors. Roofs can be of turf, succulents, wild flowers, and drought-tolerant, wetland or other species. They have a huge number of benefits: they are attractive to look at, enhancing buildings and neighbourhood; they are ecologically friendly, reducing air pollution and carbon emissions and providing insulation against heat, cold and noise, thus improving the building's energy efficiency; they provide habitats for plants and wildlife, benefiting ecology; and they reduce surface water run-off, minimizing flash flooding and acting as environmentally friendly rainwater-harvesting schemes. The nationally accredited standard for sustainable building, design and construction, 'The Code For Sustainable Homes', reports green roofs make new buildings more environmentally friendly. Sheffield City Council plans to install bio-diverse roofs for Phase 1 schools in its 'Building Schools for the Future' programme. Many green roofs are established on new builds, but they can be simply constructed on existing roofs providing certain criteria are satisfied. Buildings must support the weight, have adequate waterproofing, and roofs must not constitute danger. Simple permanent or free-standing wooden frames include grids which stop growing mediums shifting, particularly on sloping roofs. Layers consist of the following, from bottom to top:

1. Damp-proof membrane, eliminating water seepage.
2. Filter or weed suppressant membrane, allowing water through but not soil.
3. Moisture blanket or woolly fleece (Geo-textile Membrane) absorbs water.
4. Aggregate including gravel, crushed brick, or clay pellets (the Substrate) to aid drainage.
5. Growing medium of subsoil or mixtures of soil and sand.

Seeds or plants are sown directly into the growing medium. Plants provide diverse habitats attracting insects and birds. Sedums are popular: they require little maintenance, are drought resistant, they spread quickly, requiring thin Substrate, and different varieties form tapestries of colour. Taller plants and grasses require trimming. Include dressed gravel, larger stones, mosses, small trees, branches or logs, providing habitats for

ABOVE *and* BELOW: *On a much smaller scale but equally impressive, Tamarisks, Devon, has two green roofs designed by Ruth Kent. One has sedum and succulents, accessed by a small bridge from the upper garden, and the other has a diverse patchwork of plants creating good combinations of colour and texture.*

insects and birds. Ready seeded mats are available to cut to size and unroll across prepared surfaces. These include wildflower mixtures, sedums, and low maintenance grasses.

HARDSCAPING

We are an increasingly ageing population, which should be taken into account when planning gardens. Provide easy access paths, wide enough for wheelchairs; ramps rather than steps; non-slip surfaces, and level paving. Raised beds combine strong design features, ease of maintenance without bending, better drainage; they also

Living walls are stunning textured tapestries of colour, as well as having benefits to the environment and the buildings on which they are grown. The spectacular living wall at Pont Juv-nal, Aix-en-Provence, France, was designed by expert Patrick Blanc who creates living walls around the world.

allow for specific soils, while low surrounding walls form seating for weeding and planting. Beds should be conveniently sized for easy maintenance.

Hardscaping materials include wood, railway sleepers, metal, concrete blocks, bricks and stone. Sustainable local materials and timber is preferable, having travelled less far, hopefully avoiding damaging environmental consequences at source. Use permeable surfaces to reduce flash flooding. Reclamation yards are excellent sources of recycled hardscaping that looks well weathered.

LAWN

Lawns make perfect play surfaces: they show plants off to perfection, effectively cover large areas of ground, and are easily shaped. They also require a great deal of maintenance: machinery, irrigation, weeding, feeding, aerating, edging, and storage for mowers. They dry out in summer and are waterlogged in rain. Lawns should be eliminated in smaller areas, replacing with gravel, paving or decking. Grass is growing faster and over longer periods, necessitating more cutting. Heavily fertilized lawns require additional water, so feed less and only water when absolutely necessary. Letting grass grow slightly longer, and setting mower blades higher, retains moisture at the roots. Removing grass boxes means cuttings are absorbed into the ground, returning nutrients and moisture. Reduce lawn area by widening surrounding borders and paths. Create wildflower meadows or prairie gardens, limiting mowing to once

or twice a year. Grow lawn edges longer and incorporate wild flowers. Use lawn substitute plants, which supply low-maintenance green covering. Create lawn parterres with patterns of shorter and longer grass, undulating spirals, mounds, or mazes. Drought-tolerant grass cultivars stay greener without watering. New artificial turfs are often impossible to tell from real grass and maintenance is simple. Artificial grass has no die back or mud, needs no watering and is laid like carpet onto prepared ground.

LIVING WALLS

In 1970, Spanish designers Enric Tous and Josep Maria Fargas created one of the first 'Garden Curtains' or 'living walls' of plants, in Barcelona. Plants cascaded down from window boxes on balconies, forming a colourful, green curtain. The 'living wall' technique has been perfected by influential French designer, Patrick Blanc, who creates stunning vertical walls in many countries including Britain. Colourful and attractive designs grow in pocketed panels of special material attached to interior or exterior walls. Plants include climbers, trees and shrubs, densely grown in special moisture-retaining synthetic and peat mixtures. Living walls establish microclimates, using ten times less water than conventional planting.

Include *Artemisia, Bergenia, Buxus, Corydalis, Euonymus, Euphorbia,* fennel, ferns, *Geranium,* grasses, *Heuchera, Hosta, Lamium, Ligularia,* mosses, oregano, *Saxifrage, Sedum,* vines and many others. Vertical modular growing

TOP LEFT: A five-layer matrix garden with trees, shrubs, herbaceous perennials, grasses and ground cover plants.

TOP RIGHT: Wildflower meadows require careful management until they establish and form a natural balance, but then they provide a colourful display of flowers throughout summer, as well as providing excellent habitats for wildlife.

systems of polypropylene and geotextiles are used individually as extra space for growing vegetables, herbs and flowers, or create huge living walls. Fertilizer and water are irrigated through units.

Active living walls are based on biofiltration and phytoremediation techniques, which can be integrated into a building's air circulation system. Air is drawn through roots, and beneficial microbes degrade pollutants, returning clean air to the system, minimizing air pollution in large cities and aiding grey water purification. 'Hostile walls' use prickly, spiky, spiny and stinging plants, acting as natural deterrents. Plants include *Echinops*, *Eryngium*, *Yucca*, *Rubus* species and nettles.

MATRIX GARDENS

Matrix gardens create natural habitats with simply maintained, self-sustaining plant communities, which rarely suffer pests or disease. Mixes of shrubs, woody plants, perennials, grasses and bulbs, set into gravel, allow plants to seed around. East Lambrook Manor, Somerset, has a three-layered matrix garden with ground cover, perennials and shrubs. Matrix gardens take time to establish, and plants should suit local conditions, using drought-tolerant species in dry areas and moisture-loving plants in damp areas. Initially remove perennial weeds, but once established, matrix gardens require little maintenance as digging destroys the natural balance, allowing weed seeds to surface. Gardens form thick mats of roots and plants. Periodically add organic matter (which worms can drag underground) and cut as necessary to restore balance. Include annuals for cover and colour until perennials are established. Most modern varieties are hybridized versions of wild plants, with larger, more exotic blooms, and native plants are often more beautiful and useful in nature.

MEADOWS

Wildflower meadows are spectacular, but require careful management and planting until established. Use native species, as although non-native perennials and annuals are colourful they can look alien. Suit species to local conditions, create a natural balance, allow plants to seed before mowing, and remove cuttings to maintain low soil fertility. Ideally remove topsoil and sow native wild flowers and less vigorous grass species, or plug plants, straight into subsoil. Perennials establish and flowers seed, creating beautiful meadows.

MOON GARDENING

Lunar gardening has been practised for millennia, termed 'biodynamic gardening' by Austrian philosopher Rudolf Steiner. It is based on the moon's gravitational pull affecting the water within plants as it does with tides. The strong gravitational pull of a waxing moon, high in the sky, draws water into plant leaves. A distant and smaller, waning moon, benefits roots. Lunar guidebooks such as *In Tune with the Moon*, Findhorn Press, show month by month the best days for sowing, working and harvesting crops, as well as times to be avoided. Plants are divided into four main groups: fruits, flowers, leaves and roots. Many people firmly believe in moon gardening, and many sceptics have become converts.

Combination and companion planting in the kitchen garden at Painswick Rococo Garden, Gloucestershire, which has been recreated into the original geometric patterns of former years with pathways edged with cordon apple trees.

PERMACULTURE

This concept is about creating sustainable and permanent solutions, based on natural rhythms, in preserving habitats and re-establishing eco-friendly systems once destroyed. Permaculture works with nature in areas such as forest gardens and edible landscapes, making the best use of land and its responsible management, caring for the planet and those who live on it. It aims for prudent use of time, energy and resources to live creatively and harmoniously. It views the world in a different, positive way whether in gardens, farming, commerce or community, encouraging self-reliance, support and cooperation by taking control of our lives. Natural, self-sustaining systems work towards a sustainable future.

PESTS AND DISEASES

Over recent years the British climate has warmed, increasing new pests and diseases. Recent introductions include:

- Plane tree lacebug, *Corythucha ciliate*. A sap-sucking insect found on *Platanus* species.
- Harlequin ladybird, *Harmonia axyridis*. It is feared this ladybird might decimate native species of ladybird.
- Oak processionary moth, *Thaumetopoea processionea*. 700 nests destroyed in London in 2007.

- Citrus longhorn beetle, *Anoplophora chinensis*. The larvae tunnel into wood. Adults are black with white markings and long, black and blue antennae.
- Rosemary beetle, *Chrysolina Americana*. Metallic green with purple stripes found on rosemary, lavender and related species.
- Berberis and mahonia sawfly, *Arge berberidis*. Causes defoliation.
- Pests such as red spider mite and whitefly, which at one time only survived in greenhouses, are now acclimatizing outdoors.

Prevention is better than cure: don't overcrowd plants, allowing good air circulation; clear up fallen leaves and garden debris which harbour spores; burn contaminated material; nitrogen-rich feeds encourage weak, sappy growth; mulch to preserve moisture and inhibit fungal diseases; choose plants that thrive locally, as these are stronger. Encourage beneficial insects into gardens. A single lacewing for instance devours up to 10,000 aphids in its lifetime, while ladybird larvae consume between thirty and forty aphids a day.

PLANTS

Grow plants that tolerate predicted future weather conditions, and survive drought as well as flooding. Drought-tolerant plants require no additional irrigation. Strong plants, suited to local environments, require minimal maintenance. Include food plants with flowers and practise companion planting. Make sure plants have not come from wild sources.

PRAIRIE PLANTING

North American prairies are vast, sunny tracts of grassland with swathes of wild perennials. Many cultivated perennials originated in North American prairies and these grow beautifully with mixed ornamental grasses in wild style planting. Naturalized bulbs extend the flowering period, and although not usual in native grassland shrubs adapt well, creating additional interest. Prairie gardens provide excellent wildlife habitats. Merge areas of lawn into longer grasses. Clear ground before planting, and broadcast suitable grass and flower seeds in autumn. Nature does the rest. Remove perennial weeds until gardens are established, and aim for merging drifts of plants. Prairie planting also suits large borders. Simple maintenance consists of an annual mowing, removing cuttings. Plants self seed, adding to the natural effect and require no additional water to rainfall.

RECYCLING

Recycling is becoming increasingly important. Environmental issues make us question sustainability of

The wild style planting of the prairie garden forms beautiful, self-sustaining communities of perennials and grasses and leaves nature to do the rest.

The grotto at Westonbury Mill, Herefordshire, looks like a simple, unimposing, futuristic domed building …

… but once inside, it becomes clear that it has been created from recycled, coloured glass bottles, transporting the visitor into the brilliance of a stained-glass cathedral.

This hanging garden art was created from woven stems and leaves at Pinsla Gardens and Nursery, Cornwall.

garden materials with manufacture and transport. Concern about depleting peat bogs suggests we should use peat-free composts, but everything we use in our garden has had some impact, somewhere. Gardeners have been at the forefront of recycling for generations, re-using containers for seeds, gathering leaf mould, and composting.

Recycled ground coverings include gravel, crushed stone, sea shells, glass chippings, granulated CDs, and cocoa shells. Re-using old bricks, tiles, stone and paving slabs makes new gardens look established. Recycling can also introduce humour, with a little Kitsch, or pure nonsense in this serious age, although this can be boring if overdone. Examples of recycling opportunities include: upturned bottles in flower borders; designs of empty snail shells; guttering for planters; old tyres wired together for containers; steel and cable drums; arrangements of drain pipes filled with plants; wooden racks; kitchen sinks; toilet pans; driftwood; shells, and arrangements of shiny CDs.

REED BEDS

These are unobtrusive, low-cost, long-lasting ecological

and sustainable systems for waste water treatment. Reed beds are highly effective for domestic, agricultural and industrial effluent. Fully functioning systems produce stream quality, recycled water. Reed beds are economical and produce no smell when working effectively. Horizontal systems are suitable for low strength or pre-treated effluents. More efficient, vertical systems filter waste through flat beds of gravel and sand planted with reeds, *Phragmites australis*. They form smaller units and accommodate stronger effluents. Combination systems cover the full treatment of domestic sewerage as well as sludge and grey water. Water cannot be drunk, re-used in toilet cisterns or used for watering edible plants.

Filtration systems must meet Environmental Agency standards, and act by bacterial breakdown of biological components. Size is based on 1 square metre per person, and reeds are planted at 4 per square metre. Maintenance consists of removing weeds, watering until established, and occasionally loosening compacted topsoil.

SPECIAL NEEDS AND SENSORY GARDENS

Gardens of the future include higher concentrations of plants appealing to all five senses: sight, smell, touch,

Innovative use of old terracotta flower pots to create garden art at Pinsla Gardens and Nursery, Cornwall.

Reed bed systems create low-cost, long-lasting, ecological and sustainable systems for waste water management. Hillfield Cottages, Devon, uses both horizontal and vertical reed bed systems, providing complete water and effluent management for their forty environmentally friendly cottages.

Shrubs, grasses and perennials grow in self-sustaining communities without constant irrigation at Pinsla Gardens and Nursery, Cornwall.

taste and hearing. Fragrance permeates the air and plants release scents when brushed past or lightly crushed underfoot. Rustling grasses and bamboo create soothing sounds, and waxy or velvety flowers and leaves actively encourage touching.

SUPERFOODS

Grow your own superfoods, which are thought to benefit health. High in vitamins and antioxidants they include: beetroot, blackberries, blackcurrants, broccoli, cherries, elderberries, garlic, gooseberries, kale, onions, pumpkin, raspberries, redcurrants, strawberries, tomatoes and walnuts. Wild berries contain higher levels of antioxidants than cultivated; as do purple pigmentation in blackcurrants and blueberries. Levels diminish with storage so eat fresh.

WATER

Water conservation plays an increasingly important role in gardens of the future and we must safeguard this precious commodity. Many areas of the world suffer severe drought. In recent years Britain too has experienced drought, water shortages and hosepipe bans, despite enough rainwater falling to more than cover everyone's needs, causing water costs to escalate.

Excessive watering weakens plants, making them shallow rooting, stopping roots penetrating deep into the earth to find their own moisture. Over-watered plants are also more susceptible to wind damage. All plants need water until they are established but then many survive with little or no additional water, especially drought-tolerant species. If plants require water give a good, occasional soaking rather than constant small amounts that do not penetrate to the roots. Guard against wasteful water run-off. Watering in early morning or late evening limits evaporation. Never water in full sun, as this damages plants and scorches leaves. Mulches help soil retain moisture.

Irrigation systems are expensive and it is better to re-think gardens rather than using plants that require constant and expensive water. Group plants according to their waterwise needs, plants requiring water near the house for ease of maintenance, those needing little or no water furthest away. Introduce new plants in autumn to benefit from winter rain. Use rainwater, household

grey water or treated water from reed bed systems whenever possible for plants. Harvest rainwater by installing butts beneath downpipes on houses, sheds, summerhouses and greenhouses, covering tanks to limit evaporation.

New eco-friendly properties have underground water storage tanks, but these can also be installed above ground. A standard four-bedroom house captures 1,000,000 litres of rainwater each year, saving between 30 per cent and 50 per cent of domestic supplies. On average each person uses 150 litres of water every day, or 250,000 litres a year for a family of four.

Recycle grey water not contaminated with strong detergents and chemicals. Dishwasher water is not suitable, but washing machine, bath and sink water is generally re-usable. Oil traps and filters eliminate waste deposits, detrimental to tanks and plants. Simple fittings divert bathwater into separate tanks. Don't use grey water for drinking or ornamental ponds. In urban areas rainwater is taken into mains drainage systems and does not return, causing water table levels to drop.

WILDLIFE

Many natural habitats are being destroyed and bird and mammal species are declining. Gardens make valuable contributions in replacing habitats for birds, insects and small mammals, particularly in city areas. Even small balcony gardens attract numerous insects. Gardens of the future will promote holistic approaches, encouraging wildlife into gardens. This will help protect endangered species, and benefit gardens as they act as biological controls, disposing of many harmful pests.

Indiscriminate chemical use has decimated wildlife. Chemicals have entered food chains and water courses. Many plants and insects have become resistant to chemicals as nature fights back. Creating imbalances causes problems for beneficial garden organisms. For instance, by removing aphids we also lose insects that eat them, thereby upsetting the natural balance. We will never eliminate all pests, diseases and weeds from gardens, but employing organic methods helps. Providing food plants for bees, butterflies, moths, hoverflies and other beneficial insects in turn helps reduce garden pests, creating sustainable ecosystems.

Many creatures have very specific food requirements. Certain butterflies and caterpillars require nettles; Orange Tip Butterfly caterpillars need Lady's Smock, *Cardamine pratensis*, and the much-maligned ragwort supports Cinnabar Moth caterpillars. Frogs and toads devour numerous garden pests. Providing water for these to breed also attracts beetles, dragonflies, and newts into gardens. Sloping sides or small ramps in pools enable

Natural ponds are not only beautiful, they provide diverse habitats for a whole range of aquatic wildlife.

A small log pile tucked into the corner of the garden provides homes for a diverse range of insects and small mammals.

Low woven hurdles enclose raised beds in this attractive potager garden growing a wide range of vegetables and herbs.

creatures such as hedgehogs to escape if they fall in when drinking.

Milder winters see increasing numbers of insects during cold weather. Winter flowering plants ensure supplies of pollen and nectar, while berries, fruits, nuts and seeds provide food for many birds and small mammals.

Poisoning slugs and snails also kills off creatures such as the hedgehogs, frogs, toads and birds that eat them. Use natural methods of control including beer traps, halved upturned grapefruit skins and flowerpots, or planks of wood. Collect and dispose of unwanted invaders each morning.

Commercially produced shelters are available for insects, amphibians, hedgehogs and birds, but these can be simply constructed from upturned flower pots, wood stacks or piles of dried leaves. Short lengths of bamboo or bundles of hollow stems wedged into trees make perfect homes for insects. Nectar-rich plants encourage insects, which in turn aid pollination. Plants include the poached egg plant, *Convolvulus*, *Cosmos*, dill and French marigold. Hoverflies are attracted to yellow flowers, while purple, blue and white flowers are magnets for many pollinating insects. Flowers at this end of the colour spectrum often exhibit coloured markings directing insects towards nectar and pollen. Hybrids and double flowers are sterile and of less use to insects so plant traditional, single-flower varieties. Include patches of nettles as food plants for caterpillars. Grow native wild flowers and hedgerows of native species such as hazel, hawthorn and elder.

Healthier soil means happier plants, less prone to disease and insect attack. Garden with the seasons and nature's cycle, and encourage wildlife for all the benefits and few disadvantages it brings. However large or small the garden there is plenty we can do to help.

Creating gardens of the future

As we try to cram ever more into hectic lives, it is important to find time to unwind and recharge batteries. Gardens should reflect this and be pleasant, relaxing spaces to be enjoyed, rather than requiring us to spend every minute on maintenance. Gardens of the future should also be eco-friendly and sustainable, taking into account water conservation and changing climate.

We cannot and often do not want to escape what has gone before. The wonderful legacy of historic gardens, and tremendous ranges of ideas and plants will always influence our gardens. However futuristic designs become, gardens will continue with elements of the past. But gardens of the future will reflect our deeper understanding of past mistakes, enabling us to live more sustainably, both in and out of the garden, to work with nature rather than against it.

An important aspect of gardening, wherever we live in the world, is to work with local conditions and materials. These can be tweaked to maximize effect, and we can develop microclimates, but overall, it is extremely difficult to grow dry plants in waterlogged soil, shade-loving plants in sun, tender plants in arctic conditions, and acid-loving plants in alkaline soil. It is better and simpler to garden with what we have rather than fighting nature. Gardening within the natural constraints of weather patterns generally dictates the plants we grow and gardens we cultivate. Mediterranean, tropical or northern European climates diversify further into local conditions, which may be warmer or cooler than 10 miles up the road. Environments change between adjacent gardens and plants that thrive in one may not

Gardens of the future must reflect consideration for wildlife and the planet so we can all begin to live in harmony with ourselves and our environment.

survive in another. Establish what you have and then plant utilizing the advantages. Soil quality can be improved with humus and compost, while sand or gravel aid drainage.

Limit non-porous surfaces, which exacerbate water run-off. Use gravel instead of concrete, tarmac, paviors and slabs, so water escapes into the ground. Government legislation now means obtaining planning permission before covering front gardens with impermeable materials, which greatly increase dangers of local flash flooding.

Gardeners can help reduce carbon emissions and landfill waste; protect diminishing resources and energy; buy locally produced goods, minimizing road and air miles; we can also recycle, and conserve and harvest water. We can use manual tools rather than powered; banish chemicals; provide habitats for wildlife; grow plants suited to conditions; make our own compost and mulch; and exchange seeds, plants and cuttings.

Gardeners of the future must become as self-sufficient as gardeners of old. Gardens of the future will still benefit from new ideas, and push boundaries with innovative designs and materials. But it is *how* we garden and care for plants, wildlife, the environment, and fundamentally, the planet, which will be the most important aspects of twenty-first century gardening – and all gardens of the future.

Gardens of the future

Trees

Trees help maintain the planet's delicate balance. Many tolerate pollution and it will be possible to grow increasingly tender species.

Acacia dealbata
Acer campestre
Acer platanoides
Acer pseudoplatanus
Aesculus flava
Ailanthus altissima
Alnus glutinosa
Betula pendula
Betula pubescens
Carpinus betulus
Cedrus deodara
Chamaerops humilis
Cordyline australis
Crataegus monogyna
Fagus sylvatica 'Riversii'
Ensete ventricosum
Ginkgo biloba

Juglans regia 'Buccaneer'
Ligustrum lucidum
Magnolia x soulangiana
Malus sp.
Metasequoia glyptostroboides
Metrosideros kermadecensis
Morus nigra
Musa basjoo
Olea europaea
Pinus cembra
Platanus x hispanica
Populus tremula
Prunus avium
Prunus cerasifera
Prunus padus
Quercus ilex
Quercus palustris
Robinia pseudoacacia
Salix pentandra
Sequoiadendron giganteum
Sorbus aria
Sorbus aucuparia
Tilia platyphyllos
Trachycarpus fortunei

Cistus ladanifer.

Shrubs

Common and tender species for the future.

Amelanchier 'Ballerina'
Aralia elata
Arbutus unedo
Aucuba japonica
Banksia coccinea
Buxus sempervirens
Callistemon citrinus
Camellia japonica
Camellia x williamsii
Cephalotaxus fortunei
Ceratostigma willmottianum
Cistus sp.
Colutea arborescens
Daphne mezereum
Elaeagnus x ebbingei
Escallonia sp.
Euonymus fortunei
Fatsia japonica
Forsythia cvs.
Grevillea 'Austraflora Canterbury Gold'
Hibiscus sinosyriacus
Hibiscus syriacus
Hydrangea macrophylla

Hypericum sp.
Kerria japonica
Lavandula angustifolia
Leptospermum scoparium
Leucadendron discolor
Leycesteria formosa
Lonicera pileata
Magnolia stellata
Mahonia aquifolium
Olearia x haastii
Pernettya mucronata
Photinia davidiana
Protea cynaroides
Protea repens
Prunus laurocerasus
Pyracantha sp.
Rhododendron sp.
Rhus glabra
Salvia officinalis
Skimmia japonica
Spartium junceum
Syringa vulgaris
Tamarix tetranda
Taxus baccata
Torreya californica
Weigela florida
Westringia fruticosa

Garden plants for wildlife

Supplies of all important nectar and food.

Achillea filipendulina
Berberis x stenophylla
Borago officinalis
Buddleja davidii
Callicarpa bodinieri var. giraldii
Calluna vulgaris
Ceanothus arboreus
Centaurea cyanus
Chimonanthus praecox
Cistus sp.
Cytissus sp.
Cotoneaster horizontalis
Corylopsis glabrescens
Crocus sp.
Daphne mezereum
Daphne odora
Dipsacus fullonum
Erica carnea
Erigeron karvinskianus
Escallonia sp.

Hebe sp.
Hedychium coccineum
Hedychium forrestii
Helianthus annuus
Hesperis matronalis
Hypericum cvs.
Ilex aquifolium
Lavandula angustifolia 'Hidcote'
Ligustrum vulgare
Limanthus douglasii
Lonicera caprifolium
Lonicera periclymenum
Lunaria annua
Mahonia x media
Nepeta grandiflora
Osmanthus x burkwoodii
Pyracantha 'Watererii'
Rhamnus frangula
Ribes sanguineum
Sarcococca confusa
Sedum spectabilis
Thymus vulgaris
Viburnum sp.
Weigela cvs.
Wisteria floribunda

Wild plants

Gardeners are becoming more environmentally aware. Establishing wild flowers and shrubs greatly benefits wildlife.

Achillea millefolium
Agrostemma githago
Alnus glutinosa
Amaranthus retroflexus
Anthriscus sylvestris
Campanula glomerata
Campanula rotundifolia
Cardamine pratensis
Centaurea scabiosa
Centranthus ruber
Chamerion angustifolium
Clematis vitalba
Crataegus monogyna
Cytisus scoparius
Digitalis purpurea
Dipsacus fullonum
Echium vulgare
Eupatorium cannabinum
Euphrasia rostkoviana
Filipendula ulmaria

Geranium pratense
Hedera helix
Hyacinthoides non-scripta
Knautia arvensis
Lamium album
Lamium purpureum
Leucanthemum vulgare
Linaria vulgaris
Lonicera periclymenum
Lychnis flos-cuculi
Lythrum salicaria
Malus sylvestris
Melilotus altissima
Mentha aquatica
Myosotis alpestris
Oenothera biennis
Onopordon acanthium
Ornithogalum umbellatum
Papaver rhoeas
Pentaglottis sempervirens
Plantago major
Primula veris
Primula vulgaris
Prunella vulgaris
Ranunculus acris
Rhamnus catharticus
Rubus fruticosus
Salix caprea
Sambucus nigra
Silene dioica
Thymus pulegioides
Trifolium repens
Trollius europaeus
Ulex eropaeus
Urtica dioica
Verbascum thapsus
Viola tricolor

Borders

Gardens grow more eclectic mixes of plants, including many tender species.

Aeonium arboreum
Agave americana
Alocasia longiloba
Alocasia macrorrhiza
Aloe vera
Argyranthemum 'Jamaica Primrose'
Argyranthemum 'Mary Wootton'
Canna cvs.
Carpobrotus edulis

Chenopodium giganteum
Crassula sp.
Delosperma cooperi
Drosanthemum hispidum
Echeveria agavoides
Echeveria elegans
Fascicularia pitcairniifolia
Foeniculum vulgare
Mentha spicata
Persicaria odorata
Ocimum basilicum
Ocimum basilicum 'Cinnamon'
Puya berteroniana
Puya mirablilis
Rhodiola rosea
Sedum kamtschaticum
Sedum obtusatum
Sedum populifolium
Sedum spectabile
Sempervivum 'Laggeri'
Solanum lycopersicum
Thymus 'Jekka'
Tropaeolum majus

Rubus sp.

Matrix gardens

A small selection from many species that form matrix gardens.

Shrubs
Abutilon vitifolium
Buddleja davidii
Chimonanthus praecox
Clianthus puniceus
Cornus florida
Corylopsis pauciflora
Euonymus hamiltonianus ssp Hians
Fuchsia magellanica
Hibiscus syriacus
Lonicera tatarica
Magnolia stellata
Rosa moyesii
Spartium junceum
Stachyurus praecox
Viburnum plicatum
Perennials
Acanthus spinosus
Ajuga reptans
Alchemilla mollis
Alstroemeria aurea
Anemone sylvestris
Anthriscus sylvestris 'Ravenswing'

Astrantia major
Baptisia alba
Campanula latiloba
Centaurea montana
Dictamnus albus
Digitalis grandiflora
Digitalis purpurea
Eremurus x isabellinus Shelford Hybrids
Eryngium giganteum
Euphorbia characias ssp wulfenii
Foeniculum vulgare
Fragaria vesca
Helianthus atrorubens 'The Monarch'
Helleborus argutifolius
Hemerocallis 'Golden Chimes'
Hosta sieboldiana
Lamium maculatum
Lysmachia punctata
Onopordum nervosum
Paeonia officinalis cvs.
Phuopsis stylosa
Salvia x superba
Solidago 'Golden Wings'
Thalictrum delavayi
Viola cornuta
Veratrum nigrum
Verbascum olympicum

Bulbs, corms, rhizomes and tubers

Naturalize beneath trees and shrubs or with wildflowers.

Allium mollis
Anemone blanda
Camassia leichtlinii
Colchicum speciosum
Crocus speciosus
Crocus tommasinianus
Cyclamen hederifolium
Eranthis hyemalis
Fritillaria meleagris
Galanthus nivalis
Gladiolus communis byzantinus
Hyacinthoides non-scripta
Lilium martagon
Narcissus obvallaris
Narcissus pseudonarcissus
Ornithogalum umbellatum
Scilla siberica
Tulipa sprengerii
Tulipa sylvestris

Dipsaeus fullonum seed head.

Children's gardens

Eye catching flowers, leaves, perfumed plants, fruit, vegetables and sound create interest, variety and excitement in children's gardens.

Agastache foeniculum 'Blue Fortune'
Allium schoenoprasum
Allium senescens 'Glaucum'
Briza maxima
Calendula officinalis
Clarkia elegans
Cornus kousa
Cornus mas
Corylus avellana
Cosmos atrosanguineus
Cucurbita maxima
Cucurbita pepo
Drosera capensis
Fragaria vesca
Helianthus annuus
Heuchera 'Chocolate Ruffles'
Helichrysum italicum
Hosta sieboldiana 'Elegans'
Lagenaria siceraria
Lavandula angustifolia 'Hidcote'
Lavandula stoechas

Lathyrus odoratus
Malus sp.
Mentha spicata
Morus alba 'Pendula'
Nigella damascena
Phaseolus vulgaris
Phlomis fruticosa
Phyllostachys aurea
Phyllostachys flexuosa
Phyllostachys nigra
Pisum sativum
Prunus persica
Prunus serrula
Prunus tomentosa
Rosmarinus officinalis
Salvia argentea
Salvia officinalis
Sedum reflexum
Sempervivum 'Commander Hay'
Stachys byzantina
Tagetes patula
Tropaeolum majus
Vaccinum corymbosum
Vaccinum 'Northblue'
Zea mays

Plant directory

The careful positioning of plants can make or break any garden style, from the bold use of architectural plants in minimalistic modern gardens, significant positioning of essential plants in Japanese gardens, or the rampant profusion of flowers, fruit and vegetables in cottage gardens. This index covers a representative selection of illustrations from the plant lists following each chapter, all ideally suited to the various garden styles contained in this book.

Trees

Acer griseum (Paper-bark maple) 10m
Spreading, deciduous tree with orange-brown peeling bark, three-palmate leaves of oval leaflets, and good autumn colour.

Corylus avellana (Hazel) 5m
Alternate, rounded to oval leaves, golden-yellow male catkins in spring followed by edible nuts.

Crataegus laevigata (Midland hawthorn/May) 8m
Thorny, deciduous tree with glossy, shallowly lobed leaves and corymbs of white or pink flowers in late spring followed by ovoid red fruits.

Euonymus europaeus (Spindle tree) 3m
Deciduous shrub or small tree with oval, dark green leaves, turning red in autumn, and four-lobed, spherical red fruit, opening to reveal orange arils.

Ginkgo biloba (Maidenhair tree) 30m
Upright tree with furrowed, dull grey bark and flat, fan-shaped, lobed, yellow-green leaves tapered into the stalks. Pendulous yellow catkins in spring and good autumn colour.

Juglans regia (Common walnut) 39m
Spreading tree with aromatic, pinnate leaves of five to nine leaflets. Edible nuts in autumn.

Laburnum anagyroides (Common laburnum) 8m
Spreading tree with dark green leaves composed of three elliptic-obovate leaflets, hairy beneath, and racemes of yellow flowers in late spring and early summer.

Liriodendron tulipifera (Tulip tree) 30m
Deciduous tree with square, lobed, saddle-shaped leaves that turn yellow in autumn. Pale greenish-yellow, cup-shaped flowers, orange banded at base, borne in midsummer.

Magnolia × soulangeana (Magnolia) 7.5m
Deciduous shrub or tree with large, dark-green leaves and goblet-shaped flowers from white and pink to deep purple which appear before and with the young leaves in spring.

Malus × domestica cvs. (Apple)
Deciduous trees with clusters of pink buds in spring opening to scented white flowers, followed by edible fruit.

Malus × purpurea (Purple crab) 7m
Purple-red spring foliage and dark red buds open to purplish pink flowers followed by decorative dark red fruits.

Prunus avium (Wild cherry) 20m
Deciduous tree with reddish bark, and young bronze leaves which turn dark green and then red and yellow in autumn. Umbels of small, white flowers in spring followed by small, red fruits.

Prunus 'Okame' 10m
Deciduous tree or shrub with toothed, narrowly oval leaves that turn red and orange in autumn. Clusters of deep pink flowers are borne profusely in spring.

Prunus persica (Peach) 4m
Deciduous tree with slender, pointed mid- to dark-green leaves; solitary, cupped red or pink flowers are borne in early spring before the leaves appear, followed by spherical, red, downy fruit.

Quercus × hispanica 'Lucombeana' (Lucombe oak) 25m
Semi-evergreen tree with corky bark and ovate to oblong, dark green leaves. Ovoid to rounded acorns.

Quercus robur (English oak) 35m
Deciduous tree with fissured bark and short-stalked, ovate to oblong, dark green leaves with rounded lobes. Ovoid acorns in autumn.

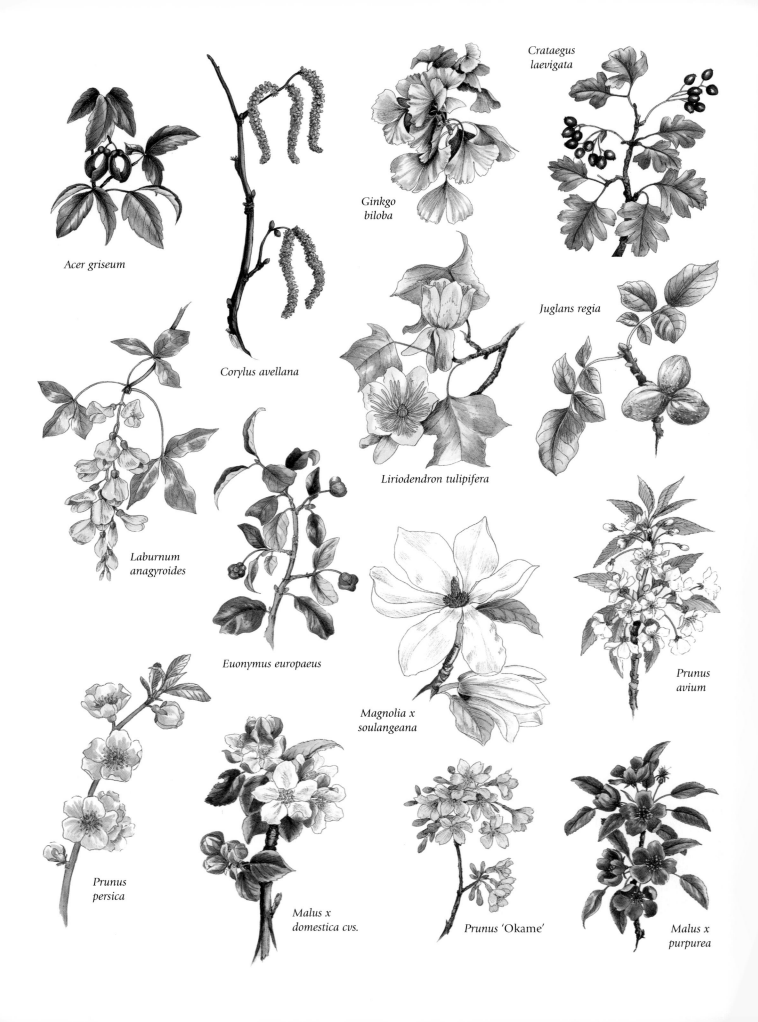

Acer griseum

Corylus avellana

Crataegus
laevigata

Ginkgo
biloba

Juglans regia

Laburnum
anagyroides

Euonymus europaeus

Liriodendron tulipifera

Magnolia x
soulangeana

Prunus
avium

Prunus
persica

Malus x
domestica cvs.

Prunus 'Okame'

Malus x
purpurea

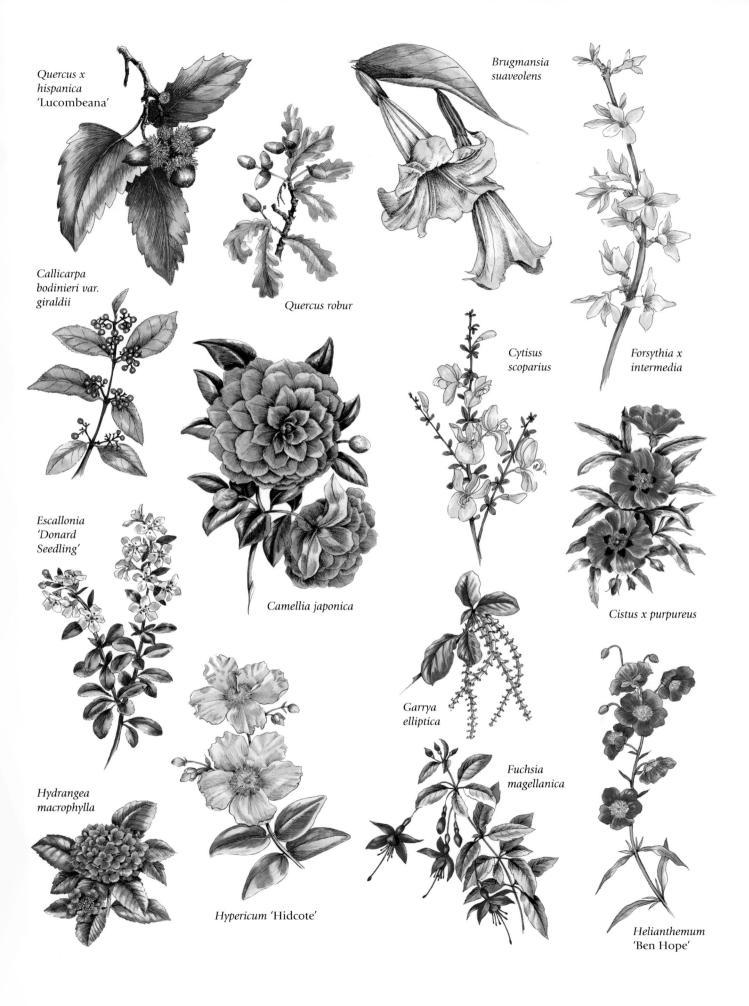

Quercus x
hispanica
'Lucombeana'

Brugmansia
suaveolens

Callicarpa
bodinieri var.
giraldii

Quercus robur

Forsythia x
intermedia

Cytisus
scoparius

Escallonia
'Donard
Seedling'

Camellia japonica

Cistus x purpureus

Garrya
elliptica

Fuchsia
magellanica

Hydrangea
macrophylla

Hypericum 'Hidcote'

Helianthemum
'Ben Hope'

Shrubs

Brugmansia suaveolens (Angels' trumpets) 5m
Shrub or small tree with large, entire leaves and scented, tubular, white, trumpet-shaped flowers in summer and autumn. Not hardy but can be outdoors during summer.

Callicarpa bodinieri var. giraldii 2.5m
Deciduous shrub with tapered, dark green leaves and cymes of tiny pink flowers in summer followed by spherical, violet-coloured fruit in autumn and winter. Good for birds.

Camellia japonica 9m
Upright to spreading shrub with glossy, dark green leaves and single or double, white, pink or red flowers, from early to late spring.

Cistus × purpureus (Gum cistus) 1m
Oblong to lance shaped, wavy margined, dark green leaves and terminal cymes of dark pink flowers with a maroon blotch at petal base.

Cytisus scoparius (Common broom) 1.5m
Upright shrub with slender shoots and small, usually trifoliate leaves, producing bright yellow, perfumed flowers in late spring.

Escallonia **'Donard Seedling'** 2.5m
Vigorous, evergreen shrub with arching shoots and dark green leaves profusely covered with short racemes of small, pink buds opening to saucer-shaped white flowers, tinged pink, in summer.

Forsythia × intermedia 2.5m
Deciduous shrub with golden brown stems and mid-green leaves massed with four-petalled, bright yellow flowers in early spring, on bare branches before leaves appear.

Fuchsia magellanica 3m
Erect shrub with scalloped or toothed leaves, occasionally tinted red beneath, and small, single flowers with dark red tubes and sepals and dark purple corollas.

Garrya elliptica (Silk-tassel bush) 4m
Evergreen, dense, upright shrub with ovate to oblong, wavy-margined leaves and showy, long, pendant, grey-green male catkins from mid-winter to spring.

Helianthemum **'Ben Hope'** (Rock rose) 30cm
Spreading shrub with grey-green leaves and bright red flowers with orange-yellow centres.

Hydrangea macrophylla (Common hydrangea) 2m
Deciduous, rounded shrub with coarsely toothed, glossy leaves and flattened corymbs of small, sterile flowers and numerous pink or blue fertile flowers.

Hypericum **'Hidcote'** 1.2m
Bushy evergreen or semi-evergreen shrub with dark green leaves and cymes of large, cup-shaped, bright yellow flowers throughout summer.

Lavandula angustifolia **'Hidcote'** (Lavender) 60cm
Compact and bushy with linear, silver-grey leaves and stems bearing dense spikes of very fragrant, purple flowers from mid to late summer.

Lavandula stoechas (French lavender) 60cm
Compact bush with linear grey-green leaves and dense ovoid to oblong spikes of dark purple flowers with conspicuous purple bracts from late spring to summer.

Lavatera arborea (Tree mallow) 3m
Woody, annual, biennial or short-lived perennial with rounded, palmately lobed leaves and open, funnel-shaped, deep pink flowers with darker veining, throughout summer.

Lupinus arboreus (Tree lupin) 2m
Evergreen or semi-evergreen, vigorous, bushy shrub with five to twelve palmate grey-green leaves of obovate-oblong leaflets and long, dense racemes of fragrant, yellow, pea-like flowers, occasionally blue, in late spring and summer.

Mahonia × media **'Charity'** 5m
Evergreen with pinnate leaves of sharply toothed, dark green leaflets and erect or spreading racemes bearing perfumed, yellow flowers from late autumn to late winter.

Philadelphus coronarius (Mock orange) 3m
Deciduous upright shrub with shallow-toothed, ovate leaves and short, terminal racemes of highly perfumed, single, cup-shaped white flowers in early summer.

Pyracantha × watereri 2.5m
Dense bush with dark green leaves and corymbs of small white flowers in early summer, followed by bright red berries.

Rubus fruticosus (Blackberry) 3m
Prickly, rampant, spreading shrub having compound leaves with thorny midribs, and clusters of white flowers in summer followed by edible, purple-black fruits.

Rubus idaeus (Raspberry) 2.5m
Lax shrubs with thorny stems and compound leaves, hairy beneath, with sprays of small white flowers which mature into edible, reddish-pink fruits.

Rubus spectabilis **'Olympic Double'** 2m
Thicket forming, upright slightly prickly, woody stems and three-palmate leaves of glossy, mid-green leaflets and very showy, double, bright carmine-pink flowers in mid-spring.

Spiraea douglasii 2m
Fast-growing, upright, deciduous, suckering shrub with dense spikes of pink flowers in summer and early autumn. Tolerates both wet and dry conditions.

Syringa vulgaris (Lilac) 7m
Small tree or upright shrub with ovate to heart-shaped leaves and conical panicles of highly perfumed single or double flowers in late spring.

Teucrium chamaedrys (Wall germander) 1.8m
Evergreen sub-shrub with small, dark-green, aromatic

Lupinus arboreus

Lavatera arborea

Mahonia x media 'Charity'

Lavandula angustifolia 'Hidcote'

Lavandula stoechas

Philadelphus coronarius

Syringa vulgaris

Teucrium chamaedrys

Rubus fruticosus

Rubus spectabilis 'Olympic Double'

Rubus idaeus

Viburnum tinus

Spiraea douglasii

Vaccinium corymbosum

Pyracantha x watereri

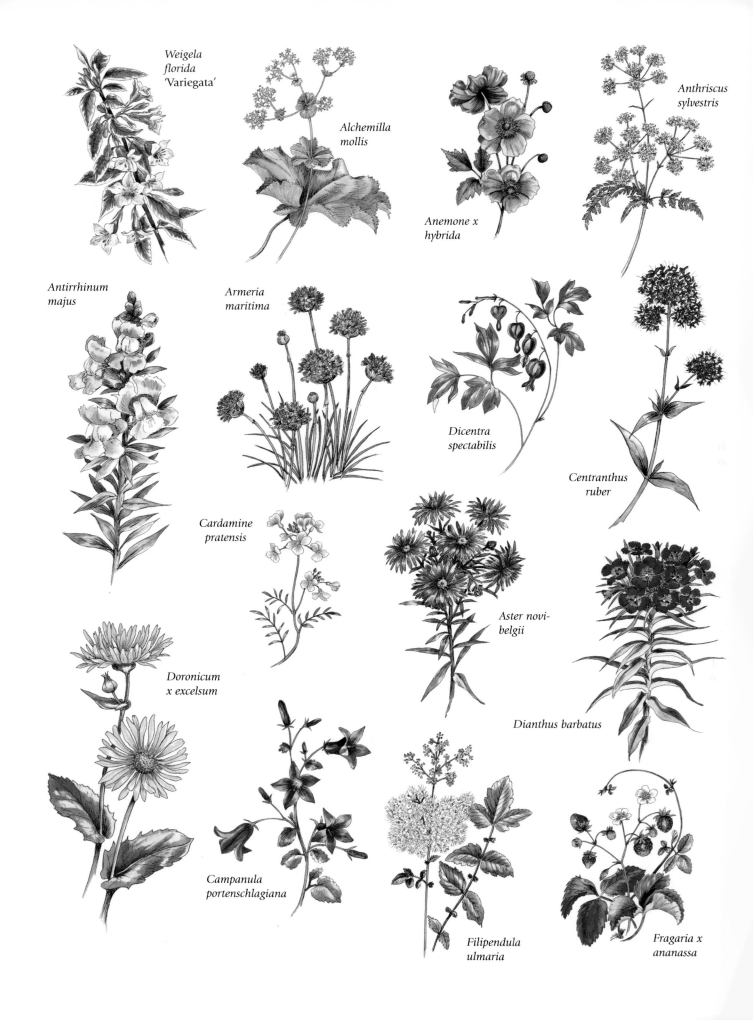

Weigela florida 'Variegata'

Alchemilla mollis

Anemone x hybrida

Anthriscus sylvestris

Antirrhinum majus

Armeria maritima

Dicentra spectabilis

Centranthus ruber

Cardamine pratensis

Aster novi-belgii

Doronicum x excelsum

Dianthus barbatus

Campanula portenschlagiana

Filipendula ulmaria

Fragaria x ananassa

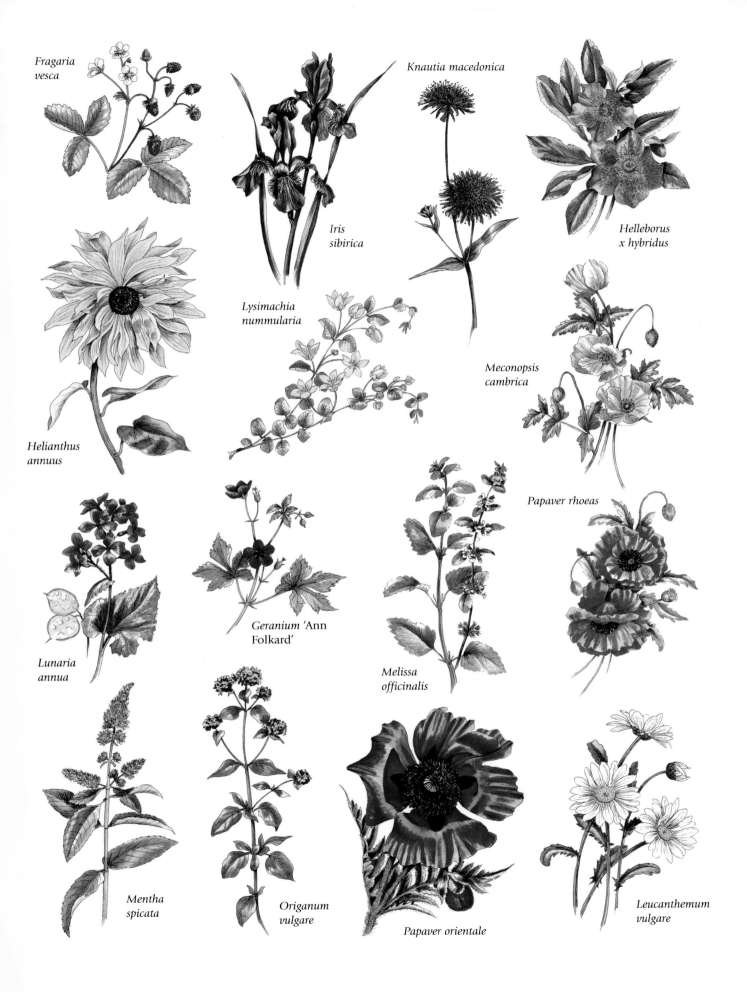

Fragaria vesca

Knautia macedonica

Iris sibirica

Helleborus x hybridus

Lysimachia nummularia

Meconopsis cambrica

Helianthus annuus

Papaver rhoeas

Geranium 'Ann Folkard'

Lunaria annua

Melissa officinalis

Mentha spicata

Origanum vulgare

Papaver orientale

Leucanthemum vulgare

leaves and racemes of pink-purple flowers in early summer. Drought tolerant.

Vaccinium corymbosum (Blueberry) 1.5m
Perennial shrub with small, simple leaves and clusters of white, tubular flowers followed by bluish-black, edible fruits.

Viburnum tinus (Laurustinus) 3m
Evergreen bushy shrub with dark green leaves and terminal cymes of small pink buds opening to white flowers from late autumn to spring, followed by purple-black fruits.

Weigela florida 'Variegata' 2.5m
Compact shrub with arching shoots and grey-green, white margined leaves, bearing corymbs of funnel-shaped dark pink flowers with white or pale pink interiors, from late spring to early summer.

Borders

Alchemilla mollis (Lady's mantel) 60cm
Clump-forming perennial having pale green, shallowly lobed and toothed, rounded leaves and slender stems bearing loose cymes of tiny, yellowish-green flowers from summer to autumn. Seeds freely.

Anemone × hybrida (Japanese anemone) 1.5m
Woody based perennial with usually three-palmate, toothed leaves and erect, branching stems with umbels of white or pink, bowl-shaped flowers from summer to autumn.

Anthriscus sylvestris (Queen Anne's lace) 1m
Biennial or short lived perennial with much dissected leaves and delicate umbels of small, white flowers from spring to summer.

Antirrhinum majus (Snapdragon) 1m
Short-lived, strongly branched perennial with lance-shaped, glossy green leaves and upright racemes bearing two-lipped flowers in shades of white, cream, pink, red, yellow and purple, including bicolours, throughout summer and into autumn.

Armeria maritima (Sea thrift) 20cm
Clump-forming perennial with narrow, dark green, linear leaves and stiff stems bearing white, pink or purple flowerheads.

Aster novi-belgii (Michaelmas daisy) 1.2m
Clump-forming perennial with slender, woody stems and lance-shaped mid green leaves bearing panicles of violet coloured flowerheads with yellow disc florets from late summer to autumn.

Campanula portenschlagiana (Dalmation bellflower) 15cm
Evergreen, mound-forming perennial with toothed ovate to heart-shaped leaves and spreading or erect stems with loosely branched panicles of funnel-shaped, deep purple-blue flowers in mid and late summer.

Cardamine pratensis (Lady's smock) 20cm
Rosettes of pinnate, grey-green leaves made up of from two to eight pairs of leaflets, and panicles of white or lilac flowers in spring.

Centranthus ruber (Red valerian) 1m
Clump-forming, branching, woody based perennial with glaucous mid- to deep-green leaves and dense cymes of tiny, funnel-shaped flowers in white, pink or red from late spring to late summer. Self seeds freely.

Dianthus barbatus (Sweet William) 70cm
Short-lived, bushy perennial usually grown as a biennial, with light to mid-green leaves and leafy bracts around dense, terminal clusters of perfumed, small, single flowers in white, pink or purple, which are often bi-coloured, in late spring and summer.

Dicentra spectabilis (Bleeding heart) 1.2m
Fleshy rooted, clump-forming perennial with pale green leaves made up of cut or lobed leaflets and slender, arching stems bearing racemes of pendant flowers with white inner petals and dark pink outer petals in early summer.

Digitalis purpurea (Foxglove) 1–2m
Rosette forming, biennial or short-lived perennial with toothed, ovate to lance-shaped, dark green leaves and tall stems of tubular, lipped, white, pink or purple flowers, spotted maroon or purple inside.

Doronicum × excelsum (Leopard's bane) 60cm
Perennial with toothed, heart-shaped leaves and branched stems bearing single, daisy-like, golden flowers in spring.

Filipendula ulmaria (Meadowsweet) 90cm
Clump-forming perennial with leafy, branching stems and strongly veined leaves, bearing dense corymbs of tiny, scented, creamy-white flowers in summer.

Fragaria × ananassa (Strawberry) 30cm
Perennial herbs with rosettes of three-palmate, toothed leaflets and cymes of white flowers in spring followed by luscious, edible, red, false fruits – actually swollen stems, with tiny fruit, achenes, on the surface.

Fragaria vesca (Alpine strawberry) 30cm
Rosettes of three-palmate, toothed leaflets and cymes of small white flowers in spring followed by small, edible, red berries.

Geranium 'Ann Folkard' 60cm
Spreading perennial with scrambling stems and five-lobed, toothed leaves with a continuous mass of saucer-shaped, bright magenta flowers with black centres and veining, from mid-summer to mid-autumn.

Helleborus × hybridus 45cm
Clump-forming perennial with dark-green, leathery, toothed leaves and stout stems bearing loose cymes of pendant, saucer-shaped flowers in colours ranging from white, yellow, green, pink and deep purple, often with purple spotting.

Helianthus annuus (Annual sunflower) 5m
Tall, fast-growing annual with broad, heart-shaped

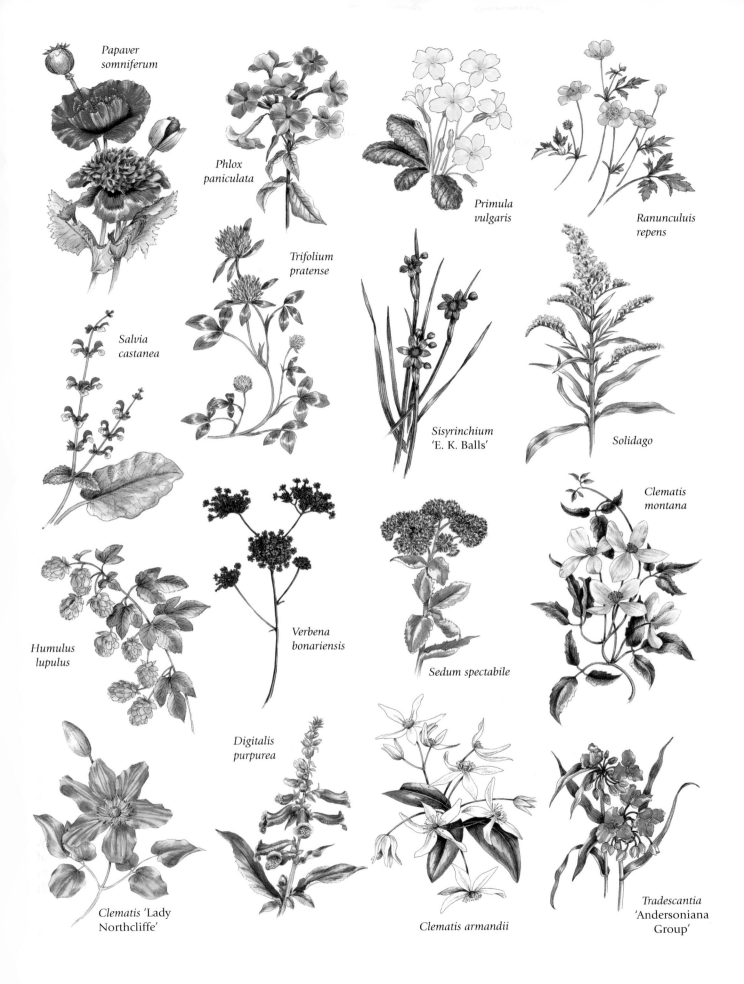

Papaver somniferum

Phlox paniculata

Primula vulgaris

Ranunculuis repens

Trifolium pratense

Salvia castanea

Sisyrinchium 'E. K. Balls'

Solidago

Clematis montana

Humulus lupulus

Verbena bonariensis

Sedum spectabile

Digitalis purpurea

Clematis 'Lady Northcliffe'

Clematis armandii

Tradescantia 'Andersoniana Group'

rough leaves and large, daisy-like flowerheads with brown disc-florets and yellow ray-florets.

Iris sibirica (Siberian iris) 1.2m
Clump-forming perennial with narrow, grass-like leaves and slender, branched stems bearing blue-violet flowers with dark veining on petal falls.

Knautia macedonica 80cm
Slender stems bearing many, long-lasting reddish-purple flowers from mid to late summer.

Leucanthemum vulgare (Ox-eye daisy) 90cm
Perennial having small, toothed, dark green leaves and solitary flowerheads with white ray-florets and yellow disc-florets in late spring and early summer.

Lunaria annua (Honesty) 90cm
Annual or biennial with coarsely toothed, heart-shaped leaves and leafy racemes of four-petalled purple or white flowers in late spring and early summer, followed by flat seed pods which split to silver.

Lysimachia nummularia (Creeping Jenny) 5cm
Prostrate, stem rooting, evergreen perennial with rounded-ovate, yellow- green leaves and upturned, cup-shaped golden yellow flowers in summer.

Meconopsis cambrica (Welsh poppy) 45cm
Deciduous perennial with irregularly lobed, blue-green leaves and stems of solitary, shallowly cup-shaped yellow or orange flowers from mid-spring to autumn.

Melissa officinalis (Lemon balm) 120cm
Upright, bushy perennial with wrinkled, light green leaves and irregular spikes of creamy-white flowers turning white or pink tinged in summer.

Mentha spicata (Mint) 1m
Spreading, perennial, culinary herb with lance-shaped to ovate, toothed and aromatic green leaves and cylindrical spikes of tubular to bell-shaped, white, pink or lilac flowers in dense whorls in summer.

Origanum vulgare (Oregano) 90cm
Bushy, woody-based perennial with small, very aromatic, rounded to ovate, dark green leaves and loose panicles of small, pinky-mauve, tubular flowers with purple-tinted, green bracts in summer.

Papaver orientale (Oriental poppy) 90cm
Clump-forming perennial with bristly, erect stems and toothed, dissected green leaves bearing cup-shaped orange to red flowers with blue-black basal spots and large bosses of purple-black stamens.

Papaver rhoeas (Field poppy) 90cm
Erect, branching annual with segmented, light-green, downy leaves and lightly hairy stems bearing solitary, bowl-shaped, scarlet flowers with purple-black stamens.

Papaver somniferum (Opium poppy) 1.2m
Annual with erect, leafy stems and glaucous, blue-green foliage, bearing single or double, bowl-shaped flowers in shades of white, pink, red and purple, often with a darker blotch at the base of the petals, followed by blue-green seed-heads that dry to brown.

Phlox paniculata (Perennial phlox) 1.2m
Herbaceous perennial with ovate or lance-shaped, narrow leaves and cymes of fragrant, white, pink or lilac flowers in summer and early autumn.

Primula vulgaris (Primrose) 25cm
Evergreen or semi-evergreen rosette-forming perennial with deeply veined, obovate to lance-shaped, scalloped or toothed leaves, and clusters of fragrant, pale yellow flowers, occasionally pink, from early to late spring.

Ranunculus repens (Creeping buttercup) 60cm
Fast-spreading, stoloniferous perennial with three-lobed and toothed leaves and branched stems bearing cup-shaped, glossy, golden yellow flowers.

Salvia castanea 1m
Herbaceous perennial with narrowly ovate to linear-lanceolate leaves and stems bearing elongated racemes of small, maroon-purple flowers with paler lip in summer.

Sedum spectabile (Ice plant) 45cm
Deciduous, clump-forming perennial with unbranched, upright stems and slightly scalloped, toothed grey-green, fleshy leaves, and dense, flat cymes of small, pink star-shaped flowers with prominent stamens in late summer. Very attractive to bees.

***Sisyrinchium* 'E.K. Balls'** 25cm
Semi-evergreen, clump-forming perennial having fans of narrow, sword-shaped leaves and stems bearing short-lived, star-shaped mauve flowers in summer.

Solidago (Golden rod) 1.8m
Tall, woody-stemmed perennial with mid-green leaves and branched heads of tiny, golden yellow flowers in late summer.

***Tradescantia* 'Andersoniana Group'** 60cm
Clump-forming, tufted perennials with narrowly lance-shaped, arching, often purple tinted leaves, and terminal cymes of flowers with three open triangular petals in shades of white, pink or blue, borne in succession from early summer to early autumn.

Trifolium pratense (Clover) 15cm
Mat-forming perennial with three-palmate leaves and dense spherical to ovoid racemes of pink flowers in summer.

Verbena bonariensis 2m
Clump-forming perennial with stiff, upright, branching stems and few toothed, wrinkled, clasping leaves, bearing panicles of purple flowers from midsummer to early autumn. Drought resistant.

Climbers

Clematis armandii 5m
Very vigorous, evergreen clematis with perfumed white flowers and cream anthers in early spring.

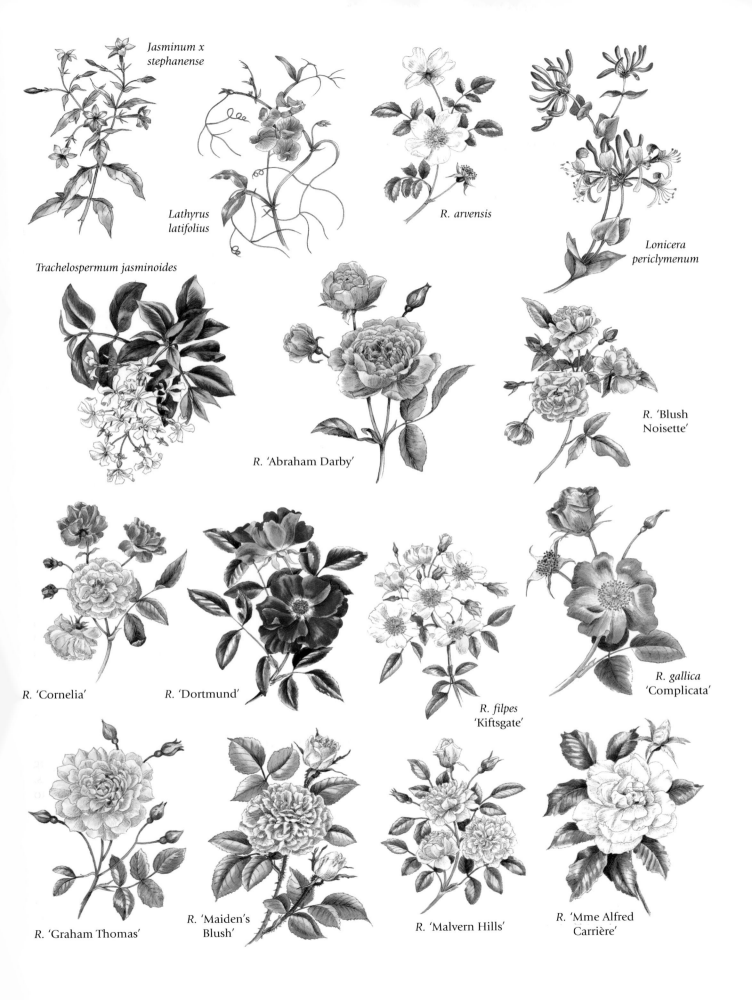

Jasminum x stephanense

Lathyrus latifolius

R. *arvensis*

Lonicera periclymenum

Trachelospermum jasminoides

R. 'Abraham Darby'

R. 'Blush Noisette'

R. 'Cornelia'

R. 'Dortmund'

R. *filpes* 'Kiftsgate'

R. *gallica* 'Complicata'

R. 'Graham Thomas'

R. 'Maiden's Blush'

R. 'Malvern Hills'

R. 'Mme Alfred Carrière'

R. 'Nevada'

R. 'Queen Elizabeth'

R. 'Roseraie de l'Hay'

Asplenium scolopendrium

R. 'The Mayflower'

Camassia leichtlinii caerulea

Alstroemeria hybrid

R. 'Swan Lake'

Colchicum byzantinum

Allium ursinum

Canna
indica

Crocosmia x
crocosmiiflora

Crocus species

Galanthus
nivalis

Cyclamen hederifolium

Dierama
pulcherrimum

Hyacinthoides
non-scripta

Hedychium
densiflorum

Iris confusa
'Brian Rix'

Iris 'Stairway to Heaven'

Iris bearded
hybrid

Iris spuria
'Media Luz'

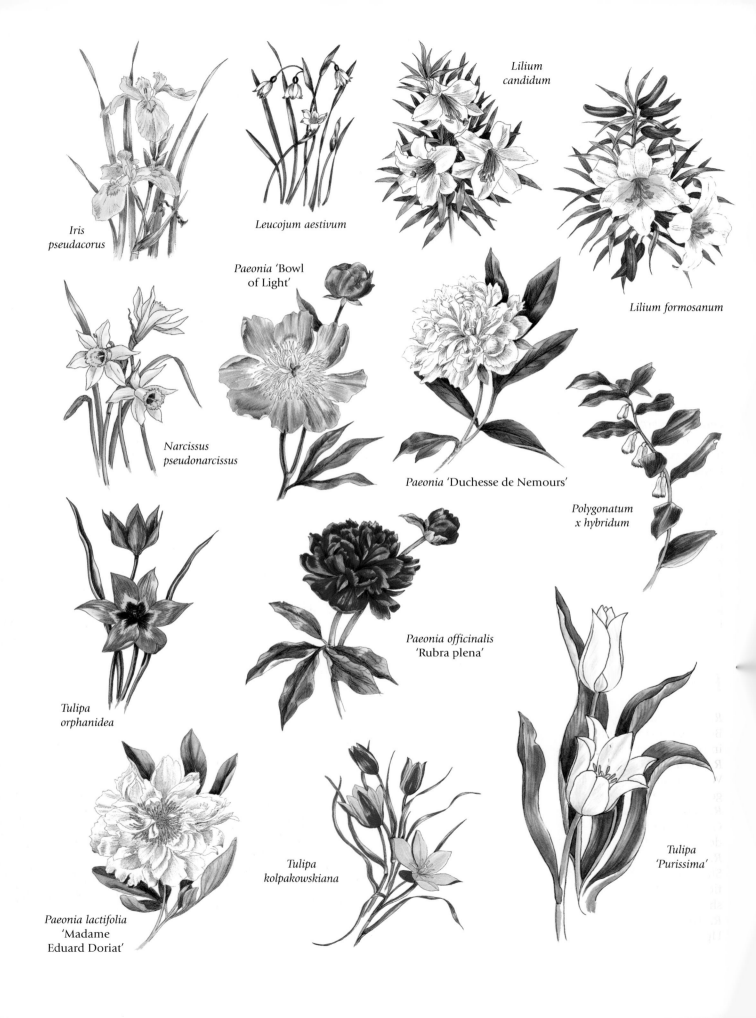

Lilium candidum

Iris pseudacorus

Leucojum aestivum

Lilium formosanum

Paeonia 'Bowl of Light'

Narcissus pseudonarcissus

Paeonia 'Duchesse de Nemours'

Polygonatum x hybridum

Paeonia officinalis 'Rubra plena'

Tulipa orphanidea

Tulipa 'Purissima'

Tulipa kolpakowskiana

Paeonia lactifolia 'Madame Eduard Doriat'

Clematis 'Lady Northcliffe' 2m
Strong-growing clematis with light green leaves and pale blue flowers, fading to Wedgwood blue, throughout summer.

Clematis montana 14m
Rampant climber with single, white or pink flowers and golden stamens, borne very freely in late spring or early summer.

Humulus lupulus (Hop) 6m
Twining perennial with rough, hairy shoots and light green, three to five lobed, deeply toothed leaves, bearing ovoid, fragrant green female flowers in summer, fading to straw colour.

Jasminum × stephanense 5m
Vigorous, deciduous twining climber with ovate lance-shaped leaves and loose cymes of fragrant, pale pink flowers in summer.

Lathyrus latifolius (Everlasting pea) 2m
Perennial, herbaceous, winged-stemmed climber with racemes of between six and eleven pink to purple flowers from summer to early autumn.

Lathyrus odoratus (Sweet pea) 2m
Annual, winged stemmed climber with racemes of two to four very fragrant flowers in shades of white, cream, pink, blue, red and purple, from summer to autumn. A wide range of cultivars available.

Lonicera periclymenum (Common honeysuckle) 7m
Vigorous, deciduous, woody, twining climber with pairs of ovate, mid green leaves and terminal whorls of highly fragrant, tubular, lipped, yellow flowers often flushed red, from mid to late summer, followed by red berries.

Trachelospermum jasminoides (Star jasmine) 9m
Evergreen, woody, twining climber with glossy, dark green leaves and cymes of perfumed, pure white, star-like flowers from mid to late summer.

Roses

R. 'Abraham Darby'
Bushy shrub rose with perfumed, deeply cupped flowers in shades of apricot, yellow and pink.

R. arvensis
Wild, scrambling shrub with small, white flowers, golden stamens and dull green leaves.

R. 'Blush Noisette'
Climber with clusters of small, clove-scented, semi-double light lilac-pink flowers.

R. 'Cornelia'
Shrub rose with trusses of small, double, pink-tinged flowers with copper centres, and dark green, lance-shaped leaves.

R. 'Dortmund'
Upright climber with clusters of single, flat, red flowers with a white eye and golden stamens, glossy, dark green leaves.

R. filipes 'Kiftsgate'
Rampant climber with large clusters of small, single, creamy white flowers and glossy, light green leaves.

R. gallica 'Complicata'
Large, rose-pink, single flowers with golden stamens and grey-green leaves.

R. 'Graham Thomas'
Medium-sized shrub rose with cup-shaped, perfumed, golden yellow flowers and bright green leaves.

R. 'Maiden's Blush'
Vigorous, arching rose with perfumed, fully double, cupped, pale pink flowers and blue-green foliage.

R. 'Malvern Hills'
Strong-growing, repeat flowering rambler massed with small, double, creamy-yellow blooms and shiny green foliage.

R. 'Mme Alfred Carrière'
Strong growing climber with large, perfumed, white, cupped double blooms, lightly flushed pink.

R. 'Nevada'
Arching shrub bearing masses of flat, semi-double, perfumed, creamy white flowers with light green leaves.

R. 'Queen Elizabeth'
Leathery, dark-green leaves and stiff stems bearing double pink flowers.

R. 'Roseraie de l'Hay'
Vigorous rugosa rose bearing flat to cup-shaped, strongly perfumed, purple-red flowers with light green leaves.

R. 'Swan Lake'
Climber with double, perfumed, white flowers, faintly flushed with pink, amidst dark green leaves.

R. 'The Mayflower'
A good disease-resistant rose with strongly fragrant, deep rose-pink flowers.

Bulbs, corms, rhizomes and tubers

Allium ursinum (Ramsons) 30cm
Flat, narrow to broadly elliptical green leaves and rounded umbels of star-shaped, white flowers in early summer. The whole plant smells strongly of garlic.

Alstroemeria hybrid (Peruvian lily) 1.1m
Fleshy, rhizome-like tubers form clumps with linear to lance-shaped, mid to grey-green leaves and upright stems bearing loose, terminal umbels of brightly coloured, funnel-shaped, six-tepalled flowers in summer.

Asplenium scolopendrium (Hart's tongue fern) 70cm
Evergreen fern with creeping rhizomes and strap-shaped, bright green fronds with heart-shaped bases.

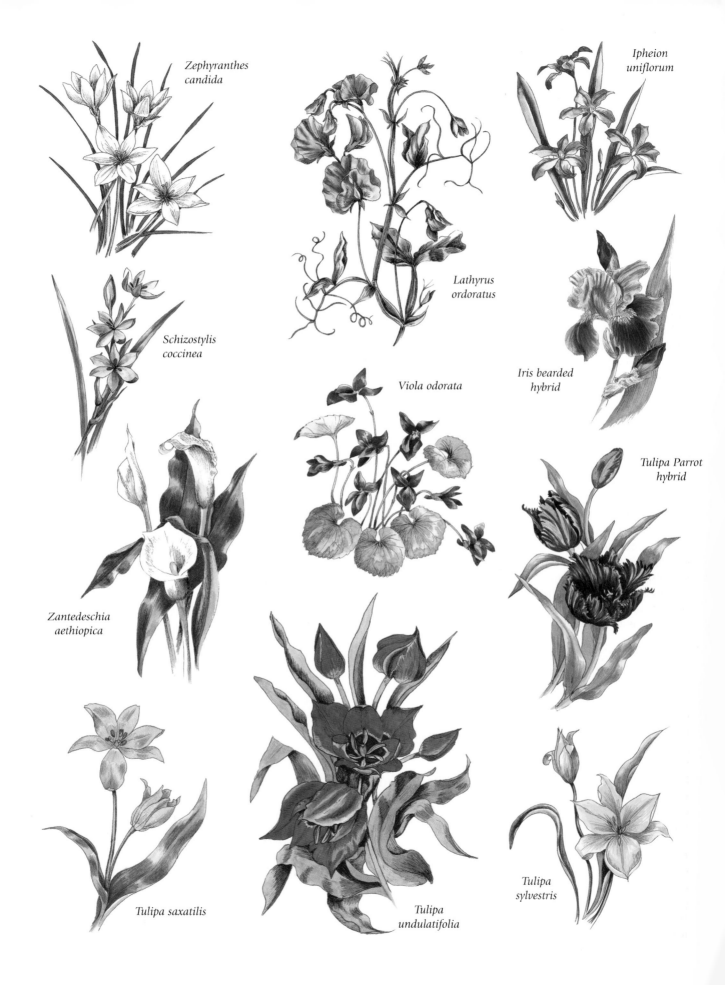

Zephyranthes candida

Ipheion uniflorum

Lathyrus ordoratus

Schizostylis coccinea

Viola odorata

Iris bearded hybrid

Zantedeschia aethiopica

Tulipa Parrot hybrid

Tulipa saxatilis

Tulipa undulatifolia

Tulipa sylvestris

Camassia leichtlinii caerulea 1.3m
Bulbous perennial with linear leaves and stems bearing racemes of blue, star-shaped flowers in late spring. Naturalizes well.

Canna indica (Indian shot plant) 2.2m
Rhizomatous perennial with dark green, ovate to lance-shaped leaves, often tinted bronze, and racemes of orange or red flowers from summer to autumn.

Colchicum byzantinum (Autumn crocus) 12cm
Cormous perennial with open, funnel-shaped, lilac flowers with tepals, in autumn, followed in spring by strongly ribbed, lance-shaped leaves.

Crocosmia × crocosmiiflora (Montbretia) 60cm
Cormous perennial with pale green, sword-like leaves and spikes of yellow or orange flowers in summer. Can be invasive.

Crocus species 10cm
Cormous perennials with grey to green leaves, usually with a central stripe, and goblet to star-shaped flowers from white, cream, yellow and gold to blue and purple in early spring.

Cyclamen hederifolium 13cm
Flattened tubers with marbled, heart-shaped to triangular leaves, often purple beneath, and white or pink flowers with five reflexed petals and deep maroon marks at the apex, in late summer and autumn.

Dierama pulcherrimum (Angel's fishing rods) 1.5m
Cormous perennial with long, grass-like leaves and slender, arching stems bearing pendant spikes of open, bell-shaped flowers in white, pink or purple-red in summer.

Galanthus nivalis (Snowdrop) 10cm
Bulbous perennial with narrow, blue-green leaves and slender stems bearing honey-scented, pendant white flowers, with three outer petals surrounding three smaller inner petals, marked with a green inverted 'V' in winter and early spring.

Hedychium densiflorum (Ginger lily) 5m
Clump-forming rhizomatous perennial with large, oblong to lance-shaped, glossy green leaves and strong stems bearing dense racemes of fragrant, exotic looking, two-lipped flowers in shades of yellow or orange in summer. Frost hardy in milder areas or with winter protection.

Hyacinthoides non-scripta (English bluebell) 40cm
Bulbous perennial having linear to lance-shaped, glossy and spreading leaves, and stems bearing pendant, narrowly bell-shaped, blue flowers, occasionally white, in spring. Naturalizes well.

Ipheion uniflorum 20cm
Clump-forming, bulbous perennial with blue-green leaves appearing in autumn, followed by silvery-blue, star-shaped flowers in spring.

Iris confusa 'Brian Rix' 100cm
Rhizomatous crested iris with erect, branching, bamboo-like stems, topped with fans of evergreen leaves, and a succession of short-lived, deep blue flowers with yellow crests, produced over a long period in mid-spring.

Iris 'Stairway to Heaven' 1m
Rhizomatous bearded Iris with grey-green, sword-like leaves and stems bearing a succession of ruffled flowers with white tinged pale blue standards, deeper blue falls, and yellow beards in mid spring and early summer.

Iris hybrid 1m
Rhizomatous bearded Iris with grey-green leaves and purple flowers, with deep yellow beards, in mid spring and summer.

Iris pseudacorus (Yellow flag) 1.5m
Vigorous, rhizomatous, beardless Laevigatae Iris with grey-green, ribbed leaves and branched stems bearing yellow flowers with purple or brown markings and a deeper yellow zone on the falls, in mid or late summer.

Iris spuria 'Media Luz' 90cm
Rhizomatous, beardless, with broad, sword-like leaves and yellow and mauve flowers in early and mid-summer.

Leucojum aestivum (Summer snowflake) 60cm
Bulbous perennial with strap-shaped, glossy, dark green leaves and green-tipped, bell-shaped white flowers in spring.

Lilium candidum (Madonna Lily) 1.8m
Narrow, bright green, lance-shaped leaves and stiff stems bearing a raceme of highly perfumed, pure white, trumpet-shaped flowers in summer.

Lilium formosanum 1.5m
Stem-rooting, rhizomatous bulb with many shiny, dark green, linear to lance-shaped leaves and very fragrant, trumpet-shaped white flowers tinged red-purple on the outside, in late summer and early autumn.

Narcissus pseudonarcissus (Wild daffodil/Lent lily) 30cm
Bulb with narrow, erect, strap-shaped leaves and stems bearing single, nodding flowers with yellow trumpets surrounded by paler perianth segments, in early spring.

Paeonia 'Bowl of Light' 1m
Herbaceous, rhizomatous perennial with mid-green leaves and stems bearing single, pink flowers with cream centres of numerous, narrow petaloids in early and mid summer.

Paeonia 'Duchesse de Nemours' 80cm
Robust, rhizomatous perennial with deep green leaves and large, fragrant, double white flowers, tinged green in bud, with unevenly ruffled, yellow-based, inner petals in early and mid summer.

Paeonia lactifolia 'Madame Eduard Doriat' 70cm
Herbaceous, tuberous-rooted peony with dark green leaves made up of lance-shaped leaflets, paler beneath, and semi-double, bowl-shaped white flowers with golden stamens in early and mid summer.

Paeonia officinalis 'Rubra plena' (Common peony) 70cm

Herbaceous, tuberous rooted peony with erect stems and dark green leaves divided into leaflets, bearing double, deep red flowers with ruffled, satiny petals, in early and mid summer.

Polygonatum × *hybridum* (Solomon's seal) 1.5m
Rhizomatous perennial bearing alternate, ovate to lance-shaped leaves and stems with tubular, pendant, green-tipped white flowers from leaf axils in late spring.

Schizostylis coccinea (Kaffir lily) 60cm
Clump-forming, rhizomatous perennial with narrow, sword-like leaves and spikes of open, cup-shaped pink or red or white flowers in autumn.

Tulipa kolpakowskiana 20cm
Bulbous perennial with two to four erect, linear, deeply channelled, grey-green leaves and single or clusters of bowl-shaped bright yellow flowers, marked crimson on outside of petals, in spring.

Tulipa orphanidea 35cm
Lance-shaped, mid-green leaves and star-shaped flowers, outside tinged buff and green, and inside orange or brownish-red with green or black basal patches.

Tulipa **Parrot hybrid** 65cm
Grey-green leaves and dark purple-red, ruffled petals with green striping, flowering in late spring.

Tulipa 'Purissima' 35cm
Grey-green leaves and white flowers in mid-spring.

Tulipa saxatilis 35cm
Spreading by means of runners and having linear, mid-green leaves and fragrant, star-shaped, lilac-pink flowers with yellow bases, in mid and late spring.

Tulipa sylvestris
Bulbous tulip bearing two to four, channelled, linear, light green leaves and fragrant, star-shaped, yellow flowers singly or in pairs, with green-tinged bases, in mid and late spring.

Tulipa undulatifolia 50cm
Reflexed, linear to lanceolate, glaucous leaves and cup-shaped, red flowers with black or purple basal marks, often edged yellow.

Viola odorata (English violet) 20cm
Semi-evergreen, rhizomatous perennial with bright green, toothed, heart-shaped to rounded leaves and slender stems bearing sweetly perfumed, spurred, violet or white flowers in late winter and early spring.

Zantedeschia aethiopica **hybrid** (Arum lily) 90cm
Rhizomatous, clump-forming perennial with bright green, arrow-shaped leaves, and white spathes tinged pink outside, with yellow spadices, from late spring to early summer.

Zephyranthes candida
Bulbous perennial with narrowly linear basal leaves and pure-white, crocus-like flowers in late summer and early autumn.

Bibliography and information

Chapter 1 – Introduction to garden style

COURSES ON GARDEN DESIGN

The English Gardening School at the Chelsea Physic Garden, 66 Royal Hospital Road, London SW3 4HS. Tel. 0207 352 4347. www.englishgardeningschool.co.uk

Garden Design information: www.gardendesign-uk.com

The Institute of Garden Design, Overbrook Business Centre, Poolbridge Road, Blackford, Wedmore, Somerset BS28 4PA. Tel. 01934 713492. www.inst.org

John Brookes Landscape Design, Denmans, Denmans Lane, Fontwell, West Sussex BN18 0SU. Tel. 01243 542808. www.denmans-garden.co.uk

KLC School of Design, Unit 503 The Chambers, Chelsea Harbour, London SW10 0XF. Tel. 0207 376 3377. www.klc.co.uk

Landscape Institute, 33 Great Portland Street, London W1W 8QG. Tel. 0207 299 4500. www.landscapeinstitute.org

The Royal Horticultural Society courses: www.rhs.org.uk

The Society of Garden Designers, Katepwa House, Ashfield Park Avenue, Ross-on-Wye, Herefordshire HR9 5AX. Tel. 01989 566695. www.sgd.org.uk

Tartendown Nurseries, Tartendown Cross, Landrake, Saltash, Cornwall PL12 5AF. Tel. 01752 851431. www.tartendown.co.uk

Reconstruction of the Elizabethan garden at Mary Newman's Cottage, Saltash, Cornwall, in conjunction with David Wilson Partnership, The Old School, Ladywell, Pilton, Barnstaple, Devon EX31 1QT. Tel. 01271 374485. www.davidwilsonpartnership.co.uk

BOOKS

Brickell, Christopher, *The RHS Essential Garden Planning and Construction* (Mitchell Beazley)

Brookes, John, *John Brookes Garden Design* (Dorling Kindersley)

Brookes, John, *Well-Designed Garden* (Dorling Kindersley)

Crowe, Sylvia, *Garden Design* (Antique Collectors' Club)

Williams, Robin, *The Garden Planner* (Frances Lincoln)

Wilson, Andrew, *The Book Of Garden Plans: Around 200 Ready-made Schemes to Help You Transform Your Garden* (Mitchell Beazley)

Chapter 2 – Formal and classical style

Modern sculpture figure by Helen Sinclair.

BOOKS

Laras, Ann, *Gardens of Italy* (Frances Lincoln)

Blomfield, Reginald, *The Formal Garden in England* (Kessinger Publishing)

Bradley-Hole, Kathryn, *Villa Gardens of The Mediterranean* (Autumn Press)

Masson, Georgina, *Italian Gardens* (The Antique Collectors' Club)

Russell, Vivian, *Edith Wharton's Italian Gardens* (Frances Lincoln)

Strong, Roy, *Creating Formal Gardens* (Little Brown and Co)

Strong, Roy, *Creating Small Formal Gardens* (Conran)

Van Der Horst, Arend Jan, *Art of the Formal Garden* (Cassell)

Whaley, Robin, *The Great Edwardian Gardens of Harold Peto* (Autumn Press Ltd)

Chapter 3 – Informal and naturalistic style

SUSTAINABLE SCULPTURE

Heather Jansch, Sedgewell Coach House, Olchard, Devon TQ12 3GU. www.heatherjansch.com. World-renowned sculptor with stunning and innovative use of recycled materials including driftwood.

Brobury House garden designed by Peter Antonius Garden Design and Build, The Furze, Aston Crews, Ross-on-Wye, Herefordshire HR9 7LW. Tel. 01989 750075. www.peterantoniusdesign.co.uk

BOOKS

Bisgrove, Richard, *William Robinson: The Wild Gardener* (Frances Lincoln)

Bisgrove, Richard, *The Gardens of Gertrude Jekyll* (Frances Lincoln)

Buchan, Ursula, *The English Garden* (Frances Lincoln)
Chatto, Beth, *Woodland Gardens* (Cassell)
Hart, Robert, *Forest Gardening* (Green Earth Books)
Kingsbury, Noel, *Natural Garden Style: Gardening Inspired by Nature* (Merrell Publishers Ltd)
Oudolf, Piet, *Dream Plants for Natural Gardens* (Frances Lincoln)
Whitefield, Patrick, *How to Make a Forest Garden* (Permanent Publications)

Chapter 4 – Cottage garden style

SOCIETIES

The Cottage Garden Society. www.thecgs.org.uk
The Hardy Plant Society. Membership Secretary Mrs Pam Adams, Little Orchard, Great Comberton, Pershore, Worcestershire WR10 3DP. Tel. 01386 710317. www.hardy-plant.org.uk.

BOOKS

Edinger, Philip, *Cottage Gardens* (Sunset Books Inc)
Hamilton, Geoff, *Geoff Hamilton's Cottage Gardens* (BBC Books)
Hamilton, Geoff, *Ornamental Kitchen Garden* (BBC Books)
Jekyll, Gertrude, *The Beauties of a Cottage Garden* (Penguin)
Lloyd, Christopher, *Cottage Garden* (Dorling Kindersley)
Musgrave, Tony, *Country Living Cottage Gardens* (Hearst)
Philips, Sue, *Cottage Garden Flowers* (Wisley Handbooks, Mitchell Beazley)
Thompson, Elspeth, *New Country Garden* (Ryland, Peters and Small)

Chapter 5 – Mediterranean and dry garden style

SOCIETY

The Mediterranean Garden Society, PO Box 14, Peania GR-19002, Greece. Tel/Fax +30 210 664 3089. www.MediterraneanGardenSociety.org.

NURSERIES

Arne Herbs, Limeburn Nurseries, Limeburn Hill, Chew Magna, Bristol BS40 8GW. Tel. 01275 333399. www.arneherbs.co.uk
Burncoose Nurseries, Gwennap, Redruth, Cornwall TR16 6BJ. Tel. 01209 860316. www.burncoose.co.uk
Downderry Lavender Nursery, Pillar Box Lane, Hadlow, Tonbridge, Kent TN11 9SW. Tel. 01732 810081. www.downderry-nursery.co.uk
Glenhurst Cactus Nursery, Station Road, Swineshead, Boston, Lincolnshire PE20 3NX. Tel. 01205 820314. www.glenhirstcactiandpalms.co.uk
The National Herb Centre, Banbury Road, Warmington, Oxfordshire OX17 1DF. Tel. 01295 690999. www.herbcentre.co.uk
The Palm Centre, Ham Street, Ham, Richmond, Surrey TW10 7HA. Tel. 0208 255 6191. www.palmcentre.co.uk
Seeds of Italy, A1 Pheonix Industrial Estate, Rosslyn Crescent, Harrow, Middlesex HA1 2SP. Tel 0208 427 5020. www.seedsofitaly.com. Seed supplies.

BOOKS

Chatto, Beth, *Drought Resistant Planting* (Frances Lincoln)
Chatto, Beth, *Beth Chatto's Gravel Garden* (Frances Lincoln)
Chatto, Beth, *The Dry Garden* (Orion)
Cox, Freda, *Designing and Creating a Mediterranean Garden* (The Crowood Press)
Gildemeister, Heidi, *Mediterranean Gardening: A Waterwise Approach* (Editorial Moll)
Lancaster, Brad, *Rainwater Harvesting for Dry Lands and Beyond*, Vol 1. (Rainsource Press)
Mus, Jean. *Mediterranean Gardens* (Flammarian)
Payne, Graham. *Garden Plants for Mediterranean Climates* (The Crowood Press)

Chapter 6 – Exotic style

NURSERIES

Amultree Exotics, The Turnpike, Norwich Road, Fundenhall, Norfolk NR16 1EL. Tel. 01508 488101. www.turn-it-tropical.co.uk
Architectural Plants, Cooks Farm, Nutthurst, Horsham, West Sussex RH13 6LM. Tel. 01403 891772. www.architecturalplants.com
Crug Farm Plants, Griffiths Crossing, Caernarfon, Gwynedd LL55 1TU. Tel. 01248 670232. www.crug-farm.co.uk
Hardy Exotics, Whitecross, Penzance, Cornwall TR20 8BZ. Tel. 01736 740660. www.hardyexotics.co.uk
Mulu Nursery. www.mulu.co.uk
The Palm Centre, Ham Central Nursery, Ham Street, Ham, Richmond, Surrey TW10 7HA. Tel. 0208 255 6191. www.palmcentre.co.uk
Urban Jungle, Ringland Lane, Old Costessas, Norwich NR8 5BG. Tel. 01603 744997. www.urbanjungle.uk.com

BOOKS

Iverson, Richard. R., *The Exotic Garden: Designing with Tropical Plants in Almost any Climate* (Taunton)
Francko, David, *Palms Won't Grow Here and Other Myths: Warm Climate Plants for Cooler Areas* (Timber Press)
Giles, Will, *Encyclopaedia of Exotic Plants for Temperate Climates* (Timber Press)

Giles, Will, *The New Exotic Garden* (Mitchell Beazley)
Lloyd, Christopher, *Exotic Planting for Adventurous Gardeners* (Timber Press)
Schrader, Dennis, *Hot Plants for Cool Climates: Gardening with Tropical Plants in Temperate Zones* (Timber Press)

Chapter 7 – Japanese style

SOCIETIES

The Japan Society, Swire House, 59 Buckingham Gate, London SW1E 6AJ. Tel. 0207 828 6330. www.japansociety.org.uk
The Japanese Garden Society, Secretary, Woodzened, Longdene Road, Haslemere, Surrey GU27 2PQ. Tel. 0845 0944584. www.jgs.org.uk

SUPPLIERS

www.japanesegardensupplies.co.uk
www.japangarden.co.uk
www.ukbamboosupplies.com

BOOKS

Albright, Brian, and Constance Tindale, *A Path Through the Japanese Garden* (The Crowood Press)
Oguchie, Motomi and Joseph Cali, *Create Your Own Japanese Garden – A Practical Guide* (Kodansha International)
Sawano, Takashil, *Creating Your Own Japanese Garden* (Shufunotoma)
Underwood, Penny, *Designing and Creating Japanese Gardens* (The Crowood Press)
Yoshikawa, Isao, *Japanese Gardening in Small Spaces* (Japan Publications Trading Co Ltd)

Chapter 8 – Islamic style

DESIGNER

Emma Clark, Islamic garden design in the UK and abroad. The Prince's School of Traditional Arts, 19–22 Charlotte Street, London EC2A 3SG. Tel. 0207 613 8500.

BOOKS

Barrucand, Marianne, and Achim Bednorz, *Moorish Architecture* (Taschen)
Clark, Emma, *The Art of the Islamic Garden* (The Crowood Press)
Clark, Emma, *Underneath Which Rivers Flow: The Symbolism of the Islamic Garden* (The Prince of Wales Institute of Architecture)
Fletcher, Richard, *Moorish Spain* (University of California Press)
Irwin, Robert, *The Alhambra* (Harvard University Press)
Preston, Diana, *Taj Mahal: Passion and Genius at the Heart of the Moghul Empire* (Walker and Company)
Stein, Achiva Benzinberg, *Morocco: Courtyards and Gardens* (Monacelli)
Tillotson, Giles, *Taj Mahal* (Harvard University Press)

Chapter 9 – Modern style

DESIGNER

Sue Butler, High Oak Garden Designs, Gladderbrook Farm, High Oak, Heightington, Bewdley, Worcestershire DY12 2YR. Tel. 01299 879923.

BOOKS

Bradley-Hole, Christopher, *The Minimalist Garden* (Mitchell Beazley)
Brown, Jane, *The English Garden Through the Twentieth Century* (Garden Art Press)
Brown, Jane, *The Modern Garden* (Thames and Hudson)
Powers, Alan, *The Modern Movement in Britain* (Merrell Publishers Ltd)
Raine, John, *Garden Lighting* (Hamlyn Gardening)
Richardson, Tim, *English Gardens of the Twentieth Century* (Aurum Press)
Shaw, Christine, *Architectural Plants* (Collins)
Wayman, Janet, *Modern Garden Design: Innovation since 1900* (Thames and Hudson)
Wilson, Andrew, *Influential Gardeners: The Designers who Shaped Twentieth-Century Garden Style* (Mitchell Beazley)

Chapter 10 – Water garden style

SUPPLIERS

Anglian Bridges, 3 Westbrook Close, Steeple Morden, Royston, Herts SG8 0NY. Tel 01763 852839.
The East Riding Koi Company, Chatterthro, Carter Lane, Flamborough, Bridlington, Yorkshire YO15 1LW. Tel. 01262 850270. www.koicarp.net and www.koi-net.co.uk
Hoselock Cyprio. Tel. 01778 344502.
Churtin Inge Associates (natural swimming pools). Tel. 01749 670070. info@gardenart.co.uk
Pond Liners Direct Ltd., Freepost, ANG 0426, Broxbourne EN10 6BR. Tel. 01992 467053. Fax 01992 478996. sales@pld.broxbourne.co.uk
Trident Water Garden Products. Tel. 01203 669020.
UK Pond Liners, Allenby Industrial Estate, Lincoln. Tel/Fax. 01522 569981/41/04.

ICE-FREE AIDS

Green Ideas, Dovecote Lane, Coleby, Lincolnshire LN5 0AD.
  Tel. 01522 789880. www.greenideasltd.co.uk
Heissner UK, Regency Business Centre, Queens Road,
  Kenilworth, Warwickshire CV8 1JQ. Tel. 01926 851166.
Interpet Ltd, Interpet House, Vincent Lane, Dorking, Surrey
  RH4 3YX. Tel. 01306 881033.
Trident, Bradshaws Direct. Tel. 01904 691169.

SOLAR POWER

Intersolar Products, Waddon Marsh Way, Purley Way,
  Croydon, Surrey CR9 4HS. Tel. 0208 6862231.
Oase (UK) Ltd, Plot 2 Northway, Walworth Industrial Estate,
  Andover, Hampshire SP10 5AZ. Tel. 01264 333225.
Solar Trend from Tricor, Longbeck Estate, Marske, Redcar,
  North Yorkshire TS11 6HT. Tel. 01642 482000.
Wagner Spraytech (UK) Ltd, Haslemere Way Tramway
  Industrial Estate, Banbury, Oxfordshire OX16 8TY.
  Tel. 01295 265353.

BOOKS

Bevan, Dave, *Creating a Wildlife Pond* (Ringpress Books Ltd)
Brewster, Bernice, *The Essential Book of Koi* (TFH Publications)
Chatto, Beth, and Steven Wooster, *Beth Chatto's Damp Garden*
  (Cassell)
Clarke, Graham, *Beginners' Guide to Water Gardening* (GMC
  Publications)
Quick, Graham, *A Practical Guide to Creating a Garden Pond*
  (Interpet Publishing)
Speichart, Greg, *Encyclopaedia of Water Garden Plants*
  (Timber Press)
Speichert, Greg, and Sue Speichert, *Timber Press Pocket Guide
  to Water Garden Plants* (Timber Press)

Chapter 11 – Small garden style

BOOKS

Billington, Jill, *RHS Really Small Gardens* (Quadrille
  Publishing Ltd)
Brookes, John, *The Small Garden* (Dorling Kindersley)
Clayton, Phil, *Planting a Small Garden: Simple Steps to Success*
  (Dorling Kindersley)
Joyce, David, *The Ultimate Container Garden* (Frances Lincoln)
Musgrave, Toby, *Courtyard Gardens: Imaginative Ideas for
  Outoors* (Jaqui Small LLP)
Nessman, Pierre, *City Gardens: Creative Ideas for Small Spaces*
  (Stewart Tabori Chang)
Newbury, Tim, *20 Best Small Gardens* (Cassell Illustrated)
Newbury, Tim, *Small Garden Design Bible* (Hamlyn)
Wilson, Andrew, *The Book of Plans for Small Gardens* (Mitchell
  Beazley)

Chapter 12 – Gardens of the future

GREEN ROOFS

www.thegreenroofcentre.co.uk
www.livingroofs.org
Designs for Tamarisks green roofs by Ruth Kent, Kingsbridge,
  Devon. Tel. 01548 842275.

LIVING WALLS

Patrick Blanc Vertical walls.
  info@murvegetalpatrickblanc.com
www.vertigarden.com
Greenscape, Tanksafe Hardform Ltd, Greenscape Division,
  Unit 4, Berewyk Hall Court, Bures Road, White Colne,
  Colchester, Essex CO6 2QB. www.resinagro.com
  info@greenscape.eu.com

ECOLOGICAL ISSUES

UK Climate Impact Programme: www.ukcip.org.uk
www.climatecare.org
www.direct.gov.uk
www.energysavingtrust.org.uk
www.soilassociation.org.

RECYCLING

www.globalgardening.org

BOOKS

Benjamin, Alison, and Brian McCallum, *A World Without
  Bees* (Guardian Books)
Brookes, John, *The New Garden* (Dorling Kindersley)
Bourne, Val, *The Natural Gardener: The Way We All Want to
  Garden* (Frances Lincoln)
Dowding, Charles, *Organic Gardening: The No Dig Way*
  (Green Books)
Dunnett, Nigel, and Noel Kingsbury, *Planting Green Roofs and
  Living Walls* (Timber Press)
Fern, Kim, *Plants For a Future: Edible and Useful Plants for a
  Healthier World* (Permanent Publications)
Gore, Al, *An Inconvenient Truth* (Bloomsbury)
Gros, Michel, *In Tune with the Moon* (Findhorn Press Ltd)
Klein, Carol, *Grow Your Own Veg* (Mitchell Beazley)
Larkcom, Joy, *Grow Your Own Vegetables* (Frances
  Lincoln)
Lavelle, Christine, *How to Create a Wildlife Garden* (Lorenz
  Books)
Lewis, Pam, *Sticky Wicket: Gardening in Tune With Nature*
  (Frances Lincoln)

Lewis, Pam, *Making a Wildflower Meadow* (Frances Lincoln)
Lloyd, Christopher, *Meadows* (Cassell Illustrated)
Mabey, Richard, *Food For Free* (Collins)
Mollison, Bill, *Introduction to Permaculture* (Tagari Publications)
Seymour, John, *The New Complete Book of Self-Sufficiency* (Dorling Kindersley)
Thompson, Peter, *The Self-Sustaining Garden: The Guide to Matrix Planting* (Frances Lincoln)
Thun, Maria, *Gardening For Life: The Biodynamic Way* (Hawthorn Press)
Thun, Maria, and Matthias Thun, *The Biodynamic Sowing and Planting Calendar* (Floris Books)
Titchmarsh, Alan, *The Kitchen Gardener: Grow Your Own Fruit and Veg* (BBC Books)
Whitefield, Patrick, *The Earth Care Manual; A Permaculture Handbook for Britain and Other Temperate Countries* (Permanent Publications)
Willis, Henry, *Earth's Future Climate* (Llumina Press)
Wong, James, *Grow Your Own Drugs: Easy Recipes for Natural Remedies and Beauty Treats*, Collins)

CHILDREN'S GARDENS

BBC Breathing Places Schools: www.bbc.co.uk/breathingplaces/schools. Help and resources for creating wildlife-friendly green spaces.
Alan Titchmarsh Gardens for Schools: www.alantitchmarsh.com/gardensforschools.asp. Financial support for school garden projects.
Gardens Organic: www.gardenorganic.org.uk/schoolsorganicnetwork. Help and advice for schools in conjunction with Duchy Originals.
Learning Through Landscape Campaign: www.rhs.org/schoolgardening. Resources, courses and advice on setting up a school garden.
Seeds of Italy: www.seedsofitaly.com. Free packs of seeds for schools.

BOOKS

Cox, Martyn, *Gardening with Kids* (Ryland, Peters and Small Ltd)
Lovejoy, Sharon, *Roots, Shoots, Buckets and Boots; Gardening Together With Children* (Workman Publishing)
Matthews, Clare, *How Does Your Garden Grow? Great Gardening for Green-Fingered Kids* (Hamlyn)
Quin, Caroline, *Gardening: Activities for 3–5 Year Olds* (Brilliant Publications)
Wilde, Kim, *Gardening With Children* (Collins)

PERMACULTURE

BCM Permaculture Association, London WC1N 3XX.
Permaculture Association, Hollybush Conservation Centre, Broad Lane, Kirkstall, Leeds, West Yorkshire L55 3BP. www.permaculture.org.uk
Courses: Workhouse Skills for Sustainability, Workhouse, Y Dolydd, Llanfyllin, Powys SY22 5LD. www.sector29.co.uk

GENERAL

Alpine Garden Society: www.alpinegardensociety.org
Garden Organic: www.gardenorganic.org.uk
Herb Society: www.herbsociety.org.uk
National Gardens Scheme: www.ngs.org.uk
The National Trust: www.nationaltrust.org.uk
Royal Horticultural Society: www.rhs.org.uk. (Membership: membership@rhs.org.uk)
Royal National Rose Society: www.rnrs.org
Wildlife Trusts: www.wildlifetrusts.org

Hillfield Cottages and Country House, Hillfield, Dartmouth, Devon TQ6 0LX. Holiday cottages with eco management.

BOOKS

Austin, David, *David Austin's English Roses* (Conran Octopus Ltd)
Austin, David, *The Rose* (Garden Art Press)
Austin, David, *Old Roses and English Roses* (Antique Collectors' Club)
Brickell, Christopher, *RHS Encyclopedia of Plants and Flowers* (Dorling Kindersley)
Hillier, John, *The Hillier Manual of Trees and Shrubs* (David and Charles)
McIndoe, Andrew, *Herbaceous Perennials* (Hillier Garden Guides, David and Charles)
Mcvicar, Jekka, *Jekka's Complete Herb Book* (Kyle Cathie)
Phillips, Roger, and Martyn Rix, *Annuals and Biennials* (Pan Books)
Phillips, Roger, and Martyn Rix, *Bulbs* (Pan Books)
Phillips, Roger, and Martyn Rix, *Climbers for Walls and Arbours* (Pan Books)
Phillips, Roger, and Nicky Foy, *Herbs* (Pan Books)
Phillips, Roger and Martyn Rix, *Perennials*, Vols 1–2 (Pan Books)
Phillips, Roger, and Martyn Rix, *Roses* (Pan Books)
Phillips, Roger, and Martyn Rix, *Shrubs* (Random House)
Rice, Graham, *RHS Encyclopaedia of Perennials* (Dorling Kindersley)
Sterndale-Bennett, Jane, *The Winter Garden* (Hillier Garden Guides, David and Charles)

Gardens index

The gardens listed below supply opening times as a guideline only. They are correct at time of going to press but many are subject to change each year so please contact individual gardens for the latest opening times before visiting. *The RHS Garden Finder* by Charles Quest-Ritson gives up-to-date information, as does the NGS Yellow Book for gardens opening with the National Gardens Scheme.

Abbotsbury Sub-Tropical Gardens, Weymouth, Dorset DT3 4LA. Tel. 01305 871387. Open daily, all year except 25th and 26th December and 1st January, from 10.00–6.00 or dusk.

Alfabia Garden, Carratera de Palma a Soller, 07110 Bunyola, Mallorca, Balearic Islands, Spain. Tel. +34 9716 13123. Open April to October, Monday to Saturday 9.30–6.30; November to March, Monday to Friday 9.30–5.30, Saturday 9.30–1.00.

Alhambra and Generalife, Granada, Spain. Check for opening times.

Alnwick Castle, Alnwick, Northumberland NE66 1NQ. Tel. 01665 510777. www.alnwickcastle.com. Open daily April to October 10.00–5.00.

Applecross House, Alveley, Shropshire WV15 6NB. Tel. 01746 780313.

Arley Arboretum, Arley, Bewdley, Worcestershire DY12 1XG. Tel. 01299 861368. www.arley-arboretum.org.uk. Open April to early November, Wednesday to Sunday and Bank Holiday Mondays, 11.00–5.00.

Arley Hall and Gardens, Northwich, Cheshire CW9 6NA. Tel. 01565 777353. www.arleyhallandgardens.com. Gardens open March to September, Tuesday to Sunday and Bank Holiday Mondays, and Sundays in October 11.00–5.00.

Athelhampton House, Dorchester, Dorset DT2 7LG Tel. 01305 848363. Fax 01305 848135. www.athelhampton. co.uk. Open Sunday to Thursday 10.00–4.30 from February to October. Closed Saturday and Sunday.

Barnsley House Garden (Hotel), Barnsley, Cirencester, Gloucestershire GL7 5EE. Tel. 01285 740000.

Beth Chatto Gardens, Colchester, Essex C07 7DB. Tel. 01206 822007. www.bethchatto.com. Open Monday to Saturday 9.00–5.00 (March to October); 9.00–4.00 (November to February). Closed Sundays.

Bicton Park Gardens, Budleigh Salterton, Devon EX9 7BJ. Tel. 01395 568465. Open 10.00–6.00 (5.00 in winter), daily except Christmas Day.

Birmingham Botanical Gardens, Westbourne Road, Edgbaston, Birmingham, West Midlands B15 3TR. Tel. 0121 454 1860. Open 9.00–7.00 (or sunset) daily all year except Christmas Day.

Blenheim Palace, Woodstock, Oxfordshire OX20 1PP. Tel. 01993 811901. www.blenheimpalace.com. Park and garden open daily 10.30–5.30.

Blickling Hall Gardens and Park, Blickling, Norwich, Norfolk NR11 6NF. Tel. 01263 738030. (The National Trust.) Garden open all year from Wednesday to Sunday, and Bank Holiday Mondays, 11.00–4.00 winter, 10.00–5.15 summer.

Bridgwalton House, Telegraph Lane, Morville, Bridgnorth, Shropshire WV16 5NP. Tel. 01746 714401. Occasional opening for NGS Scheme.

Brobury House Gardens, Brobury, Herefordshire HR3 6BS. Tel. 01981 500229. www.broburyhouse.co.uk. Gardens open daily all year.

Burrow Farm Gardens and Nursery, Dalewood, Axminster, East Devon EX13 7ET. Tel. 01404 831285. www. burrowfarmgardens.co.uk. Open daily April to October 10.00–7.00.

Buscot Park, Faringdon, Oxfordshire SN7 8BU. Tel. 01367 240786. (The National Trust.) Open 2.00–6.00 Monday to Friday, April to September; also 2nd and 4th weekends April to September.

Cambridge University Botanical Gardens, Cambridge, CB2 1JF. Tel. 01223 336265. www.botanic.cam.ac.uk. Open 10.00–4.00 winter; 10.00–5.00 spring and autumn, 10.00–6.00 summer, daily except 25th December to 1st January.

Castle Drogo, Drewsteignton, near Exeter, Devon EX6 6PB. Tel. 01647 433306. (The National Trust.) Check for opening times.

Castle Howard, York, North Yorkshire YO60 7DA. Tel. 01653 648444. www.castlehoward.co.uk. Gardens open daily all year 10.00–6.30, dusk in winter.

Chateau de Versailles, Paris, France. Check for opening times.

Chatsworth, Bakewell, Derbyshire DE45 1PP. Tel. 01246 565300. www.chatsworth.org. Open every day apart from Christmas period, 10.30–6.00 (11.00–6.00 in winter).

Chelsea Physic Garden, London SW3 4HS. Tel. 0207 352 5646. Open 12.00–5.00 Wednesdays, 2.00–6.00 Sundays, April to October, plus Chelsea Flower Show opening.

Chyknell, Bridgnorth, Shropshire WV15 5PP. Open under NGS scheme.

Cressing Temple, Witham Road, Braintree, Essex CM77 8PD. Gardens open Monday to Friday 10.00–4.00 in winter and 10.00–5.00 in summer including Saturday.

Croome Court Walled Garden, Severn Stoke, Worcestershire WR8 9DW. www.croomewalledgardens.co.

Dartington Hall, Totnes, South Devon TQ9 6EL. Tel. 01803 847147. www.dartingtonhall.com. Open all year.

David Austin Roses, Bowling Green Lane, Albrighton, Wolverhampton, West Midlands WV7 3HB. Tel. 01902 376300. Gardens and nursery open each day except Christmas and New Year. www.davidaustinroses.com.

Denmans Garden, Denmans Lane, Fontwell, West Sussex BN18 0SU. Tel. 01243 542808. www.denmansgarden.co.uk. Open

General index

Please use this general index in conjunction with the plant indices that follow each chapter.